BLUE ROAD

Windy Baboulene

SUMMERSDALE

Summersdale Publishers Ltd
46 West Street
Chichester
West Sussex
PO19 1RP
UK

www.summersdale.com

Printed and bound in Great Britain.

ISBN 1 84024 234 5

About the Author

Windy Baboulene is an award-winning film story writer. He lives in Brighton with his wife and four children.

Once a man comes to like a sea life,
He is no longer fit to live on dry land.
Samuel Johnson (1708–1784)

Author's Mitigation

Some things in life are flexible and friendly. They realise that a brittle nature does nothing for their popularity, and so adopt an admirable willingness to change. Thus our lives are enriched as we coax these considerate allies into wonderful new forms without disturbing their fundamental chemistry.

Take, for example, The Truth.

Estate agents and solicitors build highly successful careers on the malleable nature of The Truth, and I suppose all of us must admit that at some time or another, in the collar-tugging sweat of an uncomfortable predicament, we have found The Truth to be so wholly unsatisfactory in one form that we have set about it with vigour and come up with a far more pleasing Truth; one which has proven a great deal more palatable to the authorities than the original.

So, in this context, let me answer the most common question asked of me regarding this weighty tome:

'Did the tales in this book really happen? Is this book The Truth?'

And the answer is a resounding, 'Yes!'

This book represents a genuine journey, real people, places and events. I admit I have polished a little here, and pummelled a touch there, and drawn an attractive veil over unseemly detail where decorum requires. And just in case you are a libel lawyer (or are maybe thinking of calling one) it might also be worth noting that the events and characters in this book have been drawn from four years' worth of shipboard life. Additionally, within all stories depicting events involving ex-colleagues, I have changed the ranks of the individuals concerned as well as their names, so you can't get me that way either.

So liberties have been taken for the sakes of the author's marriage, vanity and bank balance, but let there be no doubt about it, this book is The Truth. As Jerome K. Jerome so (much more) succinctly put it:

'I have merely added colour, for which no extra charge is made.'

Windy Baboulene
Brighton, Sussex
2002

Global Wanderer – Personnel Rank Chart

Captain Benchmerson, aka 'The Old Man'

Navigators

Chief Officer (The Mate/First Mate) John Snape, 'Harry Tate'

Second Officer (Second Mate) Peter Cranfield, 'Cranners'

Third Officer (Third Mate) 'The Famous Dick Wrigley'

Navigating Cadets (Apprentices)
Patrick 'Patch' Gallagher
Kevin 'Giewy' Bewick
'NotNorman'
Me

Radio Officer, 'Sparky'

Engineers

Chief Engineer (The Chief) 'Chiefy', 'Plum'

Second Engineer (The Second) 'Jinx'

Third Engineer (The Third) Clive Walker, 'Skippy'

Fourth Engineer (The Fourth) 'Benny the Dog'

Fifth Engineer (Fiver) Eddie, 'SmallParcel'

Sixth Engineer (Sixth) Alan 'Crate' McCulloch

Engineering Cadet, Paul 'Gonad' Curtis

Electrician, 'MegaWatt'

Second Electrician, 'KiloWatt'

CONTENTS

Chapter 1

Mothership

A battle for supremacy. School loses out. Windy goes toe-to-toe with the Global Wanderer. *Who gets the top bunk? The Chief Officer seems upset. Work begins. The coconuts make too much of themselves.*

I was sweet sixteen and my examinations were approaching like mortar-boarded vultures over the horizon. The received wisdom amongst the academic alumni up and down the country was that I was going to fail everything, and, to cap it all, Miss Fitch was clambering along behind the tennis courts, about to find us in our hiding place in the bushes. Things did not look good.

Actually, Miss Fitch looked good. Miss Fitch was a *young* teacher. She wore short skirts and her hair dropped over one eye when she turned from the blackboard. I would have done anything to please her, and I desperately hoped she might be harbouring a deep admiration for my revolutionary spirit; a passion that was agony for her to hold inside, but which would now reveal itself at this critical junction in my life. There were two ways she could go: she could exclaim her love for me in an emotional outpouring, we could run away together and she could take my political coup in a new and full-breasted direction; or she could snub me, hand us over to the authorities, get off with one of the approaching policemen and I would have to kill myself.

As she arrived at our hidey-hole it was clear we would not find out her views immediately, because she was wheezing hard, having chased us a long way. I felt this was a Good Thing, as our punishment would be at least partially

11

hampered by exhaustion. She parted the bushes and lit up the dark of our camp with her fiery eyes. I tried to look cool for my fellow political activists, a difficult trick when you are, after all, cowering in the bushes behind the school tennis courts.

'You boys – *huerr*, *huerr* – you *huerr*, are all – *huerr*, all – *huerr*, all – *huerr*!'

She gave it up, withdrew her face from our camp and flopped against the wire fence of the tennis courts to indulge in the death rattles of an unfit person. Her whole body pumped and pulsated like a stranded heart. Beyond her, across the fields and over at the main school, the fire brigade had arrived and were setting about rescuing the chemistry lab we student activists had liberated as a first move towards overthrowing the government.

We had been watching a programme about student activists on television – in Paris, I think it was. Not only were they very cool – the clothes, the posing, the attitude – they were also thoroughly applauded the world over, didn't appear to have to attend lessons, and were allowed out very late indeed. So why wasn't it working for us?

A couple of policemen were jogging our way. I gulped and looked at my fellow gang members. Paton, Greener, Norris, Porter, Cauty (C), Cauty (J), Ludlam, Craggs and Tuckerman. Nine pairs of scared, round eyes, like baby owls in a nest. I felt reassured by the presence of Tuckerman. He took the edge off my fear. I looked around and saw others feeling calmed by the lad in the same way. In an instant a collective conscience came to a solid and unspoken agreement in those bushes. We would all blame Tuckerman.

The policemen were nearly upon us when a vision formed in the corner of my mind, and I heard the haunting tones of my Uncle Joe, reminding me of the philosophy he took into many interviews with policemen (and into each of his five marriages): 'No Problem is So Big That it Cannot be Run Away From,' he whispered.

I knew what I had to do. As my Freedom Party was ushered out of the bushes I stayed at the back. I dug myself into the darkest corner of those bushes, covered myself in leaves and simply did not emerge. The other lads were marched off and – miracle of miracles – I was left alone.

I knew the authorities would not be long establishing my presence at the scene of the crime, or my absence from the captured gang, so it was at that very moment, there and then, as I dug my way under the perimeter fence and legged it across the gardens behind the school, that I followed in the footsteps of thousands of desperados before me, and ran away to sea.

I didn't stop running until I found a careers office, established the joining procedure, filled in some forms for a merchant shipping line, and pressured the lady to make it all happen quickly. She found a company that was recruiting for an imminent intake, and asked me to sign here, here and here. I ticked the box marked 'Yes please – I would like to avoid sticky interviews with policemen' and sauntered off to find a game of football, full of the joys of that stuff that fills a man's thingy when he's slain the savage something-or-other.

And a mere fortnight later – a fortnight brim-full of teachers 'You've-done-what?'-ing, fathers bouncing off walls, and stricken mothers passing out clutching their bosoms – I had left school and was on a train to Tyneside for my induction course. It was as simple as that.

The induction course was something of an eye-opener, but they always over-egg that stuff about alcohol, ladies of the night, fighting, venereal disease, fires, narcotics, sharks and so forth, don't they? I couldn't admit it, of course, but it all sounded like a good, long list of all the things that were missing in my life.

As the planet revolved slowly beneath the aircraft, and America manoeuvred itself into position below us, I stared down at the tiny ships and miniature towns that moved with it. I was dumbfounded. Barely a month had passed since I was a mere caterpillar of a schoolboy, living a schoolboy life with schoolboy routines. Now I was a beautiful Officer Cadet Butterfly in Her Majesty's Merchant Navy, heading for New Orleans to join my first ship. My head swam. Planes? New Orleans? Ships? These were the trappings of an exciting, cosmopolitan lifestyle, not a schoolboy's lot. But it was real. A new life with a big, rusty boat in all the places I used to keep a mother.

And so it was that on 10 August 1977, I could be found on a quayside in New Orleans, my bags dropped to the floor on either side, gorping up at the steep metal sides of the mighty vessel *Global Wanderer*. They were rusty and overworked. They certainly did not appear to be in tune with the company information I had read in open-mouthed wonder. The literature had spoken of a magnificent 28,000-ton starship, with pictures of her enhancing all the famous landmarks of the world. Under the Golden Gate Bridge, in front of the Manhattan skyline, passing in front of the Sydney Opera House, the ship schmoozing at a party with John and Yoko. One of the pictures was an aerial shot of the *Global Wanderer* cutting a swathe through a turquoise sea close to a tropical island. Another depicted the scene on the bridge as masterful, square-jawed officers in smart white uniforms steered her around the world.

I *loved* the literature. It was romantic and global, adventurous and exciting. I wanted to be on that bridge and to look that important. I wanted to control a ship in turquoise waters; that would be me, setting my jaw manfully to the breeze and thinking profound thoughts about stars and navigation.

Now I had arrived, however, the real *Global Wanderer* – close up, warts and all, and with no soft focus or spectacular backdrop – was somewhat different. The romance of the literature *was* reflected by the reality, in the same sense that romance is surely present in an ageing prostitute – if the paint job is good enough and the photographs taken from far enough away.

While some of my peers on newer ships were enjoying computers, electronics and a swimming pool on the boat-deck, the *Global Wanderer* featured Morse code as its primary means of communication, and a sextant as its hi-tech positioning equipment. Satellite navigation was spoken of only as a mysterious form of black magic. This was raw Merchant Navy from a bygone era. A tramp steamer, somehow still running 30 years after its sell-by date. I felt cheated. Even the Mississippi failed to be turquoise, but there was no turning back now. Like a child facing his first hypodermic, I had no escape – just a grim notion that what was to follow might involve pain.

I struggled aboard my new home, anxious to meet some reassuring signs – a friendly face to greet me; a hand with all my luggage; perhaps an offer to phone home and tell my family I had arrived safely – but my expectations were punctured on the sharpness of reality. Any people with whom I coincided looked down their noses at me as if I was a poo on the carpet, and my cabin, when I eventually slumped through the door, gave off the still, haunted aura of a room in which there had recently been a dead body.

Suddenly I was alone. Very alone. It was the first time I had been without company for some time and I didn't like it. As I sat in the cabin I felt strange. The porthole. The bunk bed. The desk. The wardrobe. They all pretended I was not there.

'Is this all such a great idea?' I asked them. They knew, they'd seen it all before, but they were saying nothing.

I didn't have much time to contemplate my situation – or my solitude – because the significance of the bunk bed hit me at the same time as the door did – when my room-mate crashed in with his luggage. I had been led to believe that I would be sharing with one Norman Smith, so, when he arrived, I shook him politely by the hand.

'You must be Norman,' I smiled.

'And you must be Mistaken,' he said, smiling back with a certain edge. 'If you start calling me Norman, I shall set fire to you.'

'Ah. Fire, you say? Er . . . I guess that means you're not Norman?'

'Correct! And if you insist on calling me NotNorman, I will have to invent an equally excellent title for you. Judging by the smell in this room, I guess you must be Windy.'

In that short moment of misunderstanding our nicknames were set in stone for the rest of time. NotNorman became NotNorman. I became Windy.

NotNorman was a tall, skinny, accident-prone lad, with a ready smile, an eye for mischief and bags of misplaced confidence. A bit like a cross between a giraffe and a Labrador puppy. He was from the Lake District, and as he seemed to have all the answers, I stuck to him. What he did not have, however, were the *right* answers, but it's surprising how far people can get in life with the wrong answers provided that they believe in them strongly enough.

'OK, Windy, which do you want,' he shouted, (I don't know *why* he shouted) 'top or bottom bunk?' I was about to reply in the uppermost tense when he added, 'Because whichever you choose, you're having the other one.'

I eyed the man narrowly. Did he think I would fall for the old double bluff? Maybe it was a treble . . . quadruple? You know the thing, 'Now he's thinking that I'm thinking that he's thinking that . . .' ad infinitum. I was *way* ahead of him.

'Bottom,' I said, smiling knowingly.

'OK,' he said, shrugging his shoulders. 'But don't say I didn't offer.' And he clambered on to the top bunk.

'HA! You fell for it!' I yelled, assuming the bottom bunk with gritted teeth. I could see I was going to have to stay tough with young NotNorman if I wasn't going to lose the upper hand in our relationship.

We had been lying on our bunks for only a matter of seconds when the cabin door crashed open again. NotNorman and I sat bolt upright in our beds (but only I banged my head).

'RRRRight then, you SCUM!' screamed a nine-headed whirling dervish occupying the airspace. 'Let's getchooo basta . . . WHAT IN THE NAME OF SWEET JESUS ARE YOU DOING IN BED? You've not been on board three minutes and you're IN BED?' The red-faced blur roared a spine-curdling laugh and from somewhere a boiler suit flew into each of our faces. 'Get into those boilies and out on deck NOW! And don't let me ever – EVER – catch you in bed at any time of the day or night at any point in the future EVER AGAIN or your lives will NOT be worth living. I PROMISE. UNDERSTAND?'

We meekly expressed our understanding, but the door had slammed behind the hurricane long before our words reached open air.

We sat stunned for a moment as papers and dust floated down into the silence that followed the storm. We must have looked like a couple of Aborigines transplanted from the parched outback of central Australia, given a 20-second icy blast at the North Pole, then put back where we came from. It all seemed so unreal. NotNorman was first to find words.

'Did that really just happen – or have I had too many wine gums?'

I was in the middle of confirming that I had shared his hideous visitation when the door flew open once again. We both let out short, involuntary screams and drew the bedcovers up to our chins, but this time it was someone else. Someone already dressed in a boiler suit and working boots. Someone we recognised. This was Patch Gallagher, the Senior Cadet. I had chatted with him for a while on the flight over, so I knew that this was his fourth trip, and that he was in charge of us cadets. He shook his head at our flushed features and his round Scottish tones filled the room. 'Well, come on then, girls!' he laughed. 'If he has to come back for you, you may not survive the experience!'

'Who the hell WAS that?' I asked. 'He frightened the crap out of us!'

Patch's chubby cheeks wobbled. 'That,' he said, 'was Mr John Snape, the Chief Officer of this fine vessel. Also known as First Mate, also known affectionately – if men like him are ever known 'affectionately' – as the Mate or for the cockneys among you, Harry Tate. Also known as Your Boss.'

'Also known as Total Bastard,' added NotNorman, searching through his trunk for some working boots. 'I can see he's gonna be a barrel of laughs.'

'Harry Tate is one of the busiest blokes on board, so if you get in his way, you'll get trampled on,' Patch continued cheerfully. 'Rule one: do not upset him. Rule two: if you DO upset him, hide under the spare propeller on the poop deck. He is responsible for EVERYTHING: the loading, organisation and care of all cargo; ship stability; maintenance of the entire ship; the four-to-eight watch at both ends of the day; and anything else that is going spare or wrong. He has an Asian crew of around twenty-five workshy individuals to hinder his progress, and of course, he is lucky enough to be in loco parentis for US! We are his punch-bags!'

Patch began to leave the cabin, but threw in one last gem as NotNorman and I remained rooted to the spot. 'And if you're not out on deck in under ten seconds, I think you'll be in for another fairly one-sided and motivational conversation delivered from close range at high volume, with generous helpings of saliva and a headache to follow. See you out there!'

Oh Miss Fitch, Miss Fitch. Whatever have I *done*?

Nine seconds later NotNorman and I appeared on deck. Nobody had said which deck, or where, but we were out there. OK, so we looked like Laurel and Hardy with our boots on the wrong feet and both legs down one leg-hole of our respective boiler suits, but we were *there*, ready to set about our first constructive undertaking, or 'gutty job', to use Patch's technical terminology.

Patch introduced us to what is known as a 'deep-tank' – a special hold for carrying valuable liquids. The tank had just been emptied, having been full of coconut oil. The oil is transported and pipelined at a high temperature because it solidifies as it cools. Having discharged the oil, the heating had been turned off to allow us to enter and clean the tank. Of course, the tank was now relatively cool (although still very hot), so every inch of the inside of the tank was covered with a two-inch layer of sweaty coconut gunk, with the consistency of an alcoholic's stools and a smell that could drop a buffalo at 200 yards.

We lowered a light into the tank and, with our faces

screwed up like a convention of bulldogs in a perfume factory, climbed in through the only access, a small manhole in the floor, sorry – 'deck'. Beneath this manhole was a ladder welded to the deep-tank side and we began our descent of 25 feet to the dank, eerie bottom. Apart from the stench – which made me gag – the clingy, humid atmosphere began rotting away at my bones before I'd got halfway down. By the time I had reached the bottom of the ladder I was already soaked through and highly uncomfortable. As a working environment it was impossible. Everything was slippery and every rusty nook and harsh cranny was full of thick, unforgiving crap; the bilges, the ladder, the cross-girders, every footfall and handhold – everything. Patch had seen it all before.

'This,' he said, and the echo in the tank was dulled by the serrated atmosphere, 'is the worst job on earth. It is gross, unpleasant and quite staggeringly dangerous. It's hard enough just standing up, but when we are up there,' he pointed through the steamy fug to a girder running all around the tank some 15 feet above us, 'trying to wield a hose when the ship is rolling and it's as slippery as a duck on a plate of snot, we'll be breaking every safety rule in the book and have every chance of having a serious accident.' His cheerful face had become disturbingly sincere. 'Add to that our tiredness and boredom towards the end of a sixteen-hour day, and I think you can see the dangers. This job has to be finished before we refill the tanks in Houston in seven days' time.'

'Not too bad, is it?' I said, trying to strike the optimistic chord. 'There are four of us. If we get stuck in . . .'

'You don't get a choice, my son,' continued Patch, pointedly giving Optimism the red card. 'You get stuck in all right. And as far as "not too bad" goes, if you think seven sixteen-hour days of this crap is "not too bad", then I dread to think what you'd consider to be a tough one.

There are SIX of these tanks, Spanner-brain, and the inspectors in Houston will want to see their faces in five of 'em. One speck of dust and we'll have to clean the bastards all over again. By the end of this week, your "not too bad" will be "I wish I was dead." You're going to wish you'd never been born.'

He took the words right out of my mouth.

Initially the four of us worked together to get everything set up and to run through the drill. Then Patch set us into two groups of two, working eight-on eight-off, until five of the six tanks were completely clean behind the ears, under the arms, ties straight, and ready for Grandma. As the nightmare began to unfold, my mind went back to my thoughts on the plane a few hours earlier. I *thought* we'd have a couple of days (and nights) up the road in New Orleans, especially as it was the weekend. I *thought* we'd have some time to mooch around and generally get settled into shipboard life. I *thought* the cruise round the Caribbean to Houston would be spent discussing the finer points of navigation on the bridge under a clear blue sky and over a gently undulating sea.

I thought wrong.

And as if life wasn't grim enough, the cadet with whom I was paired for deep-tank cleaning purposes was a dead loss. I had felt that the team was shaping up nicely, and I have already introduced three-quarters of the squad. But I am sorry to say that there was a weak link. A runt in the litter. A bad egg in the nest. Because apart from NotNorman and me, with the experienced Patch as our leader, there was a fourth specimen making up the 'A' team.

The most striking thing that hit one upon first being confronted by Kevin Bewick was that the English language provided the perfect word for him, and that word was 'gormless'. He was a walking definition of gormless and a quite exceptional example of someone entirely without gorm – although, when I say he was a 'walking' definition, I must add that it was nothing short of a credit to his creator that a vehicle so distorted could perambulate in any distinct fashion at all; because the second thing that struck one was that he was a physical impossibility, confounding every rule of nature, balance and mechanical principle. Darwin would have chucked the towel in straight away if he had met Kevin Bewick, and I have to admit I had similar urges.

Within 20 minutes of our starting work together it became clear that he had spent his life being bitten by dogs, losing money, walking into lamp-posts and failing miserably to impress the opposite sex. Kevin was humanity's toe stubbed endlessly on the furniture of life, and yet despite all this, he was somehow convinced (and it was this that drove people to despair) that he was God's gift to shipping, mirrors, humanity, womanhood and Great Britain.

The third thing to strike one was that, for a chap of only seventeen years, he had achieved an unparalleled degree of physical degradation. He was basically skinny, but sported a paunch that would impress the purists amongst construction workers. Above the paunch was a sunken, bony chest, and atop the alleged chest was . . . nothing. He had no shoulders, and you had to look elsewhere for his head. His neck emerged horizontally from the space between the places his shoulders weren't and curved immediately downwards. It then took a U-bend back up before you got to the head. The tallest point on his superstructure was, therefore, his hunched lack of shoulders, giving him the overall appearance of life's dopiest vulture. This impression was further enhanced by his big hooked nose, goofy teeth, and his vocabulary, which consisted exclusively of a single call, the depressed expletive

'Giew!' that indicated the delivery of the latest in a lifetime of disappointments and rejection. And this was to be my partner. Perfect. Just perfect.

Despite the fact that we worked eight hours on and eight off for an eternity or two, the deep-tanks stubbornly refused to get any cleaner. We hosed the bulkheads until we ached, we scrubbed at rusty metal until our fingers bled, we hauled bucket after bucket of sludge up through the manhole, and we did headstands into the bilges to clear the pumps. It was like working in a labour camp. Pretty soon my brain lost track of right and wrong, my eyes began to deceive me, and all co-ordination and strength disappeared. The days and nights melded into one coconut hallucination, and all eight hours off were taken up with sleep, sometimes without even bothering to get out of my boilie and into the shower. Personal hygiene was simply too much effort when I emerged from the deep-tank – manky, upset and too exhausted even to eat – so a clear stretch of boat-deck sufficed for those brief moments when we were not up to our necks in recalcitrant coconut muck.

I cannot possibly put into words just how distressed I was getting with the job. Apart from anything else there was the coconut. My entire life and everything in it was impregnated, flavoured, coloured and possessed by coconut. While we were out working, someone had been in and carefully soaked our cabin carpet, our bedding and our clothes in coconut. Meals (taken, if at all, on the run in the duty engineers' mess) consisted of potato-shaped coconut, with vegetable-shaped coconut, and meat-shaped coconut, all cooked in coconut oil and covered in thick brown coconut gravy. Pudding was always a chunk of coconut (with optional coconut custard) washed down with a delicious cup of hot coconut tea. One day there was actually an item on the menu which was 'delicately augmented with desiccated coconut'. It was several weeks before the Chief Cook could safely show his face in public again.

As the ship steamed round towards Houston, the interminable drudgery of working until I dropped, sleeping until woken, then working again, continued unabated for a full week. My life consisted of nothing else.

We finished the last deep-tank two hours before our arrival in Houston. I was exhausted. No, no, don't just skip over that. Read it properly – I was EXHAUSTED. Let's have no doubt about it, we're talking shagged out here. I hadn't so much as *seen* the bridge yet, or even the officers' mess where we were supposed to eat. I had hardly seen the sun or moon. Just coconuts in the sky.

Despite my exhaustion, I was so very pleased that we had finished that I dragged my aching limbs, screaming and kicking from the sleep they so desperately craved, into the shower and gave them as good a wash as my drained muscles could muster.

The shower did nothing to alleviate the presence of coconut. It was impossible to gauge where the layers of coconut ended and my skin began, but I did feel better for it nonetheless. It was eight o'clock in the morning, and having worked all night and most of the day before without rest, I was looking forward to the deepest, most deserved sleep any man ever had. My eyes took in the humble bunk and I felt as if I had just been given a general anaesthetic as an uncontrollable desire to sleep washed over me. The bed opened up its loving arms and gathered me in like a long-lost son. I felt the pillow close around my head. My eyes began to quiver shut and – for the first time in a week – a smile drew across my coconut lips and the mists of sleep drew irresistibly into the coconut skies of my mind.

WHUNG! The door flew open. I tried to sit bolt upright (as was becoming the accepted norm on these occasions), but I was face downwards and too tired to spin, so my arse stuck up in the air instead (not a wise move in the Merchant Navy).

'FOR'D STAND-BY, WINDY! Fifteen minutes. Let's getchoo UP THEEERRRREE and . . . I THOUGHT I TOLD YOU NEVER TO GO TO BED! ARE YOU DELIBERATELY DEFYING ME? You cheeky bastard! I'll see you on the fo'c'sle in five minutes. LOOK LIVELEEEEY!'

I dragged my sleepy head up through one hundred fathoms of sleep. What? Get up? ME? I'd only been asleep three minutes! Only the echoes of his screamed commands and the recoil of the slammed door lingered. I could have cried. There must be some mistake. I had to talk to the man. To reason with him. Even at this level of exhaustion, I could not bring myself simply to turn over and go back to sleep – he'd rip my head off – so I decided to go up to the fo'c'sle and have it out with him. Surely the man had *some* compassion? Maybe he'd got the wrong cabin; he should be *pleased* with me for the work I'd done!

I blundered around trying to get myself together. I wished my mum were there to go and talk to him for me. She'd sort him out; but she was thousands of miles away, so this was down to me. I only had one pair of boots and they were turgid with coconut oil. The thought of squelching into them brought my stomach rising up into my throat. I'd given up with socks days before. They'd all rotted away. I looked through the congealed pile of boilies. They were all brown and thick with a heady mix of sweat and coconut oil. So, although I was still glowing from the luxurious shower of all those minutes ago, I had no choice but to ease myself unhappily into a cold, clingy, coconut boilie and a clammy pair of boots without socks. I tramped miserably up the foredeck trying not to come into contact with any of my clothing, but every step sent a cold, phlegmy shiver down my spine.

I took one look at the Mate and, in the absence of my mother, thought better of confronting him. I decided it would be impolite for me to turn down his invitation to participate, and besides, it's not every day one arrives in Houston. The Mate just didn't want me to miss it. Might as well enjoy it now I'm here, eh? No point in making a fuss – the Mate probably had enough on his plate without me giving him a mouthful. I would give him the benefit of the doubt this time. Maybe I'd have a quiet word with him later so he didn't wake me up unnecessarily again. I sighed and took up my position high on the fo'c'sle head for the forward stand-by.

Chapter 2

Come in, Houston

Windy meets America and injures a representative. Notes on Ugly Mobs and tobacco spitting. Life under the spare propeller.

As the ship enters or leaves a port there are three stand-by positions. Down aft with the Second Mate or on the fo'c'sle with the Mate (known respectively as the 'after stand-by' and 'forward stand-by' – both physically demanding posts) or on the bridge with the Third Mate, the Captain and the Pilot, a more cerebral and cleaner post with the added benefit of being somewhere other than where the Mate is. I had pulled the short straw. In fact, not only was it the short straw, it was the shortest of all short straws. With so little sleep and so sticky a boilie, closer examination revealed my straw to be so short that it was actually taller if it was laid down than stood upright.

So I am sorry to report that I probably did not appreciate the true wonder of arriving in Houston as much as I otherwise might. By rights I should have been at least awe-inspired and possibly even agog. In fact, I felt wretched and would gladly have skipped the whole ghastly episode in preference to an hour's kip; but as the pace picked up, the general buzz of a stand-by coupled with a few educational thoughts, roared in my direction from the Mate, helped me to find an interest. The pilots arrived on a launch and climbed a rope ladder slung over the side of the ship, ropes and winches were prepared, tugs were connected by huge wires, and the busy life surrounding the Houston Ship Canal hurried by. The walkie-talkies crackled, the sun shone and, in spite of everything, life began to look a little brighter. At least it was more interesting than cleaning deep-tanks.

Soon our berth hove into view. The Mate shouted across the two yards at me.

'RRRRIIIGGHHT, BABOULENE! Get that heaving line and, when you reckon you can make the distance, sling the heavy end on to the quay for those shore-wallahs to drag our mooring ropes ashore with. And DON'T FORGET TO KEEP HOLD OF THE OTHER END!'

I picked up the coil of cord-like line. On one end was a heavy ball to allow it to be thrown a goodly distance. I looked around at the crew looking at me and I could see binoculars trained on me from the bridge. On the quay, the wharfies were looking up expectantly for the first line to come ashore. It was up to me to make the distance. This was my moment. Anybody could clean a deep-tank, but this was a chance to make a name for myself. It was like playing for England. Here we were at our first international venue and the pressure was on me to heave that line. I stood proud and high on the fo'c'sle and the eyes of the world bore down their sternest test. Would I respond to the pressure or capitulate? The Hero or the Chump?

I wound up for the throw, let out an Olympic roar that made even the Mate jump, and gave it everything. I put my heart and soul into that heave, and as I recovered and looked out at the line, the world went into slow motion. The balled end was off like a rocket, and the entire ship held its breath as the line ate up the miles, but would it make the quayside? I believed very strongly that it would. The trajectory was perfect, the delivery fine. I had responded to the pressure and pulled out a goody. I relaxed and prepared to soak up the glory. The thought even crossed my mind that I might receive a round of applause from both bridge and wharfies for making their jobs that much easier so stylishly.

Suddenly there was a whipping rip in my right hand, and before I could say 'ouch!' my glory was disappearing over the side along with the non-balled end of the heaving line. The whole rope was now airborne. I considered this new turn of events and a couple of indisputable facts raised their ugly heads. Not only was it hard to refute the claim that I had failed to keep hold of the other end as bidden, but it was also becoming evident that I had been a little too vigorous with my throw. Because as the near end of the line left the fo'c'sle head and set off in hot pursuit of the balled end, the wharfies had their backs to us in order to watch the balled end heading off towards Canada. It was prevented in this aim only by the considerable presence of the shoreside bosun. He was oblivious to the approach of incoming enemy fire and was passing from left to right way over by the dockside buildings. He cut a curious figure (as do many Texans) in that, rather like my short straw, he would be taller lying down than he was standing up, this by virtue of the enormity of his stomach. I am able to make this statement with conviction because, after the leaden ball caught him with a sickening thud just under the right ear, he obligingly lay down, thus providing the empirical evidence required to support the theory.

Before lying down, however, he proved that he was not just a man with a stomach. He provided indications of hidden talents. Because as the balled end found its mark, he made the most of his extensive audience by spitting his chewing-tobacco a record-shattering 52 yards across the quay. I did not have time to patent the idea that a sharp and unexpected crack to the right ear is just the tonic a champion tobacco-spitter needs to break world records, because as he assumed the prostrate position, his colleagues were turning their attention back to the ship to ascertain the identity of the assailant. Sticking together like true British Bulldogs – united by our proud history and great country – I knew I was safe amongst my compatriots. As I ducked down to avoid being spotted, each of them to a man dropped what he was doing and pointed at me, crying, 'It was him! It was him!'

Hindered in their joint ambition to interview me by the lack of gangway, a queue of America's Most Ugly – all with large stomachs and mouths full of tobacco – lined up along the quay and began hurling abuse. Now we Baboulenes are well prepared for these things, so I was quick with the right response. A newcomer to ugly mobs might get the idea into his head that they are content merely to line up and present their case with vigour and volume from a respectful distance. He might stand his ground and listen with a critical ear for inconsistencies in their arguments. He would be wrong. It is my unerring experience that the verbal period of mob behaviour is merely a prelude to the main event. I would bet anybody that these stout chappies were merely filling in time with the choral stuff until they could more positively express themselves with blunt instruments. I made a dash for it.

As the gangway went down and the ugly mob (including one member with an ear like a cauliflower) prepared to get down to business, I could be found (or hopefully, could *not* be found) in a reflective mood under the spare propeller on the poop deck.

'Join the Merchant Navy,' I reflected. 'See the world, enjoy the glamour, savour the excitement, meet interesting people *and* get paid for it.'

Huh.

Chapter 3

Barbados

Lessons in how to impress girls in Barbados. Great sexual promise in the air for Welsh gardeners. Windy goes for a sex drive.

As our ship gracefully materialised into the panorama of Bridgetown, Barbados, things were beginning to settle into some sort of cohesive pattern. I was getting a rough idea of how the ship ran, I had caught up on my sleep, and the Windy brain was back in control of the world. The names and routines of the lads around me were taking shape, all the deep-tanks we had cleaned were safely full of cargo, and I was beginning to feel a lot happier with life. The thought of our impending visits to Barbados and Jamaica helped considerably, and the words of the old sages who had been there before, as they held forth in the bar, had us all champing at the bit to get out there with the red paint.

'Make the most of these ports,' saged Cranners, the posh Second Officer from Surrey. 'Most of the places you'll visit on ships are not like this. Here you may taste the fine life and mix with the glitterati; excellent restaurants, haute cuisine and splendid company, in some of the world's most glorious settings.'

'What he means,' interrupted Benny the Dog, 'is that instead of getting rat-arsed and fighting in the port, here we can go up the road to dead flash joints, pretend to be rich and pick up some upper-class skirt. They don't expect no yobbos 'ere, so we can get away with murder. Any plans, Jinx?'

The Second Engineer nodded slowly, his eyes afire with sinful designs. He was known as 'Jinx' because of his uncanny ability to secure the most attractive female companionship out of thin air, combined with his highly agreeable habit of coaxing them back to the ship to meet his friends. It was said of Jinx that, were he to find himself wandering aimlessly across the middle of the Kalahari Desert, he would be stopped by a coachload of nymphomaniac models on a day out, asking if he could find them anything to do for a week or two. His reputation preceded him as an organiser of ladies and mischief, so I was not surprised to find he was extremely well spoken and sported a dashing moustache under sparkling blue eyes.

'Barbados,' he said in a slow drawl, like that of a dastardly blackguard outlining his vile plans to a helpless maiden tied to a railway track, 'is indeed ripe for the deflowering of its high society by uncouth sailors, but it is essential that we have a plan and stick to it, or the word will get round and we won't get a look in. With a little well-placed effort in the early stages, we could be set up for a splendid time. Everybody in? Leave now if you are not prepared to stand by your mates, because my scheme involves a little . . . 'dishonesty'. Any potential squealers should leave now, or expect to lose vital organs. Here is the plan . . .' And with much twirling of moustaches, despicable laughter and rubbing of hands, Jinx outlined his devilry to his cackling cronies.

The following evening at 9.30 two pairs of eyes carefully followed the Mate from the boat-deck as he left the ship and headed into Bridgetown with the Captain and the Chief Engineer.

'Thank God for that,' said a relieved NotNorman. 'Let's go to work!'

We nipped round and knocked on half a dozen doors, and five minutes later a troop of extremely smart young gentlemen in bow ties and suits gathered on the afterdeck where Cranners, who was on cargo watch, had been unloading rather more than he was supposed to unload.

'This is the last one,' he announced, intimating the whirring cargo-wires, taut under the weight of their heavy load. As they were raised slowly upwards and drawn together to a hook, their payload swung slowly into view, emerging from the hold like a submarine from the deep. 'The other six are behind those containers.'

We peered out onto the quay and could see the dark hulks of the other six cars loitering like muggers in the shadows of the containers. 'The keys are in them. Get them back by four in the morning or we are in the deep and unpleasant. OK?'

I was beside myself with excitement. The ship was carrying a cargo of mini-mokes, and part of Jinx's plan was to unload one each and use them around the island at night. A mini-moke is like a small jeep with a Mini engine and frame. Ideal for Caribbean islands, sand-dunes and chicanery. They would be back in the hold before daybreak and nobody need be any the wiser. It was brilliant. We would majestically sweep up to one of the top night spots in seven brand new, identical cars, masquerading as 'International playboys racing each other round the world on our yachts'. Top off a scheme like that with our suits and impeccable good looks, and what girl in her right mind could resist us?

We climbed into our chariots and started them up. I had neglected to mention that I could barely drive, but there was no way I was going to be a passenger with this sort of opportunity around, so while the others snaked off into the warm night air, I brought up the rear with a hop, a skip, a jump, a backfire, and the death knell of a twisting gearbox echoing round the docks. I hoped I would get the hang of it before I had the girl of my dreams in the passenger seat. International playboys are usually racing car drivers and pilots. It would be something of a passion killer to have to attend hospital with whiplash injuries before any romance could get underway. After a while I was knocking along fairly well, and I had to admit that seven clean-cut young men flying through the night in their fashionably understated, identical machines cut an impressive swathe through the island's wide-eyed populace.

By the time we expertly swung in through the grand gateway of Alexis, Barbados's premier restaurant and nightclub, we were certainly turning heads. Nobody was looking at the guy emerging from his Ferrari; they had seen all that before. The smoothie who had landed his helicopter on the lawn a couple of minutes before us might as well have been the bin man for all the effect he was having now. Seven mini-mokes arriving in high speed formation through the trees of the long driveway, and sliding alongside one another with skids and roars, drew all the attention. We leapt out over the doors and all eyes were upon our suave personae as we horsed around, casually trying to give the impression that we did this sort of thing every night. We looked good. We were the rebels. The anti-fashion. The avant-garde. And, just as Jinx had predicted, everyone – including a large number of society's juiciest young ladies – was impressed.

The doormen opened the double doors with bows and without question. We flung our jackets at the attractive hostesses and breezed into the restaurant like a troop of James Bonds. As we clicked our fingers for menus and dispatched waitresses for drinks we could hear the buzz going round. Who were we? Where were we from? What were we doing here?

The place was packed to the rafters with girls, and I was immediately in love. I wasn't quite sure with whom, as yet, but my eyes met hers across a crowded room with about fifteen girls in as many seconds, and I wasn't fussy. Like every other lad of seventeen, I had, of course, had *loads* of sex.

Unfortunately, most of it was with myself. Tonight, however, it was going to be a piece of cake to change all that. Just look around! It was simply a matter of mingling until I found out which lady would be the lucky recipient of tonight's star prize. But my quest was halted by Jinx leaning across and speaking in a quiet but urgent undertone.

'This is the critical time,' he whispered. 'Keep calm now, and we're right in. Don't talk to *anybody*. If we go to them we've blown it. Wait for them to come to us.'

I did not see the logic in this. In fact, I could see no redeeming features to such a policy whatsoever. I wanted to strike while the iron was hot. To make hay while the sun shone. To love and be loved. These girls would certainly not remain available all night and I could see that I was not alone in feeling that Jinx had lost his grip. He should be urged to go to bed. I furtively scanned the eyes of those around me, and found the general loathing was unanimous. In fact, it was becoming difficult to remember exactly what it was that we found to commend the man in the first place. The thing to do now was to talk to these fine young ladies who were so encouragingly maintaining eye contact for just that moment too long. Make them laugh. Be erudite, witty and cultured. Be the lunatic, the lover and the poet – and don't mention sailors. I looked around hopefully for a new leader. A champion to lead the mutiny against Jinx, but I was stopped in my tracks by the approach of a tall brunette with Bambi eyes, scarily white teeth and an American accent. She could have stepped straight off the pages of *Playboy*.

'Hey, guys,' she purred in a deep Southern accent, flicking her hair and posing as if she had reached the end of the catwalk. 'Mah frayands and ah are in a little deeyasagreeyament, and we was a-wondrin' if y'all could heyalp us owut heeya?' I considered a comment about heyalping them out of their payants, but, thankfully, she continued before I could. 'Y'all British, riyut? Wale, Roxanne reckons y'all heeya for the surfin' champeenships and ah reckon y'all moosicians working up the stoodio on the Poyint. Y'all a rock bayand, riyut?'

I hadn't thought of either of these options. 'International playboys racing each other round the world in our yachts' seemed like the gravy to me, but these suggestions were match-winners. I knew the way to handle this one. We would be anything they would like us to be. Anything at all. Say, 'Shucks, you found us out,' and admit to being rock stars. Or surfers. Either would bring home the bacon. Jinx had been rescued by this turn-up, and we all turned expectantly to hear him redeem himself. He could simply tell them they were both right; that we were rock-star surfing champions. The Bee Gees. Anything! I willed him to answer along these lines, but I'm afraid he wasn't up to it. He had gone to pieces.

'Oh, we're nothing special,' he said, fiddling bashfully with his drink. 'We're just here to clean out the drains. Barbados has awful sewerage problems you know.'

I was horrified. He had completely lost the plot now. I began looking for a blunt instrument for him to wear but, amazingly, the girl did not spin on her heel and carry her spectacular body off to some men who knew what they were doing. Jinx was unbelievably lucky tonight. She patted him affectedly on the forearm and shrieked with laughter.

'Come oooon! You can *not* expeyact me to bullieve thayat! You are havin' me *on*! Say, do you mind if me and mah frayands join y'all? We're a-gittin' hayrassed bah those deyad-heyads over theyer and it would be mahty fine of you to lurk after us and git theyem offof our backs.'

She pouted pathetically.

'Of course you may,' said Jinx with chivalry. 'Make some space there lads, the ladies are going to join us.' And with that, half a dozen stunningly appetible girls abandoned their

Ferrari-driving, helicopter-piloting millionaires, and came curving deliciously over to sit with the sailors.

Half an hour later, I was deep in conversation with the most amazing-looking girl I had ever seen without staples in her face and stomach. I never once had to say that we were international playboys racing each other round the world on our yachts; firstly, because Roxanne was nineteen and talkative, and secondly, because I had come up with a brilliant idea. Inspired by Jinx's good fortune, I didn't crow about being a high-flyer; I blushed and insisted I was nothing special. And the more I talked myself down, the grander the belief in my pedigree became. She laughed aloud when I said we were escaped convicts and that our suits were really the property of the band, who could be found naked, bound and gagged in the ballroom downstairs. She wouldn't have it when I said we were private detectives, hired to find Trinidad. It got to the point where I could say, 'Listen. We're a bunch of sailors off a merchant ship and we nicked the cars out of the cargo,' and achieve nothing but delighted adulation and the further cementation of the belief that we were making a film on the plush north beaches. If Jinx had been a bit slicker he could have claimed to have planned the whole thing from the very start.

Not even Gonad – the uncouth Mancunian Engineering Cadet – could spoil things. A quite superb hostess wafted up to him as a fantasy floats into a dream. She licked her lips, then spoke in husky tones, 'While you await your main course, sir, perhaps you would enjoy whetting your appetite with a fondue on the terrace?' Long fingers indicated the French windows that opened on to an impressive balcony overlooking the gardens.

'You betcha!' enthused Gonad, tongue hanging out. 'Is that like doggy fashion?'

Even the weight of such evidence against us was laughed

off. Our lack of finesse, our accents, and the battle the poor hostess was having to disentangle herself from the puckering Gonad – all counted for nothing. The incongruities simply seemed to confirm to the cognoscenti looking on that we were in fact British royalty. We could do no wrong.

During the course of the evening, most of the lads found female companionship of a class and demeanour way above that which humble sailors would usually expect even to meet, let alone grope. I feel sure several of the finest ladies of the cosmopolitan jet set were severely traumatised that night. I would think that even the most practised, cynical gold-digger, having left a club on the arm of a supposed millionaire and arriving at 3 a.m. on the biggest yacht she had ever seen, would possibly adjudge that her ship had come in, so to speak. So as I watched three of these sweet young things heading off with their playboys to go back to the 'yacht', I could not help feeling they would be psychologically scarred for life when they awoke in the morning on a merchant ship, having been unceremoniously rogered by three cheapskates called Gonad, Crate, and Benny the Dog. It doesn't bear thinking about.

Me? Ah. I was hoping we could move on to Jamaica rather than discuss my evening. I know I was doing pretty well at the last bulletin, and as I danced opposite the heavenly body of the hot-blooded Roxanne, futures in Windy Inc. looked set fair to rise. As the lights flashed and the pulsating music whipped us into a frenzy, she began to really let go. She had a freedom of self-expression, an energetic eroticism to her dancing and that air of carefree abandon that are such potent indications of excellent horizontal prospects. She was physically superb, lithe and fit. I was actually scared of her, and yet drawn irresistibly. I could not have walked away if my life had depended on it. I was spellbound. Her long hair flew hypnotically, her eyes were shut and her full lips were gently parted. I kept finding myself staring at her. It was as much as I could do to force myself to shut my mouth and keep dancing; but as the music beat on, and her tantalising motion bedazzled my feeble male brain, I found myself standing still with my eyes on stalks time and again. Just to kiss a vision such as Roxanne, without even having to drug her first, would be the pinnacle of my life. Nothing else would ever live up to the importance of this night. And so far, if I could just control my dribbling, things were going precisely to plan.

Whenever you want a slow dance it never happens. They play upbeat, boogie-and-sweat numbers back-to-back all night. Ogling Roxanne as she writhed provocatively was all well and good but I could not excusably get my hands on her at this pace. As each song drew to its high-kicking finale, I implored the heavens to bequeath to me that soothing saxophone and gentle keyboard intro' that are the green light to leap on top of the girl you've been so carefully shepherding about the dancefloor throughout all the fast ones.

Eventually, my patience was rewarded, and I leapt. We moved into an intense clinch, entwined like climbing plants. I felt her fingers on the back of my neck. This was it. My time had come. Every inch of me tingled and shivered. I had to keep cool. Don't do anything stupid. Don't come on too strong. I decided to skip the fancy stuff and just cling on. Incredibly, fate was on my side, and as the dance built to its powerful middle eight, her upturned face appeared longingly in front of me.

We kissed.

I have no idea how long we remained locked in divine fusion, because, although my lips stuck to their post, my brain and body left the building through the roof like a firework display. After an aeon or two, Roxanne was first to come up panting for air. She licked her lips and her eyes were ablaze.

'Shall we leave?' she panted hungrily, as we returned to earth. I tried for the self-assured, 'You wanna go? Sure.' All cool and off-hand, but I just sort of whimpered meekly. Leave? Together? Just us? This could only mean one thing! This monumentally beautiful girl wanted to be alone with me! She wanted ME! My stomach hit the ceiling, then dropped through the floor. This was My Night. This was IT.

I was convinced she was finding my style and sensual expertise irresistible, and couldn't control herself a moment longer, but I guess, with hindsight, she was probably more keen to leave in order to stop me from humping her leg in public like some kind of demented spaniel. She led the way from the building, and I followed like a hydrogen balloon floating along behind her. If she hadn't been holding my hand I'm sure I would have become lost amongst the chandeliers.

On the way across the grounds to the mini-moke we stopped for another desperate grapple. I was insane with passion, and she was matching me all the way. If the owner of the car upon whose bonnet we were performing our acrobatics had not returned, it might have been all over there and then, but we had to move on. We tried again against a tree before we got to the car, but Roxanne was unhappy with all the people watching.

'Not here,' she purred. 'I want this to be veeeery special. Let's drive out to the beach.'

So with a hop, a skip and a jump, and leaving a trail of gearbox cogs in our wake, we headed off into the night towards the beach.

'This is Sam Lord's castle,' she said as she led me through the grounds of a magnificent castle and down a narrow path lined with palm trees. 'We can be alone down here.'

The path unfolded onto a moonlit tropical beach. The waves tumbled together like playful kittens all along the sandy white shoreline and the scintillating phosphorescence shimmered on their dancing crests as far as the eye could see. The palm trees leant out over the beach like dark old men looking for dropped money, the steel band played infectious, carnival rhythms and the happy sounds of the joyful revellers filled the night air as they danced on the beach and drank exotic cocktails around the open wooden bar. What? Joyful revellers? Steel band? I thought we were going to be alone?

'Oh no!' cried Roxanne as we took in the scene. 'There's a goddam party going on! Let's try further along the beach. There's a waterfall up there.'

I followed her doggedly. Anywhere. I didn't care where. Just anywhere, and the sooner the better. If ninety per cent of my mind was not being ruled by my genitals, I feel sure I would have marvelled at the beauty of the scene, but the only available ten per cent was concerning itself with the basic motor functions engaged in tracking Roxanne, so I was merely frustrated that the scene of my greatest triumph was so overcrowded. Didn't these people have homes to go to?

Further along the beach, we turned inland and walked up a track through the palm trees. The full moon lit our way as only a full moon can, and even my preoccupied grey cells could appreciate the exquisite setting of a tall, dignified waterfall, tumbling into a small lagoon. It was nothing short of breathtaking.

'C'mon!' Roxanne shouted, and ran towards the water, stripping off as she went. The picture of her naked form, reflected gently in the moonlight as she dived into the water, will remain with me until my dying day, but I had a more immediate problem. Girls are lucky. Their state of arousal is not immediately obvious to other swimmers. For men, things are different. Especially for shy young men who are too embarrassed to strip off. There was only one answer. I ran headlong for the lagoon and jumped in fully clothed. Her laughter was challenging and sexy, so I chased her energetically until I caught her. We kissed under the cascading waterfall. She tore at my clothes, and I felt her naked body press urgently against mine. I was at the gates of frantic heaven once more, and *this* time, nothing could stop us from . . .

'What did you say?' I asked her.

'I didn't say anything, I think it –'

'Last one in's a banana. Wheee!' About twenty of the revellers from the beach party were running towards us, stripping off as they ran.

'I do NOT believe this!' I said as my heart and everything else sank. 'This island is like Piccadilly Circus!' The romance faded like a burst balloon.

'Let's go back to my place,' said Roxanne dejectedly. 'My folks will be asleep by now. We'll have the whole place to ourselves.'

On the way to her father's villa, Roxanne teased me the whole time. She wouldn't let me stop driving and get hold of her, but she kept flashing her thighs and touching me, and whispering suggestive things in my ear. She was fascinated that I had maintained a steadfast erection for nearly two hours now, and she was determined to enjoy my frustration. In between teases, she would ask sensible questions and try to put me off, then start on me again, using her sexual expertise to prevent things from wilting. One of the questions she put to me was what I really did for a living. Even with the limited brainpower of a man with an erection, I could see that there was no point in lying. The truth was best. I wanted to see her again, so I might as well be honest – I just came right out with it. I was still explaining as quickly as I could when she lifted her shirt and asked me if I liked her stomach. She took my hand and brushed it over her flat, soft belly. Then she suddenly bent across my midriff and kissed me on the thigh before pulling away once more as I reached for her. Every time I tried to join in, she would back off, insist that I concentrate on driving, and then ask another question. By the time we pulled into her driveway, I was beside myself.

Her father was some sort of businessman, and, judging from the size of his Barbados retreat, I should say he was pretty successful. She opened a side door and I followed her, tiptoeing into the kitchen, then on through a large dining room. We didn't make a sound. As she reached the door at the far end, she looked back at me with big, hungry eyes and I knew my greatest moment was once more beckoning. The moment when I would finally, at long last . . .

'Oh! Hello Daddy!'

. . . meet Roxanne's parents.

'Hey, baby!' came the cheery reply. 'Come on in! We're playing cards with the Robinsons here. Wanna try a hand?'

'Er, no thanks, Pops. This is Windy Baboulene. He's the – what did you just tell me you do? – the British and Commonwealth Surfing Champion. He's here for the tournament at the weekend.'

I sidled into the room. I was not looking my best, still damp and in a bedraggled suit with no shirt, I looked like Charlie Chaplin would if they dug him up now, but what could I do? Apologise for having just been skinny-dipping with their daughter? The Robinsons looked mildly alarmed, but Roxanne's dad, after a lifetime of dealing with difficult businessmen, was equal to it all.

'Ha, ha, ha! Good nickname for a surfer, eh? Windy! And British Champion, eh? That's great! We're all keen surfers here – you could give us some tips! Say, I thought the British Champion was Grahame someone . . . Grahame Park? That's it! Grahame 'Tube-runner' Park. What's happened to him?'

My mind blanked out. How the hell did I know what had happened to him? I'd never even heard of him.

'Oh. Ah. My ol' mate Grahame. Yes. Are you sure? Is he still the British Champion?' The company nodded. They had read it just yesterday. He was still the reigning British Champion. 'Because I am actually the, er . . . WELSH Champion. Roxanne had it a bit wrong there. Welsh Champion. That's it. Out there every day on the river Avon doing my thing!' With a grin and a wink I did a quick impression of how I imagined I spent my days out taming the three-inch swell of the river Avon. The assembly looked a little bemused, but once more Father showed his true grit.

'Well now, that's great! Listen. If you're staying the night you could give us a few tips in the morning if you wouldn't mind. We only get the ten-footers over this side of the island, but they're great for learning on. What do you say?'

I gulped. Only one idea came to mind, and it wasn't one of my best. 'What? Oh! Ha, ha! You thought I said *Surfing* Champion! Ha, ha! No, no, no! You misheard. I'm the Welsh *Turfing* Champion and one of Britain's premier landscape gardeners. I can turf two acres of fallow spinney in under –' Roxanne came to my rescue.

'Oh, very funny Windy. He's so modest about his surfing. Anyway, sorry Pops, but we can't stop. We just dropped in to get some dry things and now we're off to a party. See ya!' And with that she swept me from the room. Within seconds we were back in the car, Roxanne in tears of laughter.

'Turfing Champion? *Turfing* Champion!'

'Shut UP, Roxanne.'

'Mmm-mm-mwhahaHAHAHA!'

'Where NOW?' I said, curtly. I was exasperated. Something had to give soon or I would do myself a mischief. Roxanne's sexy laughter filled the car.

'Mr Sausage never went down the whole way through!'

she giggled. 'All that turfing stuff, and he stood to attention the whole damn time! Mrs Robinson couldn't take her eyes off your groin! She believed you're a surfer all right. She thinks you carry your surfboard down your pants! So how about we go back to *your* place, and go for a ride on your surfboard?'

'Umm, OK,' I said. 'But you might not like it – my *place*, that is – not my, er . . . surfboard. I'm staying on a ship in the harbour.' I crossed my fingers as the news sunk in.

'So you really *are* a bunch of sailors? HA! That's GREAT! HAHAHA!'

She was laughing fit to burst, but I didn't feel humiliated. What was important was that she didn't care that I was a sailor! She wasn't after the glamour and wealth of a Welsh turfer – she wanted me for myself! Nothing could stop us now. If I could get her back to the ship, they would be dragging me off her exhausted body in three days' time so the ship could leave. I drove back out on to the open road with renewed belief. The rollercoaster was on the way up once more. Tonight seemed destined to be The Night, come what may, so to speak.

She began to tease me again as we flew across the island towards the *Global Wanderer*, a ship now transformed in my mind from an atrocious old rustbucket to my sexual utopia. She whispered the details of what she was going to do to me once we were alone in my ear, then she took my hand and placed it under her short skirt. She invited my hand along her bronzed thigh and took a sharp intake of breath as my fingers touched her. She wasn't wearing underwear. She threw back her head and thrust herself hard against my searching fingers. I could not believe this. She refused to let me stop the car, and kept saying, 'Faster, FASTER!' So I drove as best I could, but I wanted to look at her far more than I wanted to look at the road. She was gloriously erotic. I took a couple of bends at ten miles an hour in fourth gear, but – despite the complaints from the engine – she didn't notice. As the car built back up to speed, she built up with it. Her pelvic thrusts became wilder and wilder and her moans became screams. The engine's roar grew louder and louder, she was nearly there. The speed of the night air in her hair grew faster. She was *nearly there*. She squeezed the life out of my hand with her thighs and cried with pleasure. Nearly there. Nearly *there*. She bucked and squealed and bucked again, her rhythm getting stronger and more intense and closer and closer. Her back arched and she lifted herself completely off the seat. She cried through clenched teeth, 'Yyyyyess! Yyyyyeessss! Nooooow Aaaahhhh!' and her eyes rolled back. She froze as if she had been shot, went into the most phenomenal muscular spasm, and had a volcanic orgasm there and then in the car.

So did I.

The car went into a ditch.

Chapter 4

The Return of the Deep-tank

More deep-tanks. Windy is given a job to himself. Explosive reaction of his colleagues over breakfast. The Old Man submits his views.

From my post on the after stand-by I laughed at myself as the sun set on my vibrant paradise. I had adored Barbados, and my mind carries a thousand snapshots of the happy, dancing nights and the rhapsodic tropical ambience, and another thousand of Roxanne's outrageous eroticism. I could see that leaving people and places that had grown on me was going to be one of the hardest things to get used to on my travels. I sighed a happy-sad sigh, and began the wait for the day that I return to Barbados.

Straight from stand-by, I went to meet the other cadets on the boat-deck as agreed.

'Right lads,' said Patch rubbing his hands, 'we've had our break. Two days to Jamaica and – you've guessed it – deep-tank six has to be done before we get there.' My knees went weak and I had to sit down. I'd forgotten about the last deep-tank. 'We'll get a few hours in tonight, then steam in on it all day tomorrow. Windy, NotNorman, you get up the fo'c'sle and get the gear. Giewy, sort out some lights. I'll go and open the hatch.'

So off we went again. Deep-tanks. They didn't mention deep-tanks in the literature. I don't need to tell you how I felt. I was just wishing I'd known this was coming before we'd left port. I'd have jumped ship in Barbados and lived happily ever after. And the reality more than matched my dread. This tank turned out to be the worst of all, having had a good week or two for the coconut sludge to become crusty and solid. We worked hard throughout the evening until nearly eleven, then dragged ourselves out of the mire, tried to stay awake in the showers, then flopped into bed. No sooner had my head hit the pillow than it was six in the morning and I was being shaken awake. Before I knew which way was up, I was back cleaning the tank. Time slowed to a snail's pace as we slogged away at the unyielding tank sides, then time raced by as we had breakfast, only to slow up almost to a halt once more as we worked the endless morning shift back at the face.

The long day dragged on along these lines until we finished the actual cleaning – after some twelve hours of unremitting effort – at around seven that evening. We were all exhausted. We clawed our way out of the deep-tank manhole with what little was left of our fingers and collapsed on the tank lid. We had a five-minute smoko, and then Patch was back cracking the whip.

'Right then. One last push, boys. Home stretch now. Giewy, you clear up the gear. NotNorman, put away the lights. Windy, you put the tank bolts in and the manhole back on, and I'll organise for the tank to be pressure-tested. Go!'

'What?' I exclaimed. 'All those bolts and the manhole back on? I'll be here all night!'

'Character-building stuff, Windy. A job all to yourself – real responsibility for you. Do a good job of this, and I'll get Ahmed to put aside some dinner for you. Chin up! All part of growing up and being British. I'd love to help, but if I don't get showered up quick I'll miss dinner myself!'

And with that the three of them nipped off to do their one-minute jobs, laughing all the way. I was really peeved. Why couldn't they have helped? Four of us could have done the job in half an hour. By myself it would take two. It was totally unfair. I kicked the 'tween-deck bulkhead and hurt my foot. They would all be in the bar swilling away by eight, and I would be out here till ten finishing off their work for them. Crowd of dogs. I kicked one of the manhole bolts and would you believe it, the bloody thing went straight down the hole into the tank. I would have to go and get it back. And it was *their* fault.

'You BASTARDS!' I screamed, and kicked the bulkhead again, but nobody heard. Then I realised that the lights had been pulled up from inside the deep-tank. I'd have to set some back up again just to find that one bolt. I imagined Patch was standing there. I pointed my finger accusingly at him. 'Nuts to you, mate. And nuts to setting all the lights back up just for one bolt!' I roared sternly. 'It'll just have to stay there. Either YOU get it yourself,' I poked his chest firmly to punctuate my point, 'or your precious manhole cover will just have to make do with forty-nine bolts instead of fifty.'

I was brilliant. Masterful and succinct, firm and assertive, and yet not unnecessarily aggressive. I can be pretty devastating when my opponent is out of earshot.

I settled down to the tedious, finger-scraping job of bolting the tank lid and forty-nine fiftieths of the manhole cover back on, grizzling and grumbling the whole time. I eventually finished at 10.15 and tramped off to get showered. I could hear them all in the bar, but I was not interested. I just wanted to turn in and get the worst day of my life behind me.

The next morning was sunny, and I was surprised to find myself in a good humour. I suppose somewhere in the back of my mind it had registered that the last deep-tank was clean. There could be no more. Whatever the day ahead held for me, job-wise it could only be a happy one. I looked out of the porthole and watched the untethered Caribbean Sea flowing by. I felt cleansed and free. If leaving places was going to be hard to come to terms with, the freedom of the oceans in between them and the welcoming embrace of the next unknown new world was going to provide an equal and opposite excitement. Breakfast. There was my next worldly opportunity. One of my first chances to have breakfast in the officers' mess.

I walked off, proud and happy in my crisp white tropical uniform, but I quickly became aware that I was unable to walk in a straight line. It is quite normal to have problems walking against the pitch and roll of the ship. One moment your nose is on the deck and you are crawling up hill, the next you are involuntarily pelting downhill at a run, hoping to God that the ship rolls back before you hit the rapidly advancing bulkhead at the other end. More often than not, as you walk along a corridor, you will be entertained by a person wishing to turn into your corridor at the far end; but they don't. Instead, they slide past from left to right in the Snoopy-skateboarding pose. They want to turn, but they can't. Instead, they disappear completely out of shot but for their fingers desperately clinging on to the bulkhead, then they appear sideways around the corner as if they are climbing over a wall.

But today was different. As I navigated the first corridor, which should have had me staggering from side to side into the bulkheads, I found myself slowing down and beginning to fall over backwards. Then, as I headed across the ship along the second one, I found myself scraping along the left bulkhead. The ship was down by the head. Most definitely down by the head. Quite alarmingly down by the head. If breakfast had not been continuing unabated, I would have thought we were sinking.

'We're a little down by the head, wouldn't you say?' I asked the assembled throng on the Cadets and Junior Navigators' table.

'SERIOUSLY down by the head,' said Patch. 'There's a search party out now, and the big guys will be out there as well after breakfast to find out why. Seems we might be taking on water somewhere.'

The 'big guys' Patch was indicating with his fork full of egg on toast consisted of a Captain, a Chief Officer, a Chief Engineer and a Second Engineer, eating their food as if it was their last meal and discussing the problem of the ship's angle in the water in hushed tones.

'What will they do?' I asked.

'The problem is,' began the Third Mate, a cheerful London lad, known for some mysterious reason as 'The Famous Dick Wrigley', 'that to come down by the head by so much in such a short period of time means we must be taking on considerable amounts of seawater from somewhere. It's got to be pretty serious. They've already sent a deckside party out into each of the holds to look for signs that she's taking water on board, and they'll have an engine-room party check that all the pumps and valves are right. They've already altered course for the nearest port and put out a general call for any ships within four hours of us to head our way in case we're going down. This is really heavy shit, you know.'

'Good grief,' I said. 'If I'd known the ship was going to sink, I wouldn't have bothered cleaning that deep-tank yesterday. We could have had the day off to prepare for our funerals!'

My joke was the rambling of a nervous child. I wanted to ask if there were sharks round here, but Patch asked me a question before I could embarrass myself.

'What time did you finish last night? You didn't come to the bar.'

'No, I didn't fancy it. It was gone ten o'clock thanks to you lot. Oh yes, by the way. One of the little bolts fell into the deep-tank, so I put the manhole back on without it.'

'Eh? Sorry? Say that again,' said Patch. All three tables fell silent. All the jaws had stopped chewing and heads were raised from their plates to look at me. Open mouths full of half-chewed food were on view everywhere. It was a dentist's nightmare. I didn't see the point, but I repeated myself.

'I just said, one of those silly little bolts on the deep-tank manhole cover fell into the blasted tank. I thought forty-nine of them could do the job of fifty, so I did it up without one.'

All eight diners spat egg and bacon across the table as if they'd received a simultaneous and full-blooded whack in the small of the back. Disgusting way to behave, I thought. Uncivilised. They should save that sort of thing for late-night bars. But that was not the extent of it. There was more. All eight leapt from their seats and formed a disorderly scrum around me. It was like being on the Underground in the rush hour, the difference being that in my experience of the Underground, the nearest man does not lift me by the lapels, call me a stupid, STUPID bastard, pass me on to the next guy and run from the room, as was the case here. The next officer did the same thing, as did the next, and so on through the group, until I reached Patch at the end.

'You stupid, STUPID bastard,' he confirmed. 'Go to the poop deck and hide under the spare propeller. Do NOT come out under any circumstances. These guys will tear you limb from limb once they've got the ship back on an even keel. I'll bring you supplies. Do not come out for anything. Your life depends upon you remaining undiscovered.'

He dropped me on the floor and rushed out after his companions.

As you may have gathered by now, we Windys are not slow on the uptake. I had a hazy idea that I might in some way be to blame for the ship hobbling along at an angle of 45 degrees, and although I wasn't sure quite how, it seemed to be the news of the deep-tank bolt that had given them the clue they needed.

'Can I come out yet?' I asked Patch as he arrived with my tea and biccies at eleven.

'No, no, no. Not if you want to live. Ages yet. They're still pumping out the 'tween deck and hoping to rescue some of the cargo. It will take some forgetting, this one.'

'So let's go through it again. Once we'd finished last night, you went off to get them to pressure-test the tank while I put the manhole back on, right? That means they start a pump with a "torque knockoff". The pump filled the tank with water, and would have automatically turned itself off if the tank was sealed, right?'

'Right,' said Patch. 'But some stupid, STUPID bastard left a bolt-hole, so the pressure never got up to the point that would turn the pump off, so water fountained out of the tank up into the 'tween deck ALL NIGHT – filling half the ship with water, and nearly drowning us all. The engineers never cottoned on to it, because never in the history of shipping has ANYONE been stupid enough to leave a hole in a tank which is being pressure-tested. As stupid bastards go, you stand alone. You are head and shoulders above all the other stupid bastards in the world. You are the king of the stupid bastards, and no, you cannot come out yet. Don't move a muscle until we get to Jamaica where you can run off up the road.'

I sighed heavily. What a life.

The bolt-hole incident went to the top, to the Captain, or 'The Old Man', as he is most commonly known. I had hardly even seen him as yet, and had only communicated with him in terms of the odd shrieked, 'Yes, SIR!' in urgent response to one of his authoritatively bowled instructions. I was fetched from beneath the spare propeller by virtue of his summons to attend a personal audience. I had already been in trouble over one or two things I have neglected to tell you about –

problems with about fourteen excellent bad girls from a dance troupe who came back to the ship in New Orleans and severe upset over a teensy oil spill in the Houston Ship Canal which might, I guess, have been considered to be my fault. Now this. It was like being called by the headmaster to account for the matches in your pocket ten minutes after the Chemistry lab has gone up.

Captain Benchmerson sat me in the corner of his day room to sweat it out while he calmly completed a few items of paperwork. Then he took a deep breath and stood up. I was already aware that he came in the family-size model, but as he emerged from his seat, he looked as if he was being inflated beyond capacity. The rate he was going, I didn't think he would ever stop emerging from his seat. However, at around eight feet he tailed off in the vertical plane, continuing to around four feet in the horizontal. He didn't look overweight though – just huge.

Until now, every time I had seen him he'd looked sort of angry, but now I faced him close up his demeanour was more pained. Put-upon. He put me in mind of a bloodhound who has just heard the words 'vet' and 'neuter' in the same sentence. He put his fingertips together and began to pace. When he eventually spoke, it was with the round, authoritative tones of a Victorian headmaster.

'I have heard your name once or twice already,' he began as if reading a prepared statement, 'and it seems you have set about involving yourself in an extraordinary range of monkey business in an alarmingly short space of time. Following today's episode, it now seems we have lost a goodly amount of valuable cargo in a flooded 'tween deck, and it is only through the merciful grace of God that we have a ship left under our feet at all. You know, if you continue along the lines you appear to be following, you could quite possibly bankrupt the entire shipping line single-handedly before the end of this trip. That would put all of us out of a job, and could make you the enemy of a large proportion of the populace. Is this your intention? It certainly seems to be. You seem quite single-minded of purpose.

'Maybe you are a fiendish doppelganger from one of our rivals sent to cause as much bedlam and discord as you possibly can. Are you a fiendish doppelganger? Whether you are or not, I'm sure you are capable of seeing that, from my viewpoint, it is hard to come to any other conclusion. When I take my inventory of cadets I find myself noting "Cadets: Engineering – one; Cadets: Navigating – three; Doppelgangers: Fiendish – One." I can't help myself. There's no other rational explanation. Unless of course, you are simply a fruit cake.'

He paced thoughtfully around his desk as he considered the possibility that I was a fruit cake. His voluminous white shorts following shortly behind him.

He decided to confront me directly with it. 'Are you a fruit cake? Because fruit cake or fiendish doppelganger, it is my job to encourage you to see the error of your ways. To see the light. I would like to persuade you that there is a better life, and that causing the collapse of shipping lines is not a route to success and happiness – particularly not mine. Oh sure, in the short term it may appear to have glamour, but one really needs to take the broader view in these matters, don't you think?

'So what would you do in my position? What would you do to correct wayward fruit cakes and doppelgangers?'

He stopped and leaned on his desk, looking at me. Then his trousers stopped and his entire persona was attentive behind the desk. I got a foggy idea that maybe, for the first time, he actually wanted me to answer one of the questions he was sending towards the ceiling. The only solutions I could think of, such as 'Don't give me any work to do, then I cannot wreck anything', would not have gone down well, so I said nothing, and he set off westward once more from behind his desk, presumably for another chin-rubbing circuit. A second or two later, his shorts set off after him and soon his whole was once more on the move. He had come to his decision. 'I have a few jobs that need doing, so you shall do them for me in your spare time. That way I can train you to do one job without creating fourteen others and give you less time to yourself in which to destroy the shipping line. This is a light punishment. If you do indeed transpire to be a species of charlatan, sterner measures will befall you. You are on thin ice, and I want you to take particular care of your deportment during the rest of the trip. Each time you find yourself upon this carpet, your fate will become less and less pleasant until you will eventually find life insupportable. I hope I have made myself clear. Report to me the next time you have a few hours off, and I will take half of them from you. Good day.'

And with that he and his entourage of temporally displaced clothing collected itself back into his seat like a flock of birds landing in a tree and took up his paperwork once more.

I wasn't quite sure what to make of him. I couldn't understand him half the time, but what I did know was that he was sinister and frightening in a very different way from the Mate, and that I had had enough of both of them. I was determined to render myself anonymous from now on. Neither of them would hear a peep out of me ever again.

Chapter 5

Jamaica

Rising above racism. Windy becomes a Great Man. Philosophy? – Baloney! Fall follows pride all the way back to earth.

As we approached Jamaica, there was a special buzz of excitement amongst those present in the bar. The lads were like children on their way to a funfair. None of them had visited Jamaica before and we had made the pleasant assumption that the island would be similar to Barbados in its prospects for toothsome frolics; the thrill of the unknown added to the licking of lips and the rubbing of hands.

We arrived at four in the afternoon, and channelled our excitement into getting the berthing operations done as quickly as possible so that we could get up the road that night. However, our first contact with the shore-wallahs soundly placed a damper on any such plans. The ship's agent (a local company employed in each port to act on the shipping line's behalf) brought aboard, amongst other things, a sheet of printed paper for the attention of each of us. It said that owing to the racial tension in the area, it was not wise for white men to travel alone around Kingston, the capital. If we intended going ashore at all, it should be in groups, and only to the safer beach areas. Any unnecessary travel into Kingston should be avoided.

I was astounded. As one who had seen racism against ethnic minorities in South London, I had strong views. I even felt a certain kinship with Jamaican culture and music. Maybe this was My Moment. I could be an ambassador, bridging the gap between confused peoples. If I had any principles, I had to stand up for what was right, and I had watched enough American movies to know that courage of this nature might just kick-start a change. I would do what I knew was right. I would not be intimidated by ignorant oiks posturing and bullying people. The Empire was not built by people shrinking away every time half a dozen cowards took over the town on some trumped-up pretext! I was a civilised Englishman, and I would damn well go where I pleased. Let them try to stop me.

The bar was already staging a heated debate by the time I got there, and the general feeling was in tune with mine. We would be in a large group, we would not be looking for any trouble, and there was no way we should allow racism – which we all deplored – to stand in our way. We put on our happy clothes and set off defiantly for the town.

As we walked steadfastly towards Kingston I felt good. I was a member of a strong, united force of hairy-arsed sailors, standing up for what was right. Nobody in their right mind would tangle with *us*. In fact, I felt pretty damn hairy-arsed myself. I curled my lip at people who stared at us, and nodded threateningly at anyone who held my gaze. I've got *your* number, John.

However, as we proceeded, I became uneasy about just how many large black people were dropping into step behind us. They were not pretending to look the other way under the power of my unwavering stare, or scattering before us as we marched purposefully by. They were gathering in a disorganised pack behind us, like sharks building up their numbers before a feeding frenzy. What was worse was that they were *behind* us. It wasn't cool to look anxiously over our shoulders at them, but it was also impossible not to. Paranoia won out, and each of us in turn would sneak a worried look back at the mounting numbers following us.

This was not in the plan at all. At worst, I had expected

some verbal abuse, hurled across the street with accompanying gestures, from groups of lads who were more scared of us than we were of them, but what we were getting was more akin to psychological warfare. And as they gathered behind us, they started a chant. The chant built louder and louder – and I felt less and less hairy-arsed as the intensity of their presence and volume built to unbearable proportions – until finally they all suddenly screamed at once. It was like being shot with a blank. Then they all hooted with laughter at us and shouted crude derision in exaggerated pidgin English before the seeds of another chant began to take root.

I was alarmed to say the least, but what could I do? What could *we* do? There were already about a hundred of them, and they did not seem to know that they were supposed to show a deferential and automatic respect for our British superiority. We could not possibly turn back – our way was blocked – we didn't know where we were going and their numbers were growing all the time. I considered ducking off from the main group. There were occasional alleys on both sides, but would I fare any better alone? I would probably be in more danger. I could feel panic beginning to grip as the latest spine-chilling chant built to an overwhelming volume. *HELP!*

The group of followers was getting closer to us all the time as their numbers swelled. The leaders were almost breathing down our necks and the intimidation was insufferable. I had tried to move myself to the front of our group, but it quickly became apparent that I was not the only one with the idea of appearing to be a leader of men. I felt self-control leaving me and I broke into a trot to get to the front. Before I knew what was happening, we were all running flat out, rushing along unknown roads, with the baying mob bearing down behind us in hot pursuit. The trees and buildings swirled around me as I tried to keep running, and frantic shouts from my colleagues penetrated my sensibilities enough to keep us together. We rounded a corner and my heart was filled with dread. Ahead of us on the street was another large group of dangerous-looking black youths. They were not expecting us, but they quickly managed to add two and two, and set about cutting off our path. We were outnumbered by about two hundred to one and would have to fight for our lives. The situation was – 'Quick, in here!' shouted Jinx.

I swung round and saw a large wooden door, through which local civilians and petrified sailors were retreating like rabbits into a warren. The door slammed behind us and a cast-iron key the size of a tennis racquet turned reassuringly in the lock. I had dived in gratefully, but our troubles were far from over. Inside was a bar with around a dozen pool tables and about twenty bemused local lads. The shouts and boom of a hundred angry men hitting the sturdy door all at once rang through the air, and the fears of those locked inside – both black and white – took over. A frantic battle broke out, and the frustrated army outside expressed itself by throwing heavy objects through the (thankfully) high windows, and pummelling the door.

I observed (from my position in a corner behind a fruit machine) that a pool room and bar is a particularly unfortunate place to indulge in violence. Ready to hand are cues for splitting heads, broken bottles for removing layers of incorrectly-coloured skin, and heavy, hand-sized pool balls for attracting attention across a goodish distance. At the height of the battle, I actually noticed people desperately searching for the correct change to insert into a pool table in order to secure a fresh supply of ammunition.

Eventually, the fight on the inside became a stand-off, with the white men hiding behind the drinks counter at one end of the room, and the black men behind a line of upturned pool tables, each speculatively hurling bar-room items at the other. Bleeding individuals struggled for cover, there was even a lady lying unconscious in the centre of the bar. I have never been so scared in all my life. Outside, the police had arrived, and were calming the mob with batons and water-guns.

Around half an hour later, the door caved in and dozens of police swept purposefully through the mêlée. We were grateful to be arrested, bundled roughly into the back of an armoured van and taken off to prison. Emotions ran high as we were questioned through the night about the incident, and it was early the next morning before we were given an armed escort back to the ship.

That night there was further trouble in Kingston, and a man was murdered by muggers when he decided he would stand his ground and fight for his wallet and passport.

The atmosphere was heavy and grievous as I lay on my bunk in the dark and reflected on what had happened. I was hollow and drained with shock, and my stomach heaved as I contemplated what might so easily have been much worse. Here was I, a fun-loving easygoing kinda guy, without an ounce of malice in my soul, and here was a frenzied crowd of people who didn't even know me prepared to tear me limb from limb simply because of the colour of my skin. In South London I had thought I understood what racism meant for those suffering from it. I had had no idea, and my new-found understanding shook me rigid. Part of me wanted to hide until we got away from this god-forsaken place, and part of me wanted to march into the centre of Kingston, stand on a soapbox and preach to an astonished and respectful crowd, struck dumb by my forceful rhetoric. That was what was needed here: someone with passion and knowledge to cut through the petty racism and make these people feel that they could *do* something about the state of their country. These people did not need suppressing; they needed understanding. That's what I would be. A missionary and preacher. I would devote my life to good works, to improving the lives of the oppressed and the needy.

A day or two later I was discussing my new-found morality with an English vicar I'd met on the north shores. He was a splendid old chap, living in a beachfront house near an amazing place called Runaway Bay with his family. We sat out on his veranda for two long, hot evenings watching the props guys lower the orange sun and pull up a perfect moon. We listened to the sounds of the night and the waves lapping at the coral-white beach. We drank iced vintage whisky and talked to the stars about the problems of the world.

Reverend Hall was a wise and worldly man, but I did a lot more talking than listening. Time and alcohol were curing my cowardice. I had discovered a new and better inner me, and I was keen to tell people how soulful I was. The prevalence of evil and wrong-doing had come home to me on my travels, and I now realised that it behoved me, as an educated, civilised human being, to rise above the general desperation of the world and give something back. To educate others, to lead by example, and to give up material things. Compassion was the answer to the world's problems, and I would, from now on, devote myself to the teaching and practice of higher goodness.

And with the whisky glowing passionately behind my eyes, I meant every word.

I was becoming rather pleased with what a well-rounded chap I was turning into, intoxicated not only with the whisky, but with the depth and breadth of my capacity to forgive, to lead a good life and to resist mindlessness. I told him how forgiving I had been to the other cadets as they left me alone to work on jobs that they should have helped me with. How understanding I had been of NotNorman's puppy-like ignorance. How patient I had been with the Mate despite his megalomania. Good grief – I was virtually a saint already.

Reverend Hall raised his glass to the stars. 'Good lad,' he said, 'you're a good lad. If only there were more like you. I could lose my faith if I didn't meet the odd spark of hope like yourself. Do you know what? Only today I took delivery of a brand new mini-moke, and it seems some dirty dog has been out joy-riding in it before I've even touched the dashed thing. There's 200 miles on the clock, a big dent in the front, the gearbox is like a bowl of porridge, and the engine's had six bells thrashed out of it. Now why can't more people have your attitude and show a little respect for their fellow man? Can you answer me that?'

For some reason, I couldn't.

Chapter 6

The Planting of Seeds

Eavesdropping pays a scary dividend. Why mules die in Panama. Fear of David Attenborough. Making money from Colons. The mules live on!

After Jamaica there was a general buzz about the impending Pacific. We had finished with the Gulf of Mexico and the Caribbean, and were heading for pastures new in the agreeable shape of Australia. All we had between us and the Lucky Country was an interlude by the name of the Panama Canal, and a truly vast quantity of seawater. Not only that, but we had managed by a minor miracle to be clean enough by 8 a.m. to attend breakfast in the dining room. Breakfast is a major event on board ship, attended by men who have already clocked up a couple of hours behind the plough before the eight o'clock bell. In the case of us cadets, we would generally have been out working on deck since six, meaning an appetite is built up, and a quite astonishing quantity of food can be devoured at the first opportunity. Being present is a bit like witnessing a food fight, except the food flying into people's faces does not splatter amusingly – it gets swallowed whole.

There were five full courses. Reading from left to right, they lined up as follows: To begin, we would ingest some variety of fruit. If we were in a tropical port, this would be whatever weird and wonderful dongly things could be found and picked from the trees in the surrounding area at sunrise by hungover cadets. At sea it seemed exclusively to consist of half a grapefruit. Half a grapefruit-worth of endless giggles for the more childish amongst us as the acidic citrus content caused its recipient to curl his lip in an involuntary Elvis impersonation.

Next would come a cereal course. An innocuous matter of milk, sugar and cereal, occasionally given a sinister mobility if some insect species had set up home in the cereal store. Pouring the milk on the cereal would cause all livestock therein to panic and strike out for the shore. An off-guard first-tripper (mentioning no names) who is used to his cornflakes remaining relatively sedentary during the process of being eaten, might quite understandably fall off his chair and bang the back of his head on the floor before leaping up and down in a busy dance routine involving pointing at the offending breakfast bowl and rhythmically choking, panic-stricken, on the contents of his mouth. All good fun for the old sea-dogs, who are quite used to shovelling insects into their mouths and are grateful for the extra protein.

The first-tripper insect-dance course was followed by a fish course: variety, freshness and acceptability dependent upon region and season. After this we had 'eggs to order' in any one of their myriad manifestations. Assuming you were able to impart to the Asian Chief Cook (via several intense tutorials) the detailed specifications of your eggs, the sky, as they say, was the limit, your wish his command, and Bob a close relative. However, Asian chefs do not normally cook eggs European-style, and if you failed to communicate the essential data this course was more prone to being a globular mess somewhere between an omelette and a road accident.

Fourth came the meat course. Yes, we are still at the breakfast table. Each day saw maybe liver, or pork chops, or steak, served with one of the equally numerous potato dishes.

BLUE ROAD

The whole affair was then topped off with tea (or coffee) and toast with marmalade (or jam) and a discussion of the day ahead, with the relaxing music of the twelve-man Indigestion Concerto heaving away mezzo-forte in the background.

On this occasion, as NotNorman and I assumed the position, only the Captain, the Mate and the Chief Engineer were at the middle table. We nodded a cautious and respectful 'Good morning.'

NotNorman and I chatted self-consciously through our Elvis and insects, but by the time we were attacking our globular mess we had fallen into silence. An onlooker would think we were in that quiet, introspective mood which is so often a feature of earnest men with an honest day's toil ahead, but they would be wrong. Our ears were like satellite dishes, our eyes wide with disbelief, and our concentration intense.

We were eavesdropping.

'Surely things have improved since then?' the Captain was saying. 'It's been five years since I last went through the Panama Canal, and it was so bad then that I complained to the High Commission. I understood something was being done.'

'Apparently,' continued the Mate, waving his fork about and forcing a giant bolus into each cheek to facilitate speech, 'apparently, it's getting worse 'cos the ships they have to pull are getting bigger and bigger. It's certainly no better than the first time I came through twelve years ago. The mules still get pulled into the water, and they still can't get back out again 'cos of the Canal's steep sides. I was here last year and I saw two get pulled in. Dreadful it was. Really dreadful.'

'Ooooh, I know,' said the Chief, who, despite his enormous size, had a voice like Sybil Fawlty, 'but things have improved. They used to just let them drown. At least they shoot them now.'

THE PLANTING OF SEEDS

As the conversation continued in this vein, NotNorman and I ceased our mastication and stared at each other in silent horror. I was aghast. I'm not saying I was scared or anything. No, no. It's just that some of life's harsher realities – especially those involving the struggle of dumb animals against lethal forces they don't understand – reduce some people to tears. And I don't just mean the kind of things we all dread, like the yelp of a puppy in time with the bump under the car wheels; the three-legged mouse hobbling pathetically away from the cat; the *zing!* of the Flymo blade as my dad sliced the top off our hibernating tortoise with the lawn mower. It can be far more subtle than that. It's nothing to do with being macho – strong men can be sensitive too, you know – but just the sound of David Attenborough's syrupy narration has me reaching directly for the remote control. You can be sure his slavering tones will accompany slow-motion pictures of a pack of wild dogs tearing into an exhausted zebra, or big cats chasing helpless little bambis about. I can't take it at all, I just feel . . . excuse me a minute.

Sorry. Ahem, someone at the door. Anyway, suffice to say that the thought of watching drowning mules getting shot caused me to worry for the lads. Some of them might be squeamish. But there was worse to come.

'You'll never get –' gulped the Mate, stopping mid-sentence to force what looked like a sideboard down in his throat, 'you'll never get any change as long as it costs them nothing to use mules to pull the ships through the canal. We have to feed 'em, so they cost nothing to run, and if one breaks down they just eat it and wheel in a replacement! No problem! Basic economics – you'll never get any change.'

'Ah, but you obviously haven't seen the latest 'M' notice, have you?' said the Captain. 'They are definitely tightening up. The new directives insist that from now on, all mules, while physically engaged in the towing of ships, will have to wear a hard hat.'

'Oh good,' I thought. 'At least somebody is doing *something*.' I don't know how I thought a hard hat would help a drowning mule, but I was desperate for any hope I could cling to, and so was all for it. I could tell from NotNorman's demeanour that he had been shaken by what we had heard, poor chap. He looked a little sick. To be honest, I don't think NotNorman is really man enough for this line of work. We exited stage left with our breakfast unfinished and depressing pictures of what the next day would hold haunting our minds.

There was only one night's stop at an overexciting Panamanian port by the (rather apt) name of Colon, before our passage through the Canal. I was on cargo watch all night, so would miss out on the trip up the road, and – being macho and carefree – once I'd heard what Jinx had schemed up for *this* evening, I was dreadfully disappointed to find myself unable to attend. They were all going to go out for a penguin dance.

The story was that a handsome cash-dollar profit could be made by pretty young sailors who were not afraid to be a little cavalier with the heart-strings of Colon's substantial homosexual population. Apparently, an eyelash-fluttering cadet could, without too much expertise, tempt a woopsie Colonite to part with $20 simply by leading him suggestively by the belt up a side alley. The cadet then holds the gaze of his victim and drops sumptuously to his knees while slowly undoing the victim's belt and fly. With all the promise of the moment, the cadet licks his lips and slowly draws the Panamanian's trousers down, then in one lightening movement he does the belt back up round his victim's ankles and runs like the clappers, clutching his ill-gotten gains.

Working on the principle that a cadet with his trousers *up* can run faster than a Colonite with his trousers *down*, our protagonist is a swift $20 up on the evening for ten minutes' work. An ingenious basis upon which to start a business, but not, I would imagine, one for the faint-hearted. The expression 'penguin dance' arises from the movement a gentleman makes when trying to give chase with a belt done up around his lower legs.

So as the lads headed off up the road with such money-making adventures in mind, you can probably appreciate my chagrin at being stuck on a midnight-until-six cargo watch. I would *love* to have gone, of course, but I had to work. Great shame and all that, but there you are. And don't concern yourself on any moral grounds over such an unprincipled money-making scam. These things have a way of balancing out. For every Colonite left trouserless, hopping about in an alleyway, suffering from unrequited love and a lightened wallet, there was a sailor getting just as thoroughly laundered by one of the local ladies. As with most professions, the girls who put the most into their work reaped the greatest rewards. The most enterprising would, for an increased fee, spend an entire night with the sailor on his ship. She would then put a great deal of effort into delivering her goods until the hapless victim was reduced to a complete standstill, then delivering again until he could give no more and was begging her to stop, then delivering yet again until he was smiling but unconscious. The next thing said victim would know, it was morning. Girl? Gone. Wallet? Gone. Credit cards? Clothes? Luggage? Jewellery? Gone. Sextant? Toothpaste? Keys? Shoes? Light bulb? Toilet paper? Carpet? You name it, it was gone. Clever girl – stupid sailor. And he'd paid her as well.

Colon is one of those serious sailors' ports, where all the worst sailors' stories are acted out for real every night. Debauched, licentious, criminal, drunken, fighting nights out

69

with no holds barred. Some make money, others lose heavily. Some are hunters, others are prey. Some are streetwise and slick, others are Giewy.

The Famous Dick Wrigley and I spent the greater part of our cargo watch leaning over the side watching the intrepid adventurers come and go in their various states of dishevelment. In between returning heroes, I took the opportunity to ask him about the mules at the Panama Canal.

'Ah, you've been told have you?' he asked.

'I heard the Old Man and the Mate talking about it. Is it true that the mules fall in and get shot? It sounds dreadful.'

'Yip. I'm afraid it is. They use mules because they are free to run. The ship has to feed them as we go through, so the service doesn't cost them anything to provide. I know it's harsh, but not all the world is like Britain. The real fun, though, is that YOU are the murderer! It will be your job to feed the mules and try to stop them going in. The Chief Steward will give you a bucket of food, and you have to use it to tempt them to move. Don't give them any – just let them chase you – that way, they pull the ship along. If you give them too much, they just stop and go to sleep. Give them enough to know what's in the bucket, and to get their taste buds fired up, then run off so they follow you. Simple.'

'But what about when they get pulled in?'

'Well, when the ship begins to tug them towards the edge, it's your job to try and tempt them inland with the bucket. If they get pulled in, it's more your fault than anyone else's. If you do your job properly, they ought to be OK. But don't lose any sleep over it. It will be devastating for you to have to watch them desperately struggling to avoid drowning only to get shot, but so long as you've done your best, nobody will hold it against you. Try not to blame yourself – it will be a miracle if none get pulled in.'

This was dreadful, and I had plenty more questions, but we were interrupted by the noise of a returning sailor. Whoever it was, he was trying to get back on board without being noticed, so our curiosity naturally took us to the top of the gangway to meet him. It was 3.30 and it was Giewy. He sidled through the shadows towards the gangway. When he eventually saw us, he winced visibly at being discovered.

'Giew!' he said pointedly in reply to our raised eyebrows. 'I do NOT want to talk about it!'

We were puzzled at first, but as he got closer the course his evening had taken became clear. He was clutching $20 and was having considerable difficulty in walking properly.

Once the ship had freed itself from outrageous Colon, the canal and all the horrors it represented lay ahead. I tried to wangle myself a bridge watch for the passage in order to secure an interesting and active role at the centre of things (without any mulean death-throes to witness) but it was no use. Patch came down from the Mate with the expected bad news.

'Right, Windy. Go to the Chief Steward and get a bucket of apples. You are on the fo'c'sle for a forward stand-by looking after mules. NotNorman, you're amidships with a bucket of carrots. Gonad, you're down aft – sprouts. Right, before you go, let's run through a quick mule tutorial.'

So Gonad, NotNorman and I exchanged shrugs and began to learn the techniques for our most vital of roles: stopping mules from falling into canals. Through a series of role plays, with one of us playing a wayward mule (by bending over, using our hands as ears and braying) and another as a cadet, we learned how to extract maximum effort from them while giving up a minimum of groceries. We also learned how to tempt the mules away from death by expert proffering of the most succulent produce. For real emergencies we were additionally equipped with a Hobnob in the back pocket.

Two hours later as we approached the first cutting, I was fully prepared. I had a handsome bucket of large green apples and a giant pooper-scooper (apparently first-trippers are also responsible for tow-path hygiene).

'They're in there!' shouted the Mate, pointing to a shed-like structure on the quay. It didn't look much like a stable, but there you are. These were foreign parts.

We exchanged lines with the shoreside crew, then it was time for me to take up my position on the quay. I climbed down the ladder and walked up to the shed with my bucket of apples and my pooper-scooper. I walked all round the shed. Then all round it again, this time scratching my head. There didn't appear to be an entrance, let alone a proliferation of mules.

'COME ON, WINDY!' screamed the Mate from the fo'c'sle. It sounded like he was right next to my ear. 'Let's get a wiggle on down there!'

'But there's no entr—'

'JUST GET ON WITH IT!' he roared, his tonsils waving in the wind. I was becoming conscious that the whole operation was probably waiting on me, so I walked round again. There were various knobs and switches here and there on the shed, so I thought I'd best try a couple to see if a door would open, but as soon as I touched the shed, I regretted it. The shed exploded into life and roared at me like a lion with a V6 engine. My head swam trying to get a grip on things, then the entire building jolted a couple of feet, and set off towards me like some unearthly monster. I had heart failure and stumbled backwards shouting something along the lines of 'WuaahOOOOARGGHH!' I then fell on my arse, and my world became a mass of apples and pooper-scoopers. When it cleared, the skyline consisted entirely of delighted, laughing faces and snapping cameras. Even the Pilot was doubled up, shrieking with laughter on the bridge wing.

The realisation that the 'mule' was a machine was just dawning on me when, just audible over the sound of my cardiac arrest, there was a boom from amidships, a cry of surprise, and I saw NotNorman leap backwards, flailing his gangly arms and legs around. He too sat on his pooper-scooper, distributing carrots hither and thither. Then there was an even more distant boom from down aft where Gonad was having five years removed from his lifespan and was liberating a bucket of sprouts.

I couldn't shout at anybody, because there wasn't a soul on board who could function properly for laughter. These 'mules' were in fact dirty big engines that ran on rails to haul the ships through sections of the canal. Why I didn't notice the rails I shall never know – I tripped over the bloody things enough. We were forced to pose in front of these contraptions with our buckets and vegetables as if trying to feed them, and behind them with pooper-scoopers as if awaiting a parcel, and proper pillocks we looked too.

As if this was not enough, there was an additional blight to compound my misery. There is a code of practice on board ship regarding practical jokes, the thrust of which being that the sucker (i.e., me) has to buy each of the perpetrators who have been successful in catching him out (i.e., everybody else) a case of beer. This is apart from and in addition to the humiliation at the time and the incessant ragging from the moment the trap is sprung until the last-ever human being finally leaves this planet, wiping his eyes with mirth at me getting duped into feeding impostor mules six hundred million years before.

Chapter 7

Butterflies

A humble monster frightens the bridge watch. The homicidal nature of the washing-lines Grimm. A cross-eyed sack monster frightens the bridge watch.

The Canal can take a few days to negotiate, and although some points were man-made and perfunctory and others positively dangerous, on account of the warring factions on either side throwing explosives at one another, long stretches were extremely beautiful. With steep-sided hills climbing skyward, and teeming with tropical plants and wildlife, it was definitely good on the eyes.

I was on the bridge during one such section and life was cooking along most acceptably. The Captain was strutting about keeping an eye on things, Cranners – the Second Officer – and I were fixing positions on the chart, and the Pilot was looking through his binoculars and giving helm commands to the Seacunny on the wheel. The radar, depth sounder, and various other animated gadgets whirred and clicked reassuringly, and efficient activity ruled the bridge.

Now follow me closely here, because in two shakes things moved on from this scene of nautical bliss to one of discord and unhappiness as our mood was shattered by the entrance on to the bridge of – a butterfly. It flew in through the bridge-wing doors without so much as a by-your-leave. Well, as I am sure you can appreciate, our reaction was one of flat panic. We are but simple people, and out of the blue, as cool as you please, in flies a butterfly to ruin our day. We all screamed in unison and dived for cover as if the butterfly was packing heat.

Yes, I did say butterfly; but this thing was massive. I thought it was a pterodactyl. A pterodactyl looking mighty pissed off about something. Maybe it had just found out that the dinosaurs became extinct five million years ago. Whatever – I thought it was going to eat me.

One low flap of its mighty wings carried it about two hundred yards, and it definitely looked hungry. I wrapped myself as close to the back of the radar as I could and put my hands over my head.

'Er . . . get that, will you, Cadet!' commanded the Captain casually from his position on all fours behind the chart table.

You know what you can do, I thought, peeping out from behind the radar. I couldn't see anyone. The bridge was completely clear of people and no one was steering the ship as she steamed serenely along the narrow channel of the Panama Canal. More importantly, there were no monsters flying about. I shook my head and looked again. Nothing. If it existed at all, it must have flown directly across the bridge and cruised straight out the other side. I raised my eyes cautiously from my position of safety at the same time as other people's eyes were emerging from theirs. The eyes of the Seacunny appeared from where he had dropped like an Italian soccer striker behind the helm. The Second Mate's appeared from behind the door that led to the rest of the ship – he'd actually left the bridge – and the Pilot's peeped out from his position crammed into the cupboard. The Captain's then appeared over the chart table as he summed up the question being asked by every pair of eyes.

'Has . . . er . . . has the bloody thing gone?'

A tentative look round seemed to establish that it had, so we emerged sheepishly from our hidey-holes. We straightened our clothes and dusted ourselves off, feeling a little foolish at our reaction to what was, after all, a butterfly. It had all been so sudden. It was hard to believe it had happened at all. If there hadn't been so many others suffering the same soiling sensation as me, I would have sworn I'd imagined the beast.

As dignity returned once more and the ship was brought back on course, Cranners said that he hadn't really been scared, he'd just left the bridge by coincidence. Then the Captain said *he* hadn't been scared, he'd only jumped because of the way we incompetents had reacted, and he told us all off for deserting our posts. Then the Pilot said *he* hadn't been scared, he'd just gone to the chart cupboard to fetch something (and presumably decided on a whim to leap in and close the door behind him) and the Seacunny said he had fallen over. I was therefore blamed for my ridiculous overreaction to a piffling butterfly, and told that if I couldn't uphold basic professional standards I wouldn't be allowed on the bridge. There was no one below me in the hierarchy I could blame, so I just had to swallow my pride and apologise, swearing under my breath at the injustice of it all. Why did the buck always seem to stop with me? I moodied away at the situation and was determined to punch Giewy after my watch, but then an idea began to crawl into my razor-sharp mind. I was reminded of a night out just before I joined up, and I began to hatch a delicious plot.

It was back at home, about a year before, when my friends and I were all sixteen and terrorising the town on our mopeds. We were indulging ourselves in the usual way, riding from one pub to the next, getting steadily more unsteady. As the evening drew towards its ridiculously early close (well, you know what British pubs are like) the gathered multitude of tipsy teenagers was not yet looking for bed. We wanted more from our Saturday night. It wasn't even midnight yet, and there was plenty of dancing left in our legs and plenty of thirst yet to be quenched. So it was with sincere urgency that questions began to circulate concerning whose parents were away, and whose house could therefore be commandeered for partying purposes. And it was with one arm forced up her back that Tracey Grimm admitted to her father's absence until at least 3 a.m. Sir Isaac Newton would have been proud of the equal and opposite enthusiasm that the masses generated to counter Tracey's reluctance, and before you could say *Philosophiae Naturalis Principia Mathematica* (which we couldn't) the takeaway beers were being taken away, and the mopeds were eating up the mile and a half to Tracey's house.

Tracey had a rich father and an impressive house in a private road. However, those of us who knew her dad also knew how he got his money. With a string of betting shops, a company which repossessed cars, and a dodgy loans outfit, he ran a sort of mafia and was *not* a man to be messed with. Those who did not know him personally knew him by reputation, so despite the apparent joy at the prospect of a party, there were private fears that 'Grimbo' might return.

Anyway, like true drunk teenagers, as the music boomed, the lights went down, and Grimbo's drinks cabinet decanted itself into our brains, we quickly forgot our concerns and the party was soon doing a roaring trade.

It was about 1 a.m. and I was dancing in a huge room with a couple of hundred others when Tracey, who was looking anxiously out of the windows at the front of the house, saw a car enter the drive. None of us had cars – most of us were too young to drive anyway – so two and two quickly made four.

'Daddy!' she cried, and despite the enormous noise of the music, the whole party froze, the music ground to an ominous halt, and the only sound to be heard was that of jaws hitting the floor all around.

'Oh SHIT!' said somebody, accurately. 'He'll kill us!'

And it was with focus and determination that we all set off for the French doors at the far end of the huge room and legged it off down the garden at the back of the house.

The combination of a brain full of booze and the pack mentality of dozens of people running desperately down the garden like an Olympic 100-metre final made things rush, so I was ill-prepared for strangulation, but that was what I got. Being particularly scared of Grimbo (I upset him once with a foot pump and a Jewish parrot, but that's another story), I made good time over the first half of the course and was one of the first to make it to the washing-line that was stretched across the garden but invisible because of the dark. I was running as fast as I could when it took me perfectly by the throat. It stopped me dead in my tracks from the neck up, swinging the rest of me up in the air until I was horizontal, some eight feet off the ground.

'YEULK!' I said sensibly.

The next thing I knew my whole body from my ankles to the back of my head hit the ground with a sickening thud, the impact knocking all the wind out of me. My body convulsed and choked as it attempted to begin breathing again, and all around me my fellow revellers were: (a) being taken by the throat; (b) yeulking heartily; and (c) causing the ground beneath me to shudder as they arrived prostrate on their backs.

But my thoughts were not with them. I knew that any second now, a large and violent Grimbo (his suspicions aroused by the sound of nearby yeulking) would be round the back looking for party-goers to castrate with a rusty knife. I summoned all my strength, and with the supreme willpower of a true Baboulene, dragged my shattered body into the hedgerows. By the time the footsteps and long shadows emerged along the side of the house I was watching intently, hopeful that one of my good friends who didn't have the strength to hide would be caught and beaten up so I could nip off. However, things are not always as they seem, and, as the shadows moved into the light, I saw that it was not Grimbo at all. The footsteps, shadows and car belonged not to the Brother Grimm, but to Kev Mitchell. And he was not a Mafia hit-man. He was one of us. He had arrived late in his father's car. A seventeen-year-old kid had frightened the daylights out of one hundred and forty of the South's coolest dudes, and red faces were the fashion accessory of the evening. We crawled sheepishly from our hiding places and trudged back to the house, our pride and throats in tatters.

We sat around talking for a while, waiting for our hearts to slow down, and decided that what we had done was pathetic. Not only were our bikes lined up at the front and our coats in the house, which made running away pointless, but there were also dozens of us, and only one Grimbo. We decided that even if he did return, there was no point in running away, we would just leave his stupid house, dismissively saying 'Yeah, yeah, yeah' to his rantings and amble off into the night. There was nothing he could do about it – he would just have to lump it. Thus decided, the party began to move again, and soon it was back up to full speed.

By 2 a.m. the beer stocks were getting a little low, so my mate Nick and I decided to ride off to my house to pick up some more from my father's ample supply. We set off into the night air, and as we hurtled along the country lanes, an idea gripped me. I looked sideways at Nick, and could see from his gleeful expression that the same idea had occurred to him. We stopped and organised our strategy, then swung the mopeds round and headed back to Tracey's. As we approached the driveway, we adopted the agreed formation, side by side with around five feet between us thereby giving the appearance from the house of an approaching car. It worked like a charm. The faces of all the brave young men who were going to tell Grimbo to shove his Rolls Royce where the sun don't shine looked decidedly anxious as they whizzed past the hall window towards the French doors. As we turned off our engines, the night air was full of the throttled cries of young men yeulking – it was like a holiday in Austria – and the driveway shuddered beneath our feet as those brave yeulkers hit the unforgiving ground under the washing-line. We adopted the gruff, angry tones of a Mafia murder cell and marched purposefully around the side of the house. Desperate young men were trying in vain to drag themselves towards cover and were praying that another might be chosen. The bushes all around the garden shook at our approach, the ground beneath the washing-line was strewn with crippled bodies, and red faces glowed like Christmas lights from the trees and hedgerows all around. It was tremendous.

Nick and I needed those mopeds after that, I can tell you.

So, as I say, the reaction of the brave warriors on the bridge reminded me of Tracey Grimm and her party, and a similarly devious plan formed in my mind. After my watch, I collected NotNorman and he played Igor to my Frankenstein as we spent a constructive half-hour creating a monster butterfly. We used a black plastic bag filled with gunny sacks. Great big flappy cardboard wings, hinged to bounce up and down realistically; massive unearthly crossed eyes on the ends of long wobbly antennae, and a big angry mouth full of pointed yellow teeth. Then, while I snuck up on to the monkey island (the area of exposed deck above the bridge) Igor beetled off for his camera. I attached about six feet of thin rope to the brute's back and awaited NotNorman's thumbs up. He positioned himself to take a prime shot through the bridge-wing window, then gave me the green light. I took the hideous beast and threw it upwards and outwards as if setting it free. It set off for the sun until the rope became taut, then it changed its angle of attack and peeled off in a beautiful parabola for the bridge-wing door beneath my feet, like a World War II Spitfire beginning a strafing run. It was perfect. The creature flew directly on to the bridge with good speed, at the perfect height and, although it entered the arena bum-first (which may have been MORE frightening), it righted itself in time to present its fangs. I heard the simultaneous cries of five alarmed men in fear of their lives, and there was a bit of a scramble. Panic filled the air as the assembled officers squeezed up tight together into the limited cupboard space. I made good my escape and met NotNorman in the bar. He said that the pictures would be fantastic, featuring five men with their mouths open and their eyes on stalks as good as the butterfly's, every one of them about a foot off the deck, petrified by a cross-eyed sack and some cardboard dangling in the background.

Ha! I was definitely getting the hang of this Merchant Navy lark. I could play with the big boys when it came to this joking around stuff. These boys would have to get up pretty early in the morning to catch this puppy out, and anything they tried would spring straight back in their faces. I was definitely feeling GOOD.

Chapter 8

Water, Water Everywhere

The sea is big, Windy is small. The recalcitrant nature of propellers. Bicycles in space. The Mate's underwater brethren. Windy leaves his post. Nobby Clark and the indignity of suddenly being curried.

As Central America sank slowly into the sea behind the ship and the depth-sounder reported unbelievable information regarding the quantity of water below us, the sheer enormity of the Pacific Ocean began to dawn on our feeble brains. You know what fun it is to concentrate on one word until it loses all its meaning and shape, and goes completely crazy on you? We were getting the same sensation, only magnified one thousand-fold, by trying to imagine the ocean as being full of cars instead of water, or as a quantifiable mass of water – say, if it was all in buckets. It blew our finite minds to smithereens before the concept even halfway hit home.

Using a measure such as 'gallons' to describe the Pacific couldn't ever get the thing over, and the more we thought about it, the more our heads swam and the worse it got. Apart from anything else, as the great ocean threw the ship hither and thither like a rubber duck in a bathtub, I began to realise that a 30,000-ton ship is small and insignificant. I realised that the dozen or so mere mortals running the ship, in whose trust we placed our lives, would have no answers should Mother Nature choose to wipe us out. I felt humble and belittled, and this was before we had lost sight of land. I would have to multiply the amount of water I was unable to comprehend here by several thousand miles and nearly 20 days before we would be in Australia. I don't know if I'm getting my message across here. There simply are not the words to convey accurately the experience of being completely surrounded by – and at the mercy of – a phenomenal quantity of water. My sense of propriety was completely deranged by the mighty Pacific.

Apart from becoming spaced out at water volumes, the first few days out of Panama were relatively calm and routine as we settled into our first long haul. People seemed to hide themselves away for a day or two as if taking stock and preparing for the trek ahead, so although there was a fair degree of jollity and merriment of an evening in the bar, the tone was low-key, and the atmosphere noticeably more, well, pacific.

The lads still found time to rag me however, and I had already heard plenty about the dreaded Crossing the Line ceremony. Apparently it is traditional for anybody crossing the equator for the first time to 'declare their allegiance to King Neptune' through some sort of ritual. A humiliating and painful ritual. And 'sacrifice', whatever that meant. Nobody would be much more specific than this, but they delighted in showing me some of the disgusting array of artefacts and potions they were preparing for the big day. There were paint drums full of unspeakable muck, ropes and chains were being rigged, and, worst of all, a bottle kept under lock and key (but on view through the cabinet's glass door) in the bar was gradually filling up – and had been throughout the trip – with sperm. Yes, you're right – that's what I thought.

With my limited navigational skills stretched to their utmost, I kept an eye on the approach of my opportunity to suffer. It would not be long – just a couple of days to go – and the lads were building into a sadistic frenzy. The bottle was becoming more disgusting by the day and we four first-trippers were becoming increasingly convinced that a career in insurance would have been a wise move. However, a couple of days out of Panama we ran into a problem which set the crossing of the line back a little while – in fact, it almost wiped it out completely.

The well-oiled machinery was pushing the old girl along at a game 17 knots, and all was running as smoothly as a Swiss watch. (Did the Swiss ever make any giant, rusty, shit watches?) Three or four of us were leaning on the bulwarks watching the sea go by and making ourselves ill trying to comprehend how amazing it was that the water level rose the world over, albeit by a minimal amount, every time someone threw in a pebble (on which basis we decided that one of my dad's bellyflops could wipe out a Greek island) and whether, if you took all the sponges off the sea-bed, the sea level would rise. Ahmed – the lucky man who was looking after our every need – had brought us tea and biscuits at 3.30, and we were having a five-minute break for ten minutes. Half an hour later the Mate was taking up his post on the bridge (and was therefore unaware of our whereabouts), so we could safely settle down for another ten minutes, watching the endlessly fascinating turmoil of waves, foam, iridescence, flying fish, birds, and the fathomless shades of blue and green surrounding the ship as she cut a furrow through the ocean. An extremely civilised way to spend an hour or two, and the perfect backdrop for the discussion of the world's problems, emotional issues, political standpoints, or – more probably – bosoms. Whatever the topic was on this occasion, I have good reason to have forgotten it. Because the peaceful scene I have painted for you was ripped from the canvas, torn up and slung unceremoniously into the rubbish bin.

Ships are fundamentally designed to move in the horizontal plane, roughly in the direction in which you point them. The repetitive, easy pitching and rolling can become pleasant or even forgotten completely. It becomes a part of the day; the same as the constant engine noise, the Mate's hollering, and curry for lunch. It's just *there*.

So you can imagine our disappointment with our grand vessel when she began to vibrate. And I don't mean the kind of vibration that a car might exude at high speed on a motorway. Dismiss this imagery as less than representative. Maybe then you picture the discomfort experienced by a road worker attached to the upper regions of a pneumatic drill. Cast such wimpish analogies from your mind. Because although the vibrations were as rapid as the excitable end of a pneumatic drill, they were covering a much greater distance. Each vibration was not merely a shift of an inch or two. Or even a foot or two. We are talking about vibrations covering a displacement of a couple of yards at a time at one hundred oscillations per minute! Each of us became a 15-foot blur clinging to the rail for dear life.

Having quickly discovered that there was nothing I could do about the shape of my face under these conditions, my next thought was that life could not be supported for long, and that I should shortly be cashing in my chips with this crowd and requesting a transfer to less exciting worlds. Under these conditions I'd be pleased to see an end to it all. It was to this end that I was in the process of trying to get my head in the way of one of the rails on its upward thrash, when some bright spark had the idea that turning off the main engine might improve matters. It certainly did. The vibrations abated, the ship became dormant and strangely silent. We cadets stumbled off in the shaky style of newborn giraffes towards the nerve centre to get the score from the men in the know.

By the time we got there, the detective work was already well under way in the engine-room, but no delinquent component was immediately apparent. Soon engineers were emerging from every orifice of the great old engine, shrugging their shoulders and shaking their heads. Everything seemed to be in perfect working order. A test run of the engine was organised – to see if we were all dreaming (and to allay rumours of that giant octopus you see in all the old paintings) – but was quickly aborted. At only 'slow ahead' the vibration was appreciable, and by half ahead we were all milkshakes again. There was only one thing left that it could possibly be. The propeller. The problem here, however, was that the prop is not an easy chap to check up on. He has free rein to get up to whatever spinning mischief takes his fancy without fear of observation from above. With the ship fully laden and down by the stern, it is at least 15 feet under water and – more importantly – another 15 feet under the transom stern. Harder to get at than a nasal hair with a pair of garden shears.

It was decided that a lifeboat would be lowered into the sea, containing a special group of volunteers led by the Mate. The team could then motor round to the stern of the vessel, where one brave volunteer would dive down with a mask on and observe the condition of the propeller; the probability was that if the cause of the crazy vibes we were all digging was the prop, then there would be something fairly obvious wrong with it.

All jolly sensible. Naturally, I volunteered, with vigorous support from the Mate who helped me to secure one of the places (by my earlobe). Giewy genuinely *did* volunteer (he was grinning inanely at me as if I was Santa Claus, I mean, what is the matter with him?), along with Benny the Dog, to man the engine. Before you could say 'I'd love to help but I've got a dentist's appointment' the lifeboat was unshipped from its moorings, the davits swung out, and I was standing uncertainly at my assigned post in the stern of the lifeboat, the baying crowd a-whooping and a-cheering at the exciting prospect of severe injury befalling us.

As the boat began its descent down the side of the ship, the hullabaloo of the madding crowd became a distant buzz and I caught a glimpse of the mighty ocean rolling hungrily beneath us. My mind was suddenly awash with clear and unequivocal realisations. The first bombshell was the sheer scale of the component parts making up my predicament. People who think a 30,000-ton ship represents a large and intransigent object are fools. They should be given a wide berth and sent somewhere secure as soon as possible. Thirty thousand tons can be tossed about by the sea like a rag doll in the jaws of a Doberman. Those who consider a thousand miles to be a great distance are similarly insane. Ask them to consider such a distance – which was our distance from the nearest land – in shipping terms. In a car there are hundreds of other drivers sharing the road, as well as access to motorway services, breakdown services, police, ambulance men and overnight stops. There was no help for our ship; just a dozen or so rather strange blokes and the feeble abilities we were so pathetically arrogant about. On shore we are so reliant upon the 'authorities'. We do not see them as consisting of mere people with failings and uncertainties. The authorities are *there*, endlessly providing a God-like safety net, present at every turn to help us through life's crises. We had no authorities on board. No police. No paramedics. No breakdown services. No mummy or daddy. Not even passing fellow-travellers. Just me and Benny the Dog, and Gonad, and ... Oh, Jesus. It suddenly dawned on me how ludicrous it all was. A motley bunch of us pitting ourselves against the mighty ocean; completely out of our element and trying to steer a floating metal platform across the Pacific. Absolutely ridiculous. It's not natural for human beings to leave terra firma in the first place, and it is especially stupid to take on the might of the sea with a rusty piece of tin.

The Pacific was not particularly rough that day, but the waves no longer looked friendly. The crests, which had resembled white horses, suddenly seemed to lick at hungry lips. And this was just the surface. It went down and down and down. Five *miles* down. I tried not to think about all that deathly nothingness beneath our floating platform, and my dead bones lying at the bottom. I felt a rush of foolishness. Whatever ego I had was crushed by the sheer insignificance of my being. My muscles? Laughable. My brain? Insignificant. My opinions? My desires? My anger? The sea would not listen. Why should it? I felt I was falling through space with all my old beliefs and opinions regarding what was good and fair completely unhinged. A good analogy for going to sea on a ship seemed to be that of an astronaut travelling a mile or two away from his spaceship on a bicycle.

As the lifeboat started her jerky journey down towards sea level I had the job of patrolling one of the ropes. Two ropes are attached to the davits on the ship and coiled into the boat – one at each end – but they are not attached to the boat. They are knotted at regular intervals and, once the boat is in the water, provide (during the boat's intended employment) a means of boarding for late arrivals. It is therefore necessary to feed out these ropes as the boat descends, because if they get caught on anything, they can upset matters considerably (and literally).

Giewy was feeding out the other rope. He obviously had no grip on the inadequacies of civil authorities, the colossal nature of the phenomenon we were up against, or the significance of bicycles in space, but grinned inanely as if we were on a fairground ride. However, even he was forced to display a modicum of human awareness by what followed. When we were approximately halfway to the sea we heard shouting from above. Looking way, way back up to the bridge wing, I could see The Famous Dick Wrigley shouting and pointing to the sea.

'WOW! Look at the size of that bastard!'

I leaned carefully on the gunwale of the lifeboat and peered gingerly into the sea below. There, cruising patiently beneath us awaiting his lunch, was a huge, unbeatable shark. Although my sensibilities were already in shreds (as were my underpants), a fresh wave of desperation washed over me, but the roar of the Mate about two inches from my left ear still managed to penetrate, and I returned to my post. Then we hit the water. Or I should say, the water hit us. The crest of a wave suddenly swept us upwards. The boat came away from its retention hooks and we were in. Immediate and undiluted fear climbed all over my desperation, and stood victoriously above my insecurities. I clung to the rope with catatonic strength, frozen in horror. This is not a clever thing to do, as the rope had a separate agenda from that of the lifeboat, so there was a good chance that I would be left dangling there once the boat had gone, like a punter stranded atop his pole.

I know it sounds barely credible, but I don't believe I was thinking straight at this point, and the screamed instructions from the Mate were entirely wasted on me, so it was fortunate that a fresh wave of shouts went up from the gathered audience above. The shark! I let go of the rope and leant over the side once more. This time the water level was about six inches from me, and four feet away was the deep, black, penetrating eye of a massive hammerhead shark – one of the most efficient killing machines on earth. I remember it as being the same length as the lifeboat, which would make it 30-feet long, so even allowing for 50 per cent exaggeration, it was still a 15-footer, and there was nothing between me and this incredible monster except the flimsy wooden sides of the lifeboat. I tried to turn away, but I couldn't. That fathomless eye had a stronger grip on me than any straitjacket. I thought how feeble human beings are in the water, how superb sharks are, and how large this one was.

BLUE ROAD

From somewhere I was distantly conscious that the Mate was shouting something, but I could not hear. I stared into the shark's eye and I found no compassion. I found no hope. I was transfixed. In the age it took for the shark to pass and to release me from its grip, Benny had started the lifeboat engine, and the boat was beginning to move. I shook my head and came back to life with a start. The rope I had been feeding out was now hanging in the water about ten feet behind us, and the forward rope, which Giewy had been feeding out, was coming towards me. I caught the Mate's eye. It matched up perfectly with that of the shark, and it hit me. They were brothers. This was a conspiracy. I suddenly knew who would be chosen to dive down and look at the prop. Giewy's rope had just passed me now and was leaving us at the aft end of the boat. I ran two strides to the back, then leapt as hard as I could over the open water for the life-saving rope. I just made it. I climbed the 40 feet back up to the boat-deck in about three seconds, accompanied by the jeers and derision of my companions. I didn't care. Safety is a relative thing, and I knew where I wanted to be. As far as I was concerned, my life had just been saved. We cowards should stick together, rejecting all those who do daring things simply because they are not brave enough to be cowardly. We should form a society and practise jumping at our own shadows. Where does swashbuckling get you? OK, apart from money, girls, status, respect, self-belief, friends, fulfillment and confidence? Exactly – nowhere. Follow my advice and turn chicken.

Despite my begging to the heavens that the Mate would lose a couple of vital organs to this Nobby Clark, things went without a hitch. In fact, the water was so clear that they could see directly from the boat to the prop simply by leaning over the side with a mask. And the problem with the propeller was so obvious even from there that a closer inspection wasn't necessary. Don't ask me how or why, but the prop was missing a goodly portion of one of its blades. Although baffling and mysterious in itself (although doubtless I would be getting the blame) it did explain the vibration.

And before I become deluged by those who were paying attention earlier, I *know* there was a spare propeller – I had spent the entire journey living under the bloody thing – but it was no good. Not purely because it would involve too much upheaval for me to remove all my personal effects from beneath it, or because it could not be changed at sea – it had been done before – but because we were too heavily laden. To change the propeller required us to be at least close to light-ship. As we were, the prop was too deep, irrespective of how we altered the stability. Light-ship, the broken prop could be raised almost entirely out of the water just by making her bow heavy by filling all the forward ballast tanks and emptying the aft ones. The propeller can then be changed over using the cargo derricks. Unfortunately, sharks or no sharks, this was not possible here.

The politics and global administration of a shipping line were soon flashing around the planet in Morse code. Where were we close to? Central and South America. Both bad news for dry-docking and fixing this sort of problem, and still ages away at our new cruising speed of around four knots. Back to Panama? No good dry-dock services there. America? May as well continue to Australia. Yip, that was the way to go. We would take a month at four knots, but the problem could be easily handled there, and it would keep the cargo – the lifeblood of the shipping line – on course for the paymasters.

The engines were fired up again and people returned to their normal routines, the only differences being that the ship was going appreciably slower, and we were looking at a full 30 days more at sea, rather than the expected 15.

During the period that the ship was drifting serenely from wave to wave awaiting further instructions, the crew had not been idle. They knew from experience that sharks follow the ship, and they were ready to ambush the earliest arrivals. There are several theories as to why sharks follow ships, one of which is that the thrashing of a distant propeller in the water gives sharks the impression of a creature in distress – the equivalent of a dinner gong to our fearsome friends. Another theory is that they have learned to associate ships with the discarded scraps that are thrown overboard. Being scavengers, this too gets their saliva flowing. For whatever reason, if the ship stops deep-sea, it is soon caught up by numerous nobbies, all looking for a free lunch. But as is so common in nature, the hunter can quickly become the hunted. The crew stuck half a pig on a dirty big hook and slung it in the sea on a 22-millimetre runner wire. They followed it in with a few buckets of blood and offal to stir up the emotions, and before you could say 'Allez oop!' a dirty big nobby – not stopping to question what half a pig was doing swimming around mid-Pacific – had been plucked from the water and plonked on to the deck. So while I was climbing 40-foot ropes to escape the sea-born scourge, the crew was busy bringing it aboard for me.

When I saw the first shark they'd caught, I was fairly preoccupied by other matters, so did not dwell too long on the slow death they were inflicting upon it, but as the day wore on, I could see why they had not been quicker about dispatching it to the great sea in the sky. After they'd landed it, they sharpened up their knives, tucked in their napkins and waited for each other to curry the thing. However, a full half-hour later it was far from dead, and they didn't seem to know quite what to do about it. It lay there on the deck, apparently deep in thought, but nobody could get near it. For some reason it seemed mistrustful of its hosts. Every time someone went within 15 feet of it, there was a whirring blaze of flashing teeth and the approacher would turn tail and run like the clappers to a safe haven where he would anxiously count his limbs. After an hour or so, I was astonished to find this drama *still* being played out to the same script. I have no idea how it stayed alive, but every time they thought it was *definitely* dead, someone would venture too close with a carving knife, and Boo! It was after them again.

After a while this entertaining spectacle was simply a part of the day, and we were becoming used to the poke-the-nobby-and-leg-it routine that was by now a familiar feature of the afterdeck. So it was a surprise to return from a short diversion to find that the shark was gone and all the crew were mooching about with rotund bellies and curry round their mouths. I scratched my head in disbelief. One moment there is a shark terrorising the neighbourhood, the next moment they've curried the bloody thing and are offering you bowls of it.

I can't help but feel a little sorry for sharks really. It must be strange to be a nobby – stalking aggressively around with the gang, in your leather jacket and sunglasses, killer of the deep and all that – casually going about your normal mid-week schedule, when all of a sudden someone comes along and curries you. Most embarrassing, at the very least.

From that day forth, I vowed never to stand still too long in the presence of the Chief Cook. However, I would gladly submit myself to a convention of chief cooks rather than ever have to undergo the Crossing the Line ceremony again. However hard we tried, even the combined navigational incompetence of NotNorman and myself could not put the position of the ship at what might be termed a comfortable distance from the dreaded equator. We knew that the day was almost upon us when we would discover the purpose of the chains, the ropes, the potions and cocktails . . . and that unbearable bottle of congealed, contaminated, accumulated sailors' sperm.

Chapter 9

Standing on Ceremony

The Crossing the Line ceremony. Windy shows disarming and unexpected bravery. Spit or swallow? Gonad lets the cat out of the bag.

The Crossing the Line ceremony is every good first-tripper's opportunity to declare allegiance to Neptune upon passing over the Equator for the very first time.

Thus far, I was somewhat hazy as to what form this ritual would take, it being very difficult to distinguish the wheat from the chaff when speaking with our torturers. Most of what I was told was so unspeakably hideous that we first-trippers nervously agreed it could not possibly be based on fact, but what certainly seemed to be common to all the incidents recounted was that we would be asked to endure a number of pagan rituals, pay various forfeits, suffer numerous punishments for our sins, oh . . . and have every hair on our body – yes *those* ones as well – shaved off and committed to the deep. What the hell Neptune wanted with four sets of adolescent pubes I shall never know. From my very first day aboard *Global Wanderer*, and on every day since, everybody with whom I had spoken, upon finding out that I was a first-tripper, had shaken their heads and sucked their teeth sharply.

'Oh dear, dear, dear, first-tripper, you say? You don't want to be one of *those*. You'll have to cross the line, you know. Dear me. You want my advice? Get off NOW. Go home while there's still time. RUN AWAY!' and so on along those lines.

Similar encouragement to make with the ankles came from the various activities going on around the ship as the

95

trip progressed. The engineers were slowly but surely building up a five-gallon drum of thick, black crud with grit in it. I couldn't help but notice that it was not being thrown away with all the other waste when the opportunity presented itself. One day I came across Jinx stirring the steaming brew.

'Eurgh! What *is* that?' I asked, retching on the fumes.

'It's to do your hair and fill your pants with when you cross the line,' he said cheerfully. 'It's highly toxic, lead-based, acrid and quite extraordinarily poisonous, so try not to swallow any. Could be lethal. Mind you,' he added conspiratorially, 'your mouth will be brim full already, so there shouldn't be too much danger of eating any of this! HARHARHAR!' His laughter haunted my nights as his enigmatic words took me back to the worrying developments in that bottle locked in a glass cabinet in the bar. Its contents initially looked like some sort of mucus culture, and it grew as the weeks went by. Eventually you have to ask. You know you are going to regret it, but you have to ask.

'Oh, that,' replied the Radio Officer, blithely, 'that's the bottle of sperm we're building up specially for you to eat as you cross the line. It's a part of the ceremony.'

'Oh,' I said quietly, wishing I hadn't asked. 'I shouldn't have asked, should I?' The Radio Officer shook his head sadly.

'I should have got off the ship while I had the chance, shouldn't I?'

The head nodded, 'You certainly should have, my old mate. No good now, though, is it? I'd love to help you out, but my hands are tied. Tradition and all that, you know. You *have* to declare your allegiance to Neptune, don't you? Love to make an exception and all that, but, well, rules are rules.'

Suddenly I had a brilliant idea. The old Baboulene brainbox was in top form. I slapped my forehead.

'But Sparky,' I lied, happily, 'you *can* let me off! Didn't I tell you? I went to Australia a few years ago. I've already crossed the line! We're saved!'

'Well that's wo-o-o-nderful!' sang Sparky, brightening, the heavy responsibility for my educational advancement lifting from his shoulders. 'All you have to do is show us your certificate and you're off the hook! I *am* pleased! This means you won't have to suffer all that hideous abuse, or have your head shaved, or eat –'

'Sorry, er, hold your horses there, old chap . . . er . . . did you say, "certificate"?'

'Yes, your certificate. If you've crossed the line, then you've got one, of course, and we can call off the hounds. I *am* relieved!'

'Ah. Well. I didn't actually, er, bring my certificate with me. You see, I mean, you know how it is. Once you've crossed the line a few times like me, you don't bother carrying the old certif' anymore, do you?'

The weight returned to his overburdened shoulders.

'Ach, I'm sorry. We're back where we started. I wish I could help, but if you've crossed the line as often as you obviously have, then you know all the rules. No certificate, no reprieve. Love to help and all that, but my hands are tied, you know.'

And so it goes on throughout the time one is in hemisphere A. A slow but effective build up, irrevocably increasing its cold grip, like piano wires tightening round my heart.

On the dreaded afternoon that we crossed the Equator, the lynch mob got itself organised in the bar and built up a good head of team spirit before setting out to find us first-trippers. NotNorman was quickly tracked down to the anchor locker, but that didn't mean he could easily be led to the slaughter. He was well bedded-in, armed to the teeth, defending the small entrance admirably and was, for the moment, beyond extraction.

KiloWatt – the Second Electrician and another first-tripper – was clinging to a bulkhead 20 feet up in the engine-room. He had worked his way out along a structural girder, and was clinging on to a metal bar welded to the bulkhead. His was an effective refuge in that it was almost impossible for the enemy to get at him; however, the precarious nature of his position meant he was continually expending energy just staying up there. Like NotNorman, he too was, for the moment, unabuseable, but time would surely find him out.

Gonad was not as imaginative. He was tracked down to a toilet in the accommodation. The lock was forced, and he was shortly to be found with two heavies attached to each limb, kicking and screaming his way to the ceremonial altar on the foredeck.

And me? Well, I am proud to tell you that the mob was quite taken aback to find me lying casually on my bed with my hands behind my head, indulging in a pre-ordeal snooze. It put them right off. In fact some of them were visibly perturbed. They didn't seem to know quite what to do.

'Good grief, Windy! I would have put money on a twat like you trying to hide!'

'Yeah, we thought you'd have been hiding for a fortnight, being such a girlie!'

'Go on Windy, you're spoiling it for us! Run off and give us a chase. We'll give you ten to get away. What do you say?'

They were at once bemused and impressed by my stone-faced bravery, and it quite threw their uncivilised antics. I could see one or two of them shifting uneasily from one foot to the other as I rose above their savagery. I was prepared to take my medicine like a man and here they were demonstrably humiliated by my moral fibre. They looked like half a dozen priests caught dancing round a brothel with their pants on their heads.

As they dragged me bodily from my bunk and carried me roughly out on to the deck I could see that their hearts were not quite in it, and as they chained me up next to Gonad they cheered weakly, not feeling quite as pleased with themselves as they had supposed they might. They were unnerved by my resolve, set so firmly against the winds of adversity as I faced up to them with self-respect and pride. They could not look me in the eye and left quickly, preferring the less conscience-searching job of hunting down one of the *proper* first-trippers – those ill-equipped with moral fibre – cowering in their principle-free hiding places. They wanted the thrill of the chase as well as the ritual humiliation, and I was spoiling things for them. We Baboulenes are made of sterner stuff you see, and I was proud to be following in the footsteps of my ancestors who fought in great battles at Hastings, Dunkirk, Rorke's Drift and Yorktown, engendering new and better morals in the hearts of lesser mortals. They might abuse me this day, but they would not feel good about it. Thoroughly embarrassed, the motley crew left Gonad and me dangling and set off in pursuit of NotNorman and KiloWatt.

Despite the enormous pleasure they got from hunting down their prey, the average drunk sailor still looked upon the hiding first-tripper as an ungrateful child. They felt miffed that all their efforts towards his education were being spurned and they resolved to be firm but violent with him once he was eventually coaxed out.

KiloWatt was still clinging to the engine-room bulkhead, and the job of encouraging the shy young chap down began. The assembled masses shouted threats, detailing the present extent of the intended violence and outlined a list of special extras to be added should he fail to give himself up. But their tempting sales routine had no effect on the customer. He was not interested. He snubbed them and pretended he was not listening. They huffed and puffed with frustration, and retired to a corner where they huddled together to rethink their sales and marketing strategy. Eventually, they decided on a fresh combination of carrots and sticks he would not be able to refuse and returned to the scene. The original menu of violent intent was shouted out, the extra details enumerated (this time guaranteeing their inclusion in the programme) and a new list of envisaged atrocities was appended to the repertoire should the current package be rejected. KiloWatt provided the traditional response, chanting the sacred words 'Bugger off' and threw some nuts and bolts at them as punctuation. Heads drooping, the marauders retired once more, and so we went on around the loop again.

Some first-trippers have achieved legendary status by holding out for many hours – even days – but all give up eventually. On a ship in mid-ocean, there is simply no escape. NotNorman and KiloWatt could have saved everybody – including themselves – a good deal of heartache if they had shown a little good old British spirit and got on with it. I have no idea why some people are so yellow, it really is quite beyond me.

Eventually the hunting party that was expedited to fetch NotNorman and KiloWatt returned empty-handed. The fugitives were holding out. Neptune (more commonly known as Jinx) took charge. He stood up in his fine grass skirt, held his three-pronged cardboard trident aloft and pronounced that the proceedings should proceed (that's what proceedings do). His amassed cronies – in their equally ridiculous and ill-fitting costumes – cheered long and hard at the prospect of some action, and Neptune unfurled his scroll and began to read the sordid details written thereon.

The early parts of the ceremony were fairly controlled, with the mob chanting back the ritual responses and exercising their fingers as they awaited the opportunity to get at us; but with great tension building in line with their expectations, the whole atmosphere was becoming notably forbidding. There were no jokes or laughter and the thing had an eerie air – more like an exorcism than a lads' jape.

Soon some physical abuse featured, and another pattern began to emerge. Neptune would solemnly read out an indictment against myself, or Gonad, or both. Witnesses from the baying mob would then step forward and read out prepared statements pertaining to the incident in which we had allegedly shown ourselves to be imbecilic. For instance, Jinx – sorry, King Neptune – announced: 'That on the fifteenth inst. of this very month of this very year of our Lord, Windy here spent twenty minutes in the engine-room trying to stop a generator – which was not running. The punishment for one such heinous –'

I leapt to my defence.

'What? How can you say that? It WAS running! It was noisy in there and you just couldn't hear when I –'

King Neptune put his finger to his lips and raised the bottle containing the ceremonial sperm. I said no more. A 'witness' stepped forward and spouted some utter tripe concerning the event. I looked at the bottle and said nothing. I was found guilty as charged, and sentenced to be 'taken into custardy.'

The mob set about me with determination. My clothes were ripped from me until I was only standing in my underpants. There was a pause as they awaited the green light from King Neptune, who raised his trident aloft. 'Take him into custardy!' he shouted and they leapt joyfully into action. My pants were gripped tightly, stretched wide open and the workers began filling them to the brim with cold custard siphoned off from the galley some months before. A generous quantity of chicken tikka masala was added to my custardy pants, followed by a cupful of iron filings. They then stood back to admire my bulging underpants (a whole new experience for me). There must have been two gallons of the stuff brimming out from everywhere when Neptune gave the next order: 'PULL!'

And with that four of Neptune's helpers who were holding the sides of my underpants pulled upwards with all their might. The gunky mixture fountained out in all directions as my pants were brought up under my arms. The penance complete, they all stepped back to admire their handiwork. What a state. Covered in browny-yellow sludge (with chicken pieces), a pair of incredibly well-stretched underpants covering my nipples and a look of grim surprise on my face, I learned that day just what iron filings are capable of when left to their own devices amongst one's more sensitive nooks and crannies.

The gloves were now off. Soon a stream of crimes was being read out, and Gonad and I were undergoing an increasingly violent flow of physical abuse. What started as custard down the pants and chilli peppers rubbed on the nipples steadily built as the thirst for blood grew, and British pride in dignity and compassion got drowned under animal savagery. Soon the separation between one punishment and the next was indistinguishable and Jinx was reading out crimes faster and faster. The hair under my arms went west, as did one eyebrow and half the hair on my head. To the enormous delight of the onlookers, my penis was painted black and buff (the same colour as the funnel) with a callously ticklish paintbrush, and all my pubes were shaved off. Flowers were stuck in my ears and a dreadful mixture of black gunk and pink gloss paint (seasoned with grit) was slapped all over me.

I looked at Gonad and caught his eye between his choking on the tar they were sticking up his nose and his receiving a monk's hairdo. Like me, he had switched off and was just concentrating on surviving. Like a mouse being toyed with by a gang of alley cats, we had switched off our senses and were simply trying to hang on as the endurance test continued. I was beginning to have a degree of success in blotting out the present when I was suddenly snapped back to the here and now, because . . . oh no . . . The Bottle was brought forward.

Had I the presence of mind to think about it, I may have tried to take comfort in the probability that my life was about to hit an all-time low and could not possibly get any worse. Then it did. As The Bottle was held up in front of my face, I saw that there was a small green streak running through the contents, like the colouring in a marble. Neptune informed those gathered that the addition had been kindly donated by a very special effort from Crate who, despite having caught a dose of gonorrhoea in Jamaica, had still got into the spirit of the thing and come up with the goods. A spontaneous round of applause rippled around the assembly who appreciated the fine effort he had made despite his disease, and Crate blushed coyly and kicked a shackle.

At this point I found myself once again going up in the estimation of the lads because I resisted the traditional practice of shouting for mummy and begging for mercy. I have to admit that the reason for this was perfectly simple. The slightest hint of an open mouth and I would be eating the bodily expulsions of many unclean sailors. I was also experiencing an overwhelming desire to be elsewhere.

My problem was that I was dealing with old hands. They had years of practice in helping young lads to eat sperm, so I braced myself for a titanic battle as they tried to force my mouth open. A battle did not come. I opened one eye, and saw no such activity heading my way. Instead, Neptune strolled over with the bottle. I clamped my lips tight and tensed my jaws as hard as they could go. If he tickled me, I was determined not to giggle – matters were far too serious to fall for that kind of stuff – but all he did was to hold my nose. I opened one eye again and looked around, suspicious at the lack of brute force. What was going on? Why was he holding my nose? Then I realised that I could no longer breathe.

Oh.

I asked the Baboulene brain to analyse the situation and report back, but as it leapt into action, concentration seemed to elude it. While my body started up sirens telling me it was time to breathe in, my mind did not come back with a perfect plan. Instead it gave me a familiar face from school: Tuckerman. The same Tuckerman who took full responsibility for the Freedom Party following the combustion of the chemistry lab. It was perfectly all right to blame Tuckerman, because Tuckerman was a swot. He enjoyed maths, read books at breaktime, wore string vests and sensible shoes, would fall on his arse if he tried to kick a ball, and had the sole and expressed ambition of becoming an accountant for the same insurance firm as his four-eyed swotty old father. Us streetwise kids used to rag him endlessly for being such a plonker – we must have caused him endless suffering in those days – but now he came back for his revenge. He sat in the corner of my conscience, sitting at his accountant's desk in his warm insurance company office, smiling smugly at me. He leaned across the desk and said, 'You're going to have to breathe now, Baboulene.'

I knew it was true, but to be quite honest with you, I didn't really want to. Breathing had suddenly become a grossly overrated pastime, and the only 'hot' idea the Baboulene brain could come up with was to *pretend* to breathe in, then stop again, in the hope that they might spill the gunk. I pretended to breathe in twice, stopping again immediately despite the powerful reflex messages I was getting from my diaphragm, but to no avail. They had obviously met this trick before, and made no attempt to feed me any. They knew that my third breath would be the genuine article and were ready and waiting until I had to drink the stuff down.

I feel sure that even the most committed optimist could not convince you that my current cloud could possibly contain the remotest sniff of what might be called a silver lining; and as I stood there, naked, chained to a container, covered from head to foot in crap, with my pubes in the sea, an unspeakably bad taste searing through my digestive system, my head and genitals smarting and even bleeding from a clumsy razoring, my poor beloved willy painted black and buff, and iron filings in my most delicate neighbourhoods, I have to admit that the old '*joie de*' for which I was so well known seemed to have deserted me entirely. But I have to say that amongst this gunk-cloud there was, indeed, a silver lining. You see, I actually got off lightly. Yes, you read that correctly – I actually got off lightly.

The ordeal seemed to be abating as the savages became bored with their now-unresponsive quarry. We hung ravaged and despondent from the container chains, and they began to drift off towards the bar – their sadistic hunger satisfied, and beer becoming the foremost motivator in their simple animal brains – leaving a couple of sympathetic crew members to wash us down with a fire hose and cut us down from the container.

The ritual left me incensed with the futility of the human condition, and I vowed never to put any future first-trippers through the same degrading ordeal that I had just suffered. I decided to devote my life to the outlawing of the Crossing the Line ceremony. If I achieved nothing else in my three score years and ten, it would have been a worthy life.

While I was in the shower entertaining these honourable thoughts, NotNorman had been snared with a rope around his ankle. He would hold out for another 50 minutes, but his goose was definitely cooked. And KiloWatt was becoming weaker. He couldn't have been more than a CouplaWatts now; his position teetering high on a ledge on the engine-room bulkhead necessitated the concentrated exertion of energy every time the ship rolled. Alas, although he was a big strong lad, the unrelenting roll of the ship was grinding him down, and he too would not see out the hour. The baying hounds watched eagerly and knew the time they had to wait for the next act was shortening with every roll of the ship.

That hour was quite enough for the main combat unit to sink an appreciable quantity of additional alcohol. This was gradually making them feel more reckless, more aggressive, less capable of wielding a razor with finesse, and far less interested in the ceremonial details of the event. That hour also gave Gonad and me time to get ourselves into some semblance of order. It would take several weeks to get rid of all the gunk, remove the lead-based paints and evict the grit and iron filings from our tender parts; a further few months to regain anything remotely resembling an acceptable hairstyle, and a lifetime or two to overcome the psychological trauma of eating sperm; but we were able to shower off the worst of it, put dressings on our wounds, comb our tufts, wash out our mouths and find some loose clothing to wear. Our strength was returning and it was beginning to sink in that we had survived the dreaded Crossing the Line. It was all over.

Gonad and I were at once relieved, elated and angry. Revenge may take years, but we vowed there and then to get our own back on each and every one of those diabolical sadists who had played their part in our humiliation. We outlined plans for getting the ceremony brought to the attention of the authorities, we listed the newspapers with the highest profiles, we would contact the –

Patch's head popped round the door. 'Quick lads. You're on!'

'Wha . . ? What NOW? What have we done?'

'No, no. Nothing to be scared of. They've got NotNorman and KiloWatt and are chaining them up now. You lads have crossed the line, so you're on our side of the razor blade for this one. We thought you might like to get involved?'

'TOO FUCKING RIGHT WE WOULD!' said Gonad, putting things in a nutshell. I couldn't agree more. In a blinding flash of realisation, I clearly saw the reasons behind the ritual. The ceremony was an essential part of a cadet's education. It was character-building and sincere. I was a better person for the experience and, in time, NotNorman and KiloWatt would grow to thank us for what we were about to do. Gonad was rushing to put some clothes on, but I was already dressed, so I picked up a razor and headed for the door.

As I rushed passed the officers' lounge I was stopped in my tracks by a small party working at the bar. They had The Bottle, and were bent over it in concentration. I remembered.

They had used up the whole bottle on Gonad and me, so I wouldn't get to feed any to NotNorman and KiloWatt! This was terrible! Maybe we hadn't got off so lightly after all! Surely they weren't trying to recharge it *now*? I stormed into the bar.

'You dogs!' I said. 'You didn't keep any back for the other two! That's really unfair!'

'Don't panic,' said Benny the Dog. 'We're just making up some more. There we are! Another bottle!'

He held it proudly aloft, and sure enough, it was brim full and disgusting again. The memory nearly made me throw up on the spot. Then my eyes caught sight of the laughing faces around me, and I looked back at the counter. There, in the centre of the activity, were the essential ingredients: flour, water, lemon, sour cream and gin. The flour was lumpy and thick, and the rest just didn't taste good together. I couldn't believe it. It wasn't sperm at all. My mind flooded with anger and relief. I was beside myself with conflicting emotions and was incapable of doing anything. 'And not forgetting that extra-special ingredient,' continued the Fourth, 'provided by Crate himself . . .' The Fourth gave the bottle to Crate who produced a teaspoon with a line of bright green Swarfega on it and stirred it gently into the mix. It was unutterably disgusting once more. 'Well, don't just stand there gawping at it!' he said. 'Get out there and frighten the crap out of them!'

'Before you go,' said Crate with all the embarrassment of a big man saying something sincere, 'I have to say that we were all well impressed with your bravery today. None of us have ever seen a first-tripper cross the line with such dignity.'

I blushed and dismissed his compliments with a modest wave of the hand. Just then Gonad walked in.

'Unlike THAT wimp,' laughed the Fourth, pointing at Gonad. 'Not only did he show no bravery whatsoever, the best bloody hiding place he could think up was to lock himself in the loo! Couldn't you do better than that, Gonad?'

Gonad's lips tightened.

'What do you mean, "hiding place"?' he blurted. 'I wasn't

hiding in there, I'd gone in there for a dump! That Baboulene turkey went up to the chart-room this morning, then came down and told me there were *two more days* to go before we reached the equator! I had a great hiding place all worked out and HE would have been wimping away like no other if he didn't have the navigational prowess of a drunk turkey. On stilts. Doing bad acid. He thought we were still two days away!'

The laughter rang out, and I was sinking fast to my all-too-familiar levels of humiliation, when suddenly my purpose in life was clear. I knew what had to be done.

I took the razor firmly in one hand, snatched up the bottle with the other, and headed off with a purposeful stride towards the restrained and helpless NotNorman and the soon-to-be-earthed KiloWatt.

Chapter 10

Frottage

Muses on exercising in one's pants. The Grand Cranking Competition. We meet SmallParcel and learn of his relationship with the Post Office.

Masturbation is an issue of paramount importance to seamen. (There is a joke there if you can be bothered with it.) So despite the lowering of the tone, I am compelled by the onerous code amongst honest chroniclers to grasp the matter with both hands, so to speak.

The saying goes: 'All men are either wankers or liars' and, speaking from a purely subjective and non-self-committal viewpoint, I don't think there's much doubt about it. However, it is one of the incongruous dichotomies that occupy the great thinkers of our time that although all men masturbate, and the pastime is therefore a masculine activity, anyone who is caught in the act is immediately accused of being a Wanker. A scandalous insult, carrying the loathsome suggestion that the auto-eroticist is unable to secure female companionship, and is therefore less than a real man. In a nutshell, all men masturbate, therefore no man is a man.

So despite a healthy trade in the preferred currency aboard ship – glossy magazines – NOBODY admits to playing the organ, and anybody who is caught red-handed (I suspect there may be a joke there too) has to pay a fine in the form of the other favoured currency – beer. The fine amounts to a case of beer to every person who witnessed the shameful act or was instrumental in catching the instrumentalist. Thus all the men aboard are furiously pulling more than just ropes every day, but the stakes are high, both in beer and humiliation, so when a chap isn't conjuring himself up a quick hand-shandy in the 'tween deck of hold three, he is probably poking around the less frequented areas of the ship with a Polaroid camera trying to apprehend others. It was simply not possible to get two minutes' peace and quiet without people deciding you'd nipped off to 'rough up the suspect' (to use the vernacular).

Now why, I hear you say, does a chap with an itch not simply lock himself away in his cabin and scratch it to his heart's content? No good, I'm afraid. It is a golden rule deep-sea that cabin doors are not locked. Rarely are they even shut. Trust in one's fellows is implicit, so a locked door can mean only one thing to a bar full of drunks with the prospect of easy beer glinting in their eyes. Any seaman worth his salt (another there, don't you think?) knows just what to do upon finding a locked door:

1) Run and tell everybody you can find that Bob is masturbating. This will inspire joy and resourcefulness. The well-oiled machine will leap into action. People will run and fetch each other, collect cameras and flash-guns, and gather swiftly but quietly at Bob's door.

2) While the team is mobilising, go to the Mate's office and beg, borrow or steal the master-key.

3) Return to Bob's door where a good crowd has gathered expectantly, cameras as primed and ready to go as Bob's bits.

4) Gather closely round Bob's door. It is vital to get as many bodies and cameras through that door as you can in the shortest time possible.

5) Turn the key ever so quietly, inch by inch so as not to disturb the victim. Countdown using the fingers. Three . . . two . . . one. BANG! In we go!

From the bed glossy magazines are thrown skywards by the thunderstruck Bob. He tries to cover himself up, but he is *way* too late. Fifty photographs have been taken, and Bob is instantly in debt to the tune of a dozen cases of beer. An unwilling new star of the bar photo board is born, and doesn't he look the superstar! Naked and airborne, doing a starfish impersonation a foot above his bed, with glossy pictures floating down around his startled countenance.

Once, Gonad thought he was a tremendously clever chap. He borrowed both sets of master-keys before locking his door and setting confidently about choking the chicken. He was well into the home straight when he got the feeling that he was not alone. Looking up he saw a delighted face upside-down at his seaward porthole. We were dangling NotNorman on a rope by his ankles from the boat-deck right out over the side of the ship simply to get the solid photographic evidence we needed.

Another time we burst in on Giewy, but he didn't fling everything skyward and shrivel with embarrassment, he just kept going. He had headphones on with rock music blasting his ears off, and was so thoroughly immersed in the job at hand that he didn't even notice we were there. So with his head thrown back and his knees up, he had no idea that ten other people were standing there in the room with him. The scene could easily have been an officers' cocktail party (but for the presence of one naked person masturbating). We casually chatted of this and that amongst ourselves and took dozens of photographs of the degrading spectacle until, with toes curled, bum held high in the air and shouting, 'YES! YES! I love you, Clint!' he climaxed. He opened his eyes to be met by the entire ship's complement applauding appreciatively and awarding marks out of ten on squares of card. He jumped ship, changed his name and moved to Brazil (I wish).

One of the additional incongruities of the shipboard wanking phenomenon was that despite the highly competitive detection organisations and the adamant rebuttal of all accusations concerning the act, there were endless double standards. From the first week on board, a poster had been placed in the bar proclaiming: 'Grand Cranking Competition. Officers' Bar, 18.00 hours, First Wednesday into the Southern Hemisphere. Full uniform to be worn. Third Officer to officiate.'

I was on bridge watches with the Third Officer for a while and broached the subject. I had visions of a line of sailors trying to start old Fords, so his answer as to the definition of the term 'cranking' gave me quite a jolt.

'Surely *nobody* is going to bash one out in front of your stopwatch?' I said incredulously. 'You cannot possibly expect me to fall for this garbage, can you?' I was becoming worldly-wise and cautious in my old age and suspected another merry jape.

The Famous Dick Wrigley laughed long and hard. 'Nooo,' he said, 'don't be stupid! Nobody is going to do *that*! Would *you*? But this is an absolutely serious, bona fide, pucker cranking race. You'll find one every trip on the first Wednesday after the ship changes hemisphere. It's an ancient tradition and there's an awful lot of beer for the winner.' I furrowed the brow and eyed the Famous One. I was greatly suspicious, but he forestalled my complaints. 'To ease your troubled mind, let me give you some inside info. The lights are turned out for the full duration of heightened sexual activity. Everyone knows the routine and has done it many times before. They'll all join in because the whole thing takes place in the pitch dark; but if you don't want to, don't. First to ejaculate wins six cases of beer.'

I was still far from happy, and continued to quiz people throughout the trip. Their answers always matched. I still had no intention whatsoever of joining in, but, what with the performance of the lads in the ports to date and the kind of activities I was beginning to realise were standard among sailors, the thing was becoming almost plausible. Now, on a slow boat to Oz, the Grand Cranking Competition was almost upon us and everyone seemed to have gone into training. Men for whom the sole form of exercise was lifting beer cans suddenly took up jogging and doing press-ups on the boat-deck instead. I couldn't believe it – they were all taking it so seriously. I was still mighty unsure, but received lots of advice and encouragement.

'Bar profits will put up *six* cases of beer for the winner,' said MegaWatt, jogging past me on the foredeck. 'SIX CASES!'

'I don't know why I'm bothering at all,' panted Sparky, shadow-boxing on the boat-deck. 'One of you young bastards always wins.'

'Remember,' lectured Cranners, pointing his skipping rope at me as he strode off towards the monkey island, 'everybody will be just as nervous as you are.'

And gradually all my fears and questions were answered. I still wasn't having it, but I could not see the trick in it either. Even if there *was* some trick, they would still have to give out the beers, and most of these lads were more than happy to show off their sports department for a lot less reason than was on offer here! I couldn't make it out.

On the night of the Grand Cranking Competition, dinner was a sombre affair. Most of the competitors were preparing themselves psychologically for the forthcoming event and men who would normally put away a horse or two were studiously nibbling at pasta salad. As we retired to the bar the beers in the fridge remained untouched, and the huge pile of prizewinner's beer in the centre of the room was eyed intently. There was no chatting as resolute men with towels round their necks jogged on the spot and concentrated on their breathing.

Soon we were all gathered and The Famous Dick Wrigley called the proceedings to order. He ensured that all the entrants were seated in a circular arrangement around the cases of beer before reading in clear and solemn tones the contents of an ancient scroll containing the rules. He then had to sort out a small dispute as Sparky accused Skippy, the Australian Third Engineer, of cheating via premature stimulation. Skippy claimed he was simply 'scratching his balls' in a purely offhand and disinterested manner as he always did at this time of night. The Famous Dick Wrigley resolved the issue by forcing Skippy to stare at a picture of Princess Anne on a horse for two minutes with his hands behind his head. This engendered a second dispute as Skippy had apparently shown a treasonable interest in this picture earlier in the trip. Skippy replied, to the relief of the royalists present, that it was because he fancied the horse, which somehow placated everybody, and The Famous Dick Wrigley was able to regain control and call us to our marks. All round the room men sat back in their chairs and primed their zips ready for the off.

'Upon delumination of the lights,' pronounced The Famous Dick Wrigley, indicating the switch like a gameshow host, 'you may commence self-stimulation. I do solemnly declare that these lights will remain extinguished, and I will guard the switch personally in accordance with the scrolls, so help me God. I will rekindle the lights upon one of our number reciting the words 'Me, me, me' followed by name and rank, in the prescribed fashion. Do we all understand the rules, gentlemen?' He took the lack of response as an affirmative. 'In that case, may the biggest wanker win, and if we are all ready, on your marks,' everyone leant forward and began hyperventilating, 'get set,' the zips all came down in one crisp movement, 'you may begin.' And the room was plunged into darkness.

Now I had been reserving judgement on this affair throughout, and still seemed, for some reason, unable to throw myself into it heart and soul in the abandoned way I managed easily enough when left on my own. Despite everybody's seriousness and preparation, I was still somewhat sceptical even now, but rules were rules and The Famous Dick Wrigley had given his solemn word to keep the lights out under the penalty of buying everybody ten cases of beer apiece. I couldn't see any catch, and when the zips came tumbling down and the noises around me started up, it was quite clear that nobody else could either. A dozen zips all being unzipped in unison is a fairly interesting sound in itself – they should record it and use it on albums – but it was nothing to the noise that followed. An indescribable mix of grunts and moans, blipping and skin, sweat and machismo filled the testosterone-laden air. It was perfectly disgusting, quite unbelievable and absolutely clear that genuine masturbation was going on all around me.

The tension built very quickly, and after only a minute or so the atmosphere was already building to a feverish pitch. I sensed Gonad, to my left, was approaching his moment of beer-winning spasm, but coming up on my right was Giewy, making a noise like a hospital full of asthmatics inhaling smoke, and it was he who was first to fall to his knees.

'Argh! Uh! Uh! Yyeess! Ugh! Ugh!' but the stupid sod was so carried away with his orgasm that he hadn't said the right words by the time NotNorman came up on the stand side with a tremendous last minute spurt.

'Wugh! ME! ME! Wugh! ME!' he cried. 'Not . . . Wugh! . . . Norman – Navigating Cadet!'

The lights crashed on and suddenly the awful reality hit.

FROTTAGE

In a small circle on their knees in the centre of the room around the beer cases were all the first-trippers (and Giewy) with their shorts round their knees and their excitement in evidence. Everywhere else around the room dignified officers sat back relaxing in comfortable chairs, resplendent in their uniforms, and as innocent as wild flowers. They all hooted with laughter and took photographs of the depraved spectacle before them. They congratulated one another on the great joke and reprised the groaning and wet slapping noises they had all been making. They had all been sitting back in their chairs making wanking noises while all the first-trippers (and Giewy) were masturbating furiously in front of them. What made them doubly delighted was that because of the rules regarding catching others wanking, all the first-trippers (and Giewy) would now have to buy all of those present a case of beer each. Even NotNorman, who had genuinely won six cases would have to part with twelve, so once again we had been suckered.

It was quite brilliantly done. All that trouble we had gone to in order to catch people masturbating – knocking down doors, dangling off the boat-deck on ropes and so on – and we had been tricked into cranking away in the middle of the officers' bar in front of the entire assembly.

I hid myself in about ten pints of beer and spent the night trying to decide what my new name would be when I moved to Brazil.

Before I leave the topic of masturbation, I must just tell you one more story. It's not that I wish to dwell on base matters, but, following the revelations of the previous story, the more people I can drag into the field with me, the less conspicuous I'll feel, if you see what I mean.

I have not yet introduced the Fifth Engineer. His name

was Eddie, but everybody called him SmallParcel following the event I am about to relate. The reason you have not yet met SmallParcel is that he didn't really exist, at least not in any tangible sense. He was a pale, thin chap with scraggy hair, an unshaven, vacant face and a body you felt you could put your hand straight through and out the other side. Do you remember in *Star Trek* when the people on the *Enterprise* got the co-ordinates wrong beaming someone up and they *sort of* beamed up, but got stuck in a faded and translucent state in the transporter room? That's how SmallParcel looked all the time – half beamed up.

One of the main reasons he was like this was that he provided for himself an almost continuous supply of mind-expanding drugs. And not just one type – he liked plenty of variety in his diet. This meant that any conversation with him was very unlikely to advance matters. For instance, if you came across him on the deck somewhere, instead of saying 'hello', it was always a good game to hit him with a randomly selected word, such as 'cauliflower' or 'theodolite'. If you caught him right it would drive his scrambled brain to new extremes of surreal delirium. He would freeze, pole-axed by the word, then jerk his head around trying to make it slot in somewhere. He would repeat the word a few times, a look of wonderment creeping over his face, then he would crack up into raucous, emotional fits of laughter and tears that could go on for hours. You then went on your way, leaving the man reeling from the blatant delivery of a single word.

One night we were having a few beers in the bar when the door burst open and Gonad's delighted face poked into the room. 'Stations lads! Eddie's having a chieftain in his cabin!'

We all leapt into gear and two minutes later a crowd of us were sardined around his door ready to burst in. We got ourselves organised for maximum effect, the master-key was turned and, BANG! In we went. The usual glossy magazines went up, the cameras flashed and the laughter rained. The normal, everyday humiliation of a man playing with himself. But then someone noticed that there was something different about this particular catch. The glossy magazines that had been thrust skyward by SmallParcel were not the usual range featuring bad, rude excellent girls. There was not a single curvaceous blonde to be found. This in itself was not unheard of – chaps had been caught with every imaginable variation of fetishist material from a Crufts' catalogue to a book on amoebic dysentery – but SmallParcel was indulging an interest in neither of these. Nor was he a rubber fetishist or one of those guys who like to dress as babies, wet the bed and get punished by a gothic tractor mechanic wearing flippers. Any of these would have raised appreciative eyebrows without surprising anyone too much; but the shocking perversity of SmallParcel was beyond the experience of even this worldly bunch of sailors.

SmallParcel was sexually aroused – and you must follow me closely here, because it's all rather strange – by letterboxes. Mmmm, letterboxes. And this was no passing fancy or whimsical attraction – he could fall in love with the doors to which they were attached. This is absolutely true, and the evidence was there for us in the glossies being examined with wide eyes. Although the majority of them were the advertising literature from builders merchants on the various front doors available in the marketplace, the one that stood out above all was an American-published magazine – called something like *Remember Your ZIP* or *CosmoPostman Magazine* – for people who shared his front door and letterbox fetish. Inside were contact advertisements for this like-minded, happy-go-lucky bunch to meet one another, advertisements for the various letterboxes you could buy, 'ready and willing' to receive your advances, and stories and letters on the various adventures these people had. (Apparently the American way of life is a particular tease for those sharing SmallParcel's predilection, as American doors do not *have* letterboxes. These doors were referred to by the magazine as 'prick-teasing bitch doors'. Need I add that trips to Europe were a major advertising feature?)

SmallParcel was disarmingly unembarrassed at being caught in the act. Indeed, he was more wrapped up in evangelical enthusiasm to convert us to the wonders of his religion. He was more than happy to share his convictions with us, presumably in the hope that he might recruit more members for the clan. He showed us a contraption, which he had made himself, that looked like a sort of hollowed-out cucumber fixed to a flat, rectangular piece of wood. It was actually made of Tupperware lined with polystyrene, and was so constructed as to fit snugly into a letterbox, thus allowing SmallParcel to consummate his love with the door of his choosing. Putting it plainly, this fitting – which he referred to as a 'lobby-shunter' – allowed him the luxury of shagging letterboxes. He told us, in his own inimitable fashion, that this was extremely exciting for him, not simply because of the emotional fulfilment in making love to a door you are fond of – which is rather touching in itself – but because, if there was anybody *inside* the house he was rogering, there was no way he could know what their reaction would be upon encountering a womb's eye view of the sexual act in the form of a huge Tupperware cucumber wobbling about in the letterbox. Nor could he predict what action they might take, and the prospect of some overwrought housewife setting about his genitalia with a food processor excited him above all else.

So SmallParcel had become a postman. Wandering from door to door, trying to hide his excitement, it was the perfect job for a man who wished to establish the prospects for love in the district. As he posted a letter, he would close his eyes and get a feel for the letterbox – strength of springs, size, make, material, flexion and general cuteness. When he found a good one his knees would turn to jelly. He would pray that the door was a beauty and that the view of his bottom from the road was none too clear. Then he would retreat, and the door would quake on its hinges, for she knew that SmallParcel would return after dark to 'do his funky thang' (as *Remember Your ZIP* so aptly put it). The act of making love to a door was also given its own verb – 'to starfish' – presumably from the splayed nature of the position the Don Juan needed to adopt up against the door.

Anyway, SmallParcel ended up in prison. He had been unable to resist a tempting young 'Pine Mastif' (half-glazed with a brass twin-sprung letterbox) in Southampton, and an old woman – thinking it was her husband – had crept up on him from the inside with a carpet beater. SmallParcel passed out, and woke up in a cell. He was ordered to visit a psychologist who told him his job as a postman exposed him to too much temptation, and that he should try to find an environment entirely devoid of puckering front doors with teasing letterboxes. He was also told to come out of the closet and tell his friends he was an abuser of letterboxes. He took this instruction to heart and following a sympathetic reaction from family and friends, he went a little too far, going around confessing to people that he'd been buggering their houses. Unfortunately, rather than engendering the sympathetic response the psychologist had envisaged, this had the opposite effect. Irate house-owners threatened SmallParcel with whatever domestic items were nearest to hand, and he became all the more aroused.

SmallParcel felt a burning need to get away to a sex-free

environment. The Merchant Navy seemed the ideal answer, but now he was here, he was yearning to be back amongst the knobs and knockers. His enforced separation from his loved ones was too much for him to take.

To try and get closer to his desires he was writing a short story to send for publication in the magazine. He showed it to us and it was a remarkable piece of work, which I would like to share with you here. What follows is the result of a drugs-inspired, half-beamed-up letterbox enthusiast putting pen to paper for the benefit of his fellow worshippers. It is written from the viewpoint of a house-owning couple whose front door is being sullied:

'Dear Sir,

My wife and I were sat at the breakfast table, wondering why the mail was late this morning, when your missive came squeezing through our front door's front door. My front door is now in the post-pubescence phase common in kiln-dried hardwoods, and, for the first time in our experience, showed signs of being in ecstasy. Of course, we were shocked, but mostly we were concerned for the welfare of our front door, so we decided that it would be best for the time being if we blocked up her letterbox with a wet chamois. To our utmost amazement, she enjoyed this more than a *Reader's Digest* Prize Offer, but we hoped, with the chamois there, she would have no more problems until she grew a little more mature. But then the postman started ringing the bell (our front door enjoyed that too). He told us that he was 'frustrated' by our actions, and that if we did not restore our front door's receptive capability forthwith he would take (a) umbrage, and (b) action. Which we thought was a bit much on top of (c) liberties.

Let me fill you in. It's important for us to protect our front door from the ravages of the harsh world outside lest she become distorted. We want to protect her so she can 'open out' and not feel that people just walk straight through her when she does. You see, she's very young. She may look strong and reliable, but we've seen her come off her hinges a couple of times, I can tell you. She was left on our doorstep the very first day we moved into this house, and we didn't have the heart to shut her out. I suppose we should accept that she needs to be given more space – she's a good seven feet tall now. Do you know, she used to have just a tiny little bell? Now she's got two huge knockers and that letterbox and . . . well . . . when we found out what the postman was doing before we were up in the morning, we couldn't believe it. Anyway, we took suitable measures to stop the postman and, as documented above, he got uppity about her chastity. There was nothing he could do though, so things quietened down.

Then, just as diplomatic relations with the Post Office were being restored, our disgust was redoubled by the discovery that this postman – having declared passionate and devoted allegiance to *our* front door – was indulging himself in a sordid affair with a 74-year-old 'Suffolk Sturdy' round the corner, and a terrace of 'Jewson Reliables' in Kemptown village.

Well, we were distraught. I mean, what with the fear of Dutch Elm disease and Postman's Knock, which are both going around at the moment, we called in a Gyknockologist straight away. He took a look through our letterbox and – apart from telling the old gyknockological joke about needing to redecorate the hall – he said there was a good chance we might shortly be taking delivery of a parcel. Well, that sealed it. We had a furious row with our front door during which she gave us some rubbish about French letters and the postman's forced entry. Her arguments fell flat when we discovered a large battery-powered, vibrating, rubber latch-key called 'The Juggernaut', an inflatable 'Male Yale' and a pair of skimpy lace draught-excluders disguised as a fluffy snake.

These horrific discoveries are every door-owner's nightmare, and it was at this point that we realised just how bad things had become. It was time to get tough. She shrieked and begged us not to get a porch. Anything but that. She accepted that she had let us down and that the whole incident was a stain upon her woodwork, but said she loved her postman and that nothing we could do would change that.

'Love him?' we said incredulously. 'Can't you see he's just junk male? We're getting a porch, and that's that.'

The next morning there was a ladder up to front door's bedroom window and she was not in her bed when we took her up a morning cup of Cuprinol. She and the postman had eloped.

We hired a private Timber Merchant, and he did what he could. He discovered that the postman had escaped from a 'home-for-people-who-like-doors-too-much' in Northamptonshire and that he should never have been allowed to become a postman in the first place. He had also heard that our door and her postman were living on a caravan site in North Wales, and that she too was now beyond restoration. She was 'doing parcels' every day, and getting right up the drive on second-class registereds.

So there you are. The postman wins again, and we have lived in a broken-hearted (and draughty) world since then. We haven't received any letters since March because we're too traumatised to get another letterbox.

That's why we didn't receive the summons, Your Honour, and concludes the evidence for the defence.'

So be warned. Learn the lessons of this story. Tell the truth, don't do drugs and get a porch. You know it makes sense.

Chapter 11

The Electric Hammer

The untrustworthy nature of electric hammers. The unexpected existence of windy hammers.

Following the Grand Cranking Competition, the spirits of the majority were extremely high. The company seemed pleased to have wrought wholesale embarrassment on the first-trippers, and the feeling of a job well done in psychologically damaging young men for life was abundant. Even the few who were not directly in high spirits (i.e. the victims) were understandably keen to drown their sorrows, so the flow of beer (all paid for by the victims) and the fact that nobody had eaten much came together to produce a high-stepping evening of some note.

All I remember is that by 7.30 things were going so well that many of those present were once again dropping their trousers (this time voluntarily and under bright lights). I have no recollection of anything after about 8.30 – actually, that's not quite true. I remember that as I fell back on to my bunk at about two in the morning my pillow exploded around my head, and everything became decidedly damp as a result; however, I am not a man who lets trivial matters stand between me and my beauty sleep, so I did not so much as turn a wet hair. The surprise was only enough to give me a faint memory of the event the next day, but I must not become sidetracked into a discussion on the causes and effects of exploding pillows. However intrigued you may feel about this, I am afraid it must wait for a future chapter, probably entitled 'One Hundred and One Things To Do With a Condom, Two Litres of Water and a

Pillowcase'. For now, I shall remain on the prescribed course.

In fact, what I said was completely untrue, because now I think about it, I have some decidedly hairy recollections of some of the things that were going on when Animals' Night was hotting up. Sparky was out cold on the floor, stark naked. He had a lighted cigarette stuck in his bottom and was having half his beard removed by four drunks. I would have confidently wagered that he was completely unconscious, but when the cigarette keeled over and the lighted end nestled gently into the back of his testicles he proved me wrong by leaving the room in something of a rush.

Two rubber dolls (Clarabel and Elvis) were suffering horrendous indecency and the entire bar was two inches deep in beer. Crate was trying to establish who had so carefully used one of his flip-flops as a toilet, NotNorman and Benny the Dog were having a fight, wrestling violently on the carpet without anyone paying any attention, a deputation had returned from a thieving raid on the galley for some munchies, and Cranners was in the hospital attending to Patch who had 'Got some glass in his back playing darts'.

So it should come as no surprise to you to find out, firstly, that my pillow exploded, and secondly, that the next morning the bar was found to be in what might euphemistically be referred to as 'a state of disrepair'. Mind you, weren't we all? I have no idea how anyone managed to get me up at six, or how I survived the deck-work until breakfast. I was still thoroughly drunk, let alone hungover, when I went up to the Mate for the jobs after breakfast. (A job delegated to me by Patch who was too busy snoring in the rope store to do it himself.)

'Ah, morning Windy!' screamed the Mate, delighting in my condition. 'Good night last night, was it? Someone tells me you lads were wanking in the bar while I was on watch. Tut, tut now. Surely not! Hardly the stuff of officer material, eh? Ha, ha, ha! Anyway, I hope you didn't drink too much 'cos I've got an important job for you. Seems there was a bit of a jolly-up in the bar afterwards. The crew have been in for the last two hours clearing up, but there's some structural damage that has to be fixed very carefully. Some of the rosewood panels and trim have come away from the bulkheads and they are very valuable. You lads can spend the morning fixing it all back up again, but BE VERY CAREFUL. See the electricians for the correct driver-nails and the electric hammer, and don't set it higher than torque level two. Those panels don't come cheap, OK?'

No, I was *not* OK, but I nodded in all the right places.

In the bar we surveyed the mess that remained even after the strenuous efforts of the crew to clean up.

'Wow!' exclaimed NotNorman, examining some damaged rosewood wall panelling and shaking his head. 'I'm surprised the ship stayed afloat through last night!'

And it certainly was a mess. This was hardly surprising, however, because little did I know that a team of four men had spent the last hour painstakingly *causing* the apparent devastation in the bar – not clearing it up – and all for my benefit. They had taken down pictures, ripped off panels, torn down trimming and, just for good measure, completely dismantled the bar. The place looked like a family of bears had been fed a bucket of cocaine each, then given 20 minutes to find the honey.

'Where do we start?' implored Giewy.

I took charge. 'Right. What we need here are some specialist tools.' I rubbed my chin thoughtfully. I was not going to let on that I was just repeating the Mate's instructions. 'NotNorman, you go to KiloWatt and get some driver-nails. Giewy, you go and wake Patch – you're good at upsetting people – and I will get the electric hammer. We'll meet back here asap.' And with the heady taste of leadership swelling my head, I started off for MegaWatt's cabin.

MegaWatt was the Chief Electrician and was a quiet, polite unassuming Welshman. That was until he got a few beers inside him, when he turned into a loud, angry, aggressive and violently patriotic Welshman. As I knocked tentatively at his door, I knew that I was more likely to be waking the latter Welshman than the former, and I feared he would not appreciate being woken now.

'Cooee – MegaWatt?' I ventured round his door. 'You've slept in, you naughty lad. Ha, ha! Have you got the electric hammer?'

There were some grunts and mumbled swear words, then a growl like an engine starting. He roared through gritted teeth and launched out of bed straight for me with his fingers outstretched towards my throat. One of the things my family has always been good at is reading people's moods. I divined, in the split second it took him to motor across his cabin, that if he did intend to give me an electric hammer it would be in the form of an enema. I slammed the door on his fingers and legged it.

Shaken but unbowed, I decided to try KiloWatt, the Second Electrician. He would be on the bottom plates of the engine-room on watch. I sighed and trudged round the accommodation and into the noisy, hot engine-room. I should mention here, for those who are not familiar with ships, that the engine-room is massive. It is fully six flights of stairs from the door to the bottom plates. It is rather like walking around a car engine, with the people equating roughly to the size of a spark plug. When something goes wrong, the engineers can climb inside the engine block and wander about looking for the problem. We are talking sizeable here. As you can imagine, such a beast generates a great deal of heat and noise, so the engine-room was the very last place I wanted to take the kind of hangover that would show up on a photograph.

Having negotiated the metal steps to the bottom plates, I was disappointed to find that the electric hammer was not there. KiloWatt told me that SmallParcel had apparently taken it to carry out some essential work on the motor that hauls up the anchor. He could be found on the fo'c'sle head attending to that. I couldn't believe it; that was a mile away, and half of it was stairs! I stomped back up the six flights to the exit, round the back of the accommodation and trudged on to the foredeck for the long haul up to the fo'c'sle head. At least there was the benefit of some fresh air outside and the chance of a peaceful minute or two watching the world go by. It's always a pleasure to taste air that has not even seen land – let alone a car exhaust – and to soothe one's eyes on the passing sea and sky. I was particularly needful of their restorative qualities today because I was tiring fast, and my head felt as if every three seconds or so, someone was inflating a medicine ball inside my brain to a size roughly four times larger than my head, then popping it with a tent mallet. My skull was having to resist the pressure to burst like a smashed watermelon on each inflation.

Upon arrival at the fo'c'sle head I was greeted by the gargoyle-like countenance of SmallParcel, looking like the Ghost of the Confused Fo'c'sle Dead Man. He had been hideously drunk the previous night, and stoned out of what he laughingly called his mind, and I could see him struggling manfully with his brain to get it to tell him who I was and whether or not I was a feature of *his* reality or of *real* reality. He gave up the unequal struggle and smiled wanly at me. He was waiting to see if I had human attributes or if I was about to turn into a dragon. It was at this point that a well-delivered 'cauliflower' or 'theodolite' would hit home beautifully, but I was short of time so I gave it a miss.

'Mornin' SmallParcel! You all right?' His ears turned towards me like satellite dishes as I spoke, then he threw his head around a bit and snorted, as if trying to get his brain around all those words spoken in one go. I always envisaged his brain as being like one of those children's games where you have to get the marbles to fall into the right holes before anything can happen. When he threw his head about, I could picture them all jumping around and falling back into a new configuration. He would try that one, and if he didn't get a result he would throw his head around some more. Anyway, no answer was forthcoming from this configuration, so I hit him with the biggy, 'Have you got the electric hammer up here?'

He shook a little as if someone had walked over his grave, then looked around his feet at the miscellany he had accrued. The winch was in bits, and lots of tools, cogs, bolts and cables were strewn around the fo'c'sle. He jumped as if he had no idea how all this electrical and mechanical instrumentation had materialised around him. Then he broke into a sweaty panic as he realised he had no idea what any of them were for. This would not do his career any good. How could he be an engineer if he didn't know the purpose of any of the tools? He tried to remember how he got the job in the first place and I could see him fading fast with the enormity of it all. It was not simply that he was drunk or hungover. Sure, he had got wasted last night, but he did that *every* night. The addition of some more people and some animal tomfoolery in the bar simply blended in with the friends and bizarre scenery his addled brain gave him as standard. No, it was the battle of interacting with other people that was hampering him. My case was especially tough because I'd asked two questions. He had them both stacked up over Luton, and I was beginning to wonder if he would ever be able to land one. Suddenly, he threw his head back and snorted again, as if he'd just received a carpet beater in the 'nads. He had remembered several things. Firstly, that he had clear and specific knowledge on the subject of electric hammers. Secondly, that he had qualified in Mechanical Engineering (Ordinary National Certificate) at Portsmouth Polytechnic in 1972, and thirdly, that eight out of ten cats preferred Whiskas.

'Errrrr . . .' he began. It sounded as if a little fan had started up in the back of his head somewhere, but there were signs of better things to come, so I nodded encouragingly. 'Errrr . . . the errr . . . yeah.' The fan stopped. We were back where we started. His mouth was still open, but sweet words did not fill the air. Then he got it again. 'Errr, electric hammer, you know? It's, like, Not Here. We're talking . . . *somewhere else*. Right? Not here.' He nodded vigorously to try and coerce me into agreeing. 'I found something out,' he continued with an air of collusion, 'from a statistical analysis of engineers who own cats, they found that eight out of ten cats that expressed a preference preferred Portsmouth Polytechnic. Chiefy's got the hammer – he's on the boiler flat.'

He spun round to see who had said the last bit. He had no idea it was him. I turned and left him to it. In my condition I could not face quizzing him on felines in further education. Another time, maybe. As I walked away, he was shouting with heartfelt passion to an empty sky, 'Why, WHY? Why are there no LEAVES on this ship?' He seemed close to tears. 'What are they trying to DO to us?'

I didn't worry about him. I knew that as soon as the ship rolled back the other way, the marbles would all roll into different holes, he would forget the lack of foliage and be happy again. I was more concerned about my personal plight. The boiler flat? I was already getting sore feet and – Jesus my *head* – and the boiler flat was way, way up in the funnel. I was also aware that by now the guys would be waiting for me back at the bar, so I picked up the pace and battled on.

It was another major distance, primarily involving steep stairs upwards and when I got to the boiler flat I was doubled over and wheezing from the exertion. I was in no condition for all this exercise. The Chief Engineer stared at me with some concern as I put my hands on my knees and stared at the floor, striving to force the correct words out between my wheezes. I had a feeling he wouldn't simply give me an electric hammer, and I was right. He had used it, and last he knew Jinx had it on the poop deck.

I stumbled down the companionways from the boiler flat, crawled the length of the afterdeck and dragged my half-dead body up on to the poop, only to be told by Jinx that Benny the Dog had it, and that he was on watch in the engine-room.

And so we went on. Benny told me that The Famous Dick Wrigley had just that moment been using it on the bridge, who, it transpired, had given it to Crate who was working on the propeller-shaft. That was back down into the engine-room, down to the bottom plates and out along the shaft tunnel to the very farthest end where the shaft exits the ship to join what remained of the propeller. What remained of me was told by Crate that Skippy had the electric hammer working on the bilge pump at the bottom of hatch number one, right up near the foc's'le then down a 50-foot ladder to the deck of the hold. And so it went on. Everyone I spoke to had just that very moment passed it on to someone else who always seemed to be at the furthest imaginable point on the ship from the point I was presently occupying. Incredibly bad luck.

THE ELECTRIC HAMMER

Had I the mental capacity to analyse what was happening, I might have wondered if perhaps these cheeky chappies were not being quite as co-operative as they might be, but a combination of hangover, nausea, and the convincing line in patter of each of the people I had to visit kept me from suspecting that this might all be a merry jape. As it was, I never believed for one moment that the hammer did not exist, which was just as well, really, because it did indeed exist, but I was still a long way from getting my hands on it.

Skippy sent me to Sparky up in his 'shack' near the bridge, who sent me to Cranners in the number five hatch down aft, who sent me to the fo'c'sle rope store, and so on until I had visited everybody on the ship apart from the Captain himself. Each person I visited duly sent me somewhere else, then unbeknown to me, went to the bar, where they met up with all the others and tracked my progress. Finally I arrived at the Captain's day room, gasping like Chitty Chitty Bang Bang on a cold morning and coughing fit to throw up my legs.

'Good Lord!' he exclaimed. 'Cough it up, there Baboulene; it might be a lung! How can I help you – apart from cardiac massage?'

'The electric . . . the electric . . .' I put my hands on my knees and waved at the Captain to indicate that I would be with him shortly. Luckily he came to my rescue.

'The electric hammer? Certainly! It's in the top drawer of that desk. Bring it back when you've finished with it – I'm going to have it framed!' And with that, he left the room and headed off to the bar.

I was too weak to be puzzled by his last remark, and too overwhelmed with relief to care what he had said. I had finally got my hands on the bloody thing! I opened the drawer as if I was awakening a princess, and there was my jewel, as large as life. I held it up and it shone out like a visitation of angels. To me this was not a power tool; this was the holy grail. It was of no consequence that I was reverently holding aloft a perfectly ordinary two-pound hammer with a bit of wire stuck in the back and a three-pin plug on the end. To me, my life's work was over. My quest complete. Beholding the electric hammer meant I could die a happy man. With the renewed energy of a mission completed, I headed off for the bar with my prize.

As I opened the door I was about to start talking to the other cadets about what a business I had had trying to find the thing when I suddenly became unaware of which planet I was on, what my name was or how I fitted into the general scheme of things. I still remember that feeling every time I see one of the thousand photographs taken at that instant. I see my dumbfounded face registering innocence, ignorance and shock in equal measure. I see the hammer in one hand (PROVING innocence and ignorance) and the pointless plug in the other, just to rub it in.

The delighted chant went up for me to buy the breakfast beers. I had been caught out again. Then MegaWatt hushed the gathered throng and asked me to explain exactly what I thought would happen were the electric hammer plugged in. He took it from me and plugged it into the wall socket. Then to roars of approval he threw the switch. The hammer flashed up and down, beating the life out of thousands of unseen nails. MegaWatt, his face gripped by fear, held tightly with both hands as the hammer gradually took over his whole body. First his arm, then his head, and soon he was entirely possessed by the manic motion of the electric hammer. He unplugged it just in time and managed to survive the experience.

Which was more than I did. From that day to this, whenever I bump into a member of that ship (or one of the many more who have heard the tale) they pretend to be in the merciless grip of a hyperactive electric hammer, and begin hammering away uncontrollably, shouting, 'TURN IT OFF! TURN IT OFF!' Dreadfully boring it is, and juvenile in the extreme.

For years afterwards I tried to get other first-trippers to nip off and get the electric hammer, and not one of them has ever fallen for it. Irrespective of whatever greatness I achieve in life – be it musical superstardom, literary genius, sexual infamy, academic excellence – I am afraid I shall go down in history as 'that donkey who fell for the electric hammer routine.'

The issue came up again about a week later. Giewy was in the doghouse for something-or-other – being astoundingly ugly while on duty or something – and Harry Tate said to him that as a punishment he couldn't have his timetabled, cushy study afternoon. Instead, he was to collect himself a 'windy hammer' and help the crew who were chipping and painting the foredeck. Giewy furrowed his brow and pushed out his lower jaw. He had never heard of a 'windy hammer' in all his months of experience, and wasn't going to be fooled, and he told the Mate so. This led to the inevitable transfer of information and abuse (from close range and with a three-part chorus of tasty saliva) about how the windy hammer was an air-powered, triple-headed power tool, used in the removal of surface rust and scale from metalwork. It was very noisy, highly unpleasant, and could be obtained from the Serang, the Asian crew equivalent of the Bosun, immediately, if not sooner, and was equally effective on recalcitrant cadets' genitals. Giewy's nerve held. He knew the Mate would respect him if he stood his ground and avoided the trap.

'Righto,' said Giewy, winking at the Mate. He crinkled his nose and added, 'No problem.' Then he patted him on the shoulder, tweaked the Mate's cheek and walked happily from the bridge, chuckling with self-satisfaction. The Mate was too stunned to do anything about it. In 20 years at sea nobody had ever tweaked his cheek. Giewy cheerfully ignored the orders and settled down on his bunk for his study afternoon. I'm sure you don't need me to tell you that it was not very long before Giewy was lifted bodily from his repose, pinned up against the wall, and requested to explain why he was not in extreme discomfort at the business end of a windy hammer. Giewy also needs no reminding that a windy hammer is indeed a triple-headed pneumatic device for chipping decks. He also knows they are especially unpleasant when employed on bulkheads in the cramped and sweaty confines of the after-peak (another tank, but with no elbow room) and anchor locker, and that to make the chipping and painting of such areas your very own responsibility, all you need to do is wink at the Mate, pat him on the shoulder and tweak his cheek when he asks you to do something. Simple.

Chapter 12

Bridge Watch

Deep wonderment on a tropical bridge watch.

After all the fun and games of the previous few weeks, it was a great contrast – and something of a relief – to find myself away from the bustle of daily deck-work and on the midnight-to-four bridge watch. This is the Second Officer's watch, and despite the unsociable hours is arguably the most pleasant of the three watches. The twelve-to-four afternoon session is busy and alive, with sunsights to complete, people coming and going and plenty of business to get through. Then, at the other end of the clock, the midnight-to-four stint is dark and quiet as the ship sleeps, and there is little to do at sea but think deep thoughts and chat deep chat.

There is no better time or place to contemplate life than leaning on the bridge wing at 2 a.m. in the balmy equatorial Pacific. Without an artificial light for a thousand miles, a million stars twinkle their secrets to you as few men have seen them. The warm breeze strokes your face, and the easy motion of the ship rocks you into a most pleasant mood of happy reflection. The haunting, mysterious darkness of the deepest of all seas contrasts brilliantly with the sparkling iridescence of the moon reflected in the bow wave. Way down aft, a crewman is hunched over the light from his stove, and above him hangs the reassuring presence of a great albatross. This is the time to take stock, to talk in hushed, sincere tones of the meaning of life, and to see it not as a tragedy, but as a miracle and a privilege.

Never have I found a more wondrous place than this. I would recommend to anyone and everyone that they do whatever they must to experience these circumstances at least once in life. It is the eighth wonder of the world, but it cannot be seen or touched. It is a feeling. An aura. A sensation.

I leant on the bridge wing and placed my chin on my arms. I stared out at the stars as they rocked to and fro, and sighed happily. From here I could laugh at the practical jokes and the hardship. And with a week of the midnight-to-four lying ahead of me, and Sydney, Australia – a place I had been burning to visit – sitting just over the horizon after that, the old Merchant Navy began to look as though it wasn't such a bad idea after all.

Chapter 13

Harbouring Grudges

Australia runs off and hides. Argumentative pilots in Sydney. Egg on the face? Lady Luck has a flannel.

On the afternoon that we finally arrived on the Australian coast, I was lucky enough not only to be on the bridge, but also to see, first-hand, a stretched and decidedly nervous navigation team at work. The previous day's noon sunsights had not worked out because of bad weather, nor had the Mate's starsights, so our last reliable position had been more than 24 hours earlier. In these circumstances, with the ship known to be heading towards a great continent and a cunningly concealed shelf of underwater reefs, the navigating crew understandably tend to become edgy.

The estimated position put us 15 miles off the coast. If we were a few miles north of our actual position, we would be about to run onto the reef. A few miles south would give us a similar fate, so tension was high as we played hide-and-seek with Australia. It was still raining and visibility was poor, so two Seacunnies, Cranners, the Captain, and I were all scouring the veiled horizon, anxiously searching for the first signs of land.

To be honest, I had no real idea what to do, but I had learned that the way to handle these circumstances was to fix a severe expression on my face and march about purposefully as if greatly troubled by the gravity of the situation. In fact, I was greatly *excited* by the gravity of the situation, but I adopted the acceptable pose and joined the circuit shifting from chart table to bridge wing to radar – shaking my head and tutting at the lack of information –

to depth-sounder, to binoculars and back for any clue as to our precise position.

The radar had not been giving us too much information because it was picking up rain, clouds and wave-tops (known as 'clutter') ahead of all else, so no land could be distinguished. I had still been spending a lot of time staring into it because I liked to fiddle with the knobs and watch the pretty green line swing round and round. I was thus engaged when I twiddled the wrong button; the clutter disappeared, and there, clear as a bell, was a headland. I reported my find with due composure (although with hindsight I might perhaps have missed out the 'Yippee!'). And sure enough, once they had all had a look, relief abounded amongst the cognoscenti as they agreed it was indeed Australia.

Now the circuit shifted to a trot between the radar and the chart to try and match the landfall with a known *piece* of Australia. Within five minutes another headland blinked shyly into view, and the Captain and Cranners needed only a few seconds poring over the chart table before agreeing our position. The headlands were the North and South Heads at the entrance to the Sydney Harbour itself, and they congratulated each other on a marvellous piece of navigation. To set a course from a position 30 hours previously, taking into account wind and current, and hit the target smack on the nose takes some doing (or so the Captain told me) and the Old Man was not just relieved, he was full of himself. You could see him thinking that the old instinct was still there, that he had done us all a great favour by helping make those key decisions at nine that morning when sunsights had looked like a washout. He picked up the radiotelephone and spoke with the kind of voice Churchill must have used to announce victory in Europe.

'Sydney pilots, Sydney pilots, this is the British merchant vessel *Global Wanderer*, over.'

I could imagine the pilots looking at each other and saying, 'Oh Jesus, listen to *this* Pommie jerk!' before they replied formally – or at least as formally as Australians get – 'Yeah, go ahead, mate. Tell us all your stories.'

The Captain took the instrument from the side of his head and looked at it as if it had just run its tongue round the inside of his ear. This was not correct radio protocol, but he batted on regardless.

'Ah good, Sydney pilots, Yes. We have a landfall of two-niner decimal seven, two-niner decimal seven miles east of the South Head and can give you an ETA between the heads of eighteen hundred hours. Is this acceptable to you, over?'

Another gap, then the correspondent came back with the sound of restrained giggles in the background. He sounded as if he was speaking from the centre of a particularly serious drinking session. I imagined the pilots all crashed out drunk on a wharf somewhere.

'Is it acceptable to me? Y'know, I reckon we could fit you in there, mate. See ya later.' And the radio went dead. The Captain was extremely unhappy and called them straight back.

'Sydney pilots, Sydney pilots, this is the British merchant vessel *Global Wanderer*, over.' He stood tapping his foot and fuming as they left the customary pause before answering. Then a bored voice came back.

'Yeah mate, we're here. Can we do something else for you?'

'You certainly can! Firstly, I am NOT your "mate". Secondly, you can start using proper radiotelephony protocol in your communications! Really! We didn't invent all these rules and regulations just for you damned colonials to ignore. They may not make a lot of sense to someone of your intellect, but there is a purpose to each and every one, and if you do not begin to employ them forthwith I shall be visiting your superiors as a priority upon my de-embarkation. Do I make myself clear?'

I was embarrassed by the Captain's outburst, and from what I had heard of Australians thought it would be best to try and be friendly, so I was surprised when he did not receive a stream of abuse back from the other end. In fact, quite the reverse.

'Er, yeah, sorry about that, Captain. Yeah. Er, rendezvous at the designated pick-up point to collect your pilot at eighteen hundred hours. Roger and out.'

The Captain snorted as he replaced his receiver and stalked out on to the bridge wing, muttering something about forefathers and the last bastions of Western civilisation.

We were about ten minutes early arriving between the heads, so were not surprised that the pilot vessel was not there yet. However, when six o'clock came and went and we couldn't even pick it up within five miles on the radar, the Captain began to think they were deliberately messing him about.

'Sydney pilots, Sydney pilots, this is the British merchant vessel *Global Wanderer*, over.'

'Oh, er, roger, Captain. We can't seem to find you. Are you er . . . having trouble with your position there, eh? Er, over.'

The Captain flew into a rage. He snatched up the instrument and began working it over. 'I have been at sea for over thirty years, both man and boy. I was working with no navigational aids except for a lead-line, a brain and a pair of eyes before you were out of nappies, and I do NOT expect to be treated with anything less than the respect I deserve. WE are in position between the heads awaiting a pilot, and you are nowhere to be seen. I will be on to the Admiralty and you will be struck off before you can draw breath if I don't get a pilot within the next half hour. DO I MAKE MYSELF CLEAR? OVER!' He breathed in for the first time and puffed his chest out like a rooster. Then a new voice came over the radio.

'Good evening, Captain. This is your pilot here. Listen, I've spent TWENTY years piloting these waters. You are NOT where you are supposed to be. We are precisely between the heads, bearings one-nine-two and zero-zero-four, and you are not here. Over.'

Cranners nipped over to the radar and took the bearings, then ran them up on the chart. 'We're in the same place as they say they are,' he said, shrugging his shoulders.

'They are NOT going to get away with this,' said the Captain, boiling across to the radio. 'Sydney pilots, THIS is the British merchant vessel *Global Wanderer*, over.'

'Go ahead, Captain, over.' The Captain drew himself up to his full height and pursed his lips.

'Now you listen to me. You people had better get your act together pretty damn quick-smart or there will be trouble. I am a reasonable man, and I accepted your apology for letting your standards drop. However, your subsequent behaviour has been abominable. You clearly lack suitable leadership and I refuse to become the butt of your mindless retribution just because I am man enough to point out your failings. You have pushed me just about as far as I am prepared to go, and unless I get some co-operation from you IMMEDIATELY, I am getting straight on to the . . .'

'Captain!' I called. 'Red light on the port beam, sir!'

'. . . bloody insulted in all my . . . sorry?' He put down the radio. 'Red light, you say?'

'Yes, sir! Flashing red three every ten seconds.'

'Ah, good lad. Let's get a precise position, then two-oh. Then we can sink these scallywags once and for all.' Cranners was poring over the chart table, but no position was springing happily from his lips. In fact, he looked decidedly pale.

'Well come on then, two-oh. You can work a pair of dividers, can't you?'

'Er, yes, sir. Flashing red three in ten, was it?' Cranners knew how the light felt – he too was flashing red three in every ten seconds.

'Yes yes, that's it. That must be the light on the headland.'

'Well, yes, sir, but not the headland you're thinking of. We are *not* between the North and South Heads of Sydney Harbour, sir. We appear to be between a *different* set of heads, around twenty-five miles south of Sydney's heads, sir.'

The Captain's eyes bulged out like boiled eggs, a klaxon sounded from the back of his mouth and his knees clacked together like an alarm clock going off.

'WHAT?' he cried, stupefied. 'You mean we are sailing gaily around some of the most dangerous reefs in the world without knowing where we are to the nearest . . . *twenty-five miles*?'

He had hit the nail on the head. That was exactly what we were doing. We had mistaken these heads for Sydney's heads and were talking to Sydney pilots 25 miles away. It was nothing short of a miracle that we had not run aground and sunk the ship in shark-infested waters. The enormity of our mistake – and our escape – hung heavy in the air. Nobody spoke for some time. Suddenly the radio crackled into life.

'*Global Wanderer*, *Global Wanderer*, this is Sydney pilots. Come in, over.'

The Captain had gone white. He made no move to answer them.

'Good God,' he said, falling into the pilot's chair and wiping his brow. He was shaking visibly. 'I . . . I . . . could have lost . . . lost the ship – maybe some crew. I could have killed everybody! Get me a glass of water, cadet. My lord, what a thing.'

'*Global Wanderer, Global Wanderer*, this is Sydney pilots. Come in, over.'

The Captain looked mournfully at the radio.

'Whatever am I going to tell *them*? My career will be in tatters once they get blabbing. This will be in the papers tomorrow. Tell them I'm unavailable two-oh. I can't face them just now – but don't tell them anything! We have to think.'

Cranners walked silently to the radio and picked it up. He did not know what he was going to say.

'Sydney pilots, this is *Global Wanderer*. Go ahead, over.'

'Ah, good evening *Global Wanderer*. This is Captain Mollineaux here. I gather you've been having a few problems tonight, over?'

'Ah,' said Cranners. What could he say? He gulped and was about to say something vague in order to play for time, when Captain Mollineaux came back.

'Yeah, well, I'm real sorry about what you've been put through tonight. I don't know how to tell you this, but I've just turned up for my shift, and the blokes here are all drunk. They had a big win on the horses earlier on, and they've been, er . . . celebrating. I don't know how to apologise, and I'm sure you must be raging out there, but what can I tell you? The guys are all lying around here – they say they couldn't find you.'

We stared at each other dumbfounded while the radio continued apologising. 'These things happen, eh? Ha ha. We were all boys once, eh Captain? So listen, I'll be coming on board tomorrow with an invitation for you to come back here to our offices and I'll help you with the formalities of your complaint, but until then I've pulled the pilot back in, so I'm going to have to ask you to put down an anchor, Captain, and wait until we can get a sober pilot out to you. I know this is disgusting behaviour, but I don't see any other way round it.' I could hear the poor chap wringing his hands as he spoke.

Our Captain, on the other hand, seemed to have found a whole new lease of life. He strode once more to the radio, a fully restored, belligerent old bastard. He picked up the radio, stuck his nose in the air, and spoke in clear, majestic tones.

'Sydney pilots, I shall give this matter my deepest consideration. What has happened tonight could well have had grave consequences, and you have been fortunate to get away without disastrous results. I shall expect a pilot here at oh-six-hundred hours, and I shall want to talk to you first thing when we come alongside. Over and out.' He then turned to Cranners. 'OK, two-oh. As far as I'm concerned, we have not yet arrived. Plot a course for Sydney and put the ship there as if nothing happened. In fact, as far as you are concerned, nothing DID happen this evening, OK?' He looked at me, then Cranners. 'Good,' he said. 'If anyone wants me, I shall be in bed.' And he left the bridge looking decidedly older than he did when he'd arrived.

I shrugged my shoulders at the Second Mate, who was looking a little bewildered. He went out on to the bridge wing and stared at the hulking shadow of the continent of Australia on the misty horizon. He spread his arms to the looming land mass and shouted into the vastness, 'Will the REAL Sydney Harbour please stand up!'

Chapter 14

The Wizard of Oz

Australian workers don't work. The appropriate treatment of a gift horse. Windy gets a life in Sydney. Lessons in adjusting the sobriety of beautiful girls while maintaining the condition of one's shins. Meeting the parents.

Australia is a wonderful country. Let's have no doubt about it, it is a wonderful, wonderful country. I suppose one could argue that anybody who has been incarcerated on a fifties ship for 36 days with a bunch of animals would find any land relatively wonderful, but I hope to convince you that my love for the Lucky Country was based on more than the fact that it was somewhere other than the *Global Wanderer*.

It may also be argued that my view was tainted by our having run out of fresh water. We had drinking water but were showering in seawater and, rather like the ship herself, we were all struggling to get up a good lather. So as we plodded across that famous natural harbour towards the Opera House and that great coat-hanger bridge – leaning on the tugs like a marathon runner being helped the last few yards to the finishing post and with a hundred colourful yachts dancing attendance like butterflies around a fragrant bush – we were more than just a little bit fragrant ourselves.

I suppose anywhere would have been a blessing, but we, by virtue of our broken propeller, were heading for a dry dock in one of the planet's high spots: Sydney, Australia. I got a rush just saying the words, but there was more good news to come.

The ship flopped into the Cockatoo Island dry dock as if it were a hospital bed. A long gangway made its incision from the shoreside on to the foredeck, a drip-feed of mains electricity was brought aboard, and the *Global Wanderer* had her generators switched off. She was put to sleep for her operation, and it was just as well because I think she would have taken her own life had she seen the surgeons. Dozens of laughing, crude Australian workers came ambling on board, full of self-assurance and caustic wit. They were in charge now. *Global Wanderer* was our ship – we were there to provide the tender loving care – but now that she'd been placed on life support, our role was suspended. It was a strange feeling really. Like being possessed. I had invested a lot of time and effort in her wood and brass; we had been through a lot, and crossed half the world together, and here was a bunch of insensitive invaders making jokes at her expense because she was an old girl. I felt sad and impotent.

But whatever else they were, they set about their business with vigour, and by the next afternoon they had whipped the old propeller off. Happy estimates of a week in dry dock and a week alongside for cargo were bandied about as if there was no conceivable way things could go awry. But they had not accounted for the good old Aussie unions.

We cadets were on the boat-deck end-for-ending the lifeboat wires and slagging the Mate off for not allowing us the day off. We were spotted in our endeavours by a couple of Australian workers skiving off for a ciggie. They saw us at our labours and, to our utmost surprise, called an immediate strike. That was it. All out. Some someones were doing some work, and those someones were not Australian someones, so they all marched off the ship. Gone. Within minutes the place was like a morgue. This was at 9.30 on the Tuesday morning. The Captain could not even find anybody to complain to; they had all disappeared. It was Wednesday before he managed to find out what the matter was and desperate negotiations with a committee of bolshy union representatives could begin.

Marooned in dry dock with no propeller is not a strong negotiating position, and after a spittle-laden diatribe on the subject of colonies, forefathers and the last bastions of Western civilisation, the Captain signed his name to the effect that if there was ANY work to be done, an Australian would do it. The Captain headed for his cabin to lie down in a darkened room, the union man ambled off to the pub to bring the poor, injured workforce back, and the Mate came up to the boat-deck shouting and screaming at us.

'Will you STOP WORKING!' he roared. 'STOP IT THIS MINUTE! And don't let me catch you bastards working AGAIN! You've caused enough bloody trouble as it is, so just KNOCK IT ON THE HEAD!'

His words did not quite sit right at first. We stared blankly at each other as he stomped off, then we shrugged our shoulders and began to pack up, discussing what sort of a practical joke this could be.

The union man didn't have too much luck getting the shore-wallahs back on board. They were deeply scarred by the rough treatment meted out to them, and poor sensitive lads that they were, they didn't return until the Thursday, and then only with an air of great reluctance. Their hearts just did not seem to be in it now that the trust was gone from our relationship.

They mooched about kicking stones and staring off into space, unable to thrive in this atmosphere of conflict and discord. The Captain was at his wits' end. Every hour that passed was costing the company thousands of pounds, and there didn't seem to be anything he could do about it. The Captain tried bribing someone, but he turned out to be a sneak and news of the bribery spread like wildfire. Before you could say 'More than my job's worth, mate' the gangway was once more alive with departing workers. The Captain, in a rare moment of inspiration, shouted to them that it was *not* a bribe, and that he was going to give *everyone* the same thing; it was a gesture of friendship. They all turned round and marched back aboard again, forming a queue outside the Captain's cabin and wasting another half-day collecting their 200 fags and a bottle of whisky each. Things were looking grim for the Captain at this stage. He was steaming mad, but had to pretend that he was delighted to give these fine men their gifts. What he actually wanted to give each of them was a chainsaw in the stomach, but he kept his face in a rigid smile.

Finally his patience was rewarded when one of them revealed to him what the problem was. It seemed these lads were sad because all their friends in the pub were out of work. They were ship painters and maintenance men and they had no work for the full duration of the *Global Wanderer*'s time in dry dock. The Captain kept his fixed smile and spoke through clenched teeth, 'Well if you get on and swap the propeller over, then the next ship can get in and the poor wee petals will all have work again, won't they.'

The informant was not overawed by the Captain's attitude. 'Tell you what, mate. I've got a better idea. The lads would be employed immediately if you were to ask them to chip and paint *this* ship, wouldn't they?'

The Captain knew he shouldn't have sworn like that, and jumping up and down on the spot and throwing a tantrum is for children, not ships' Captains, so he offered his sincerest apologies to the deputation that finally returned to the ship on the following Monday (Sunday being a religious celebration amongst propeller-swappers, who place a high value on their worship time) and agreed to have the entire ship painted. By the following Tuesday, there were five times as many Australians doing as much nothing as the original number managed in half the time. It was amazing.

The Mate was so agitated he made a bit of a faux pas too. The day after we'd received the order to down tools ourselves we went up to the Mate to ask what we should do. He hadn't thought about us and was under great pressure. Recently, everyone he had shouted at had stuck their nose in the air, grabbed their mates, and stalked off the ship in a huff. He welcomed the opportunity to shout at us because we couldn't follow suit. Unfortunately, he was not careful with his choice of words.

'WHAT CAN YOU DO? You can BUGGER OFF, that's what you can do! Do what you like. I don't give a shit. Study or something. Just get out of my face – AND DON'T DO ANY WORK! I don't want to see ANY of you ugly bastards until . . . until . . .' he paused, huffing and puffing, and scrutinising his watch. 'Until December! Now BUGGER OFF!'

We buggered off to our cabins in disbelief. It was November the third. A meeting was hastily convened in Patch's cabin.

'Right,' said Patch. 'You heard the man, we've got to bugger off. He will greatly regret saying that when he next wants us for something, so we have to act fast. We have to pack some kit, get off the ship and not come back at any cost. We mustn't sleep in our bunks or drop by for meals. Nothing. We must leave the ship now and stay away for the next twenty-seven days. Meet here fully packed in ten minutes. We have to sneak off together. GO!'

This was incredible. We trotted round the alleyway to our cabins all chatting at once. We packed a haversack each, and ten minutes later we were back in Patch's cabin. Patch had bribed Ahmed to trace the whereabouts of the Mate so we could nip off unseen, and as soon as we got the signal we went over the side like the SAS and off into the town as quickly as we could. As we left we could see the Mate high on the fo'c'sle shouting at some people. Soon we were disappearing into the anonymity of Sydney's happy throng for the holiday of a lifetime.

I knew it was called the Lucky Country, but I didn't realise that the luck was all mine. I looked around at the bustling city and my heart flew high in my mouth. I got that pit-of-the-stomach sensation you get when something exciting is about to happen. I didn't know exactly *what* was going to happen, but that was what was so exciting. I didn't even know where I would be sleeping that night. For 27 glorious days – and nights – we were out of the Mate's grasp, on full wages, and totally free.

So what do you do when you unexpectedly find yourself young, free, single, randy, rich and at large in the most vibrant paradise on earth? Add to that brim-full of self-confidence and very, very determined not to go back to the ship, and you have yourself a Windy Baboulene, all revved up with all sorts of places to go.

By lunchtime the four of us were eating happily on Manly Beach without a care in the world. It was indeed paradise. I felt so adult. I was completely in charge of my own destiny. Nobody knew where I was. Nobody would be telling me where to go or what to do and even *I* did not know what was going to happen next. All I did know was that it would be my choice. It was the most deliciously exciting feeling, and I could make all the hairs on the back of my neck stand up just by thinking about it.

However, as the afternoon wore on, it became evident that my optimism and excitement were not entirely shared by all. There was concern over such mundane issues as where we were going to sleep, what we would do and what might go wrong. I was at once disgusted and amazed at their lack of adventurous spirit. I was not remotely interested in sleeping, was fizzing with life *because* I didn't know what was going to happen, and knew precisely what we should do.

'We find the local groo-oo-oovy kids and PAARRRTTEEE!' I enthused, pushing home the idea. 'If you haven't got laid by the time everyone else has, you sleep here on the beach. Loads of people stay here all night, eating and drinking and dancing and smoking and licking each other. No problem!'

NotNorman was happy with this, but a distinct uncertainty resided in the more cautious Giewy. NotNorman and I went through the entire 'You-only-live-once-seize-the-day-climb-every-mountain-live-life-to-the-full' routine, but Patch was going to get a train and visit his Nan in Brisbane, and Giewy decided Sydney was boring and that it was high time we were getting back to the ship. He said he'd seen it all before, and that he wanted to get some study done rather than prat about with children like us. He set off back for the ship despite our gentle coaxing, our convincing line of argument and our very best chicken impersonations.

So, from left to right, Giewy was scared, Patch was off to visit rellies, I was covering my insecurity with blind enthusiasm, and NotNorman didn't need to be scared or excited because he'd met a girl a couple of nights before and was already sure of having stuff to do and somewhere to sleep. He'd organised to meet his new-found love in town, so, having agreed that we would meet at midnight in case either of us (i.e., me) needed help, he too headed off. By and by, they had each gone their own way and I was alone.

There were dozens of people enjoying the day on the beach

– in and out of the sea, buying drinks and ice-creams, playing around in the sand, and so on – but I was completely and utterly alone. A bevy of butterflies flitted around in my stomach. The world was my oyster and I was determined to make the most of it. I wandered among the people, revelling in my invisibility. Everything would be exactly like this even if I were not here. I was anonymous. I watched and shared. Soon, if things went well, I would become involved with some people. I would be affecting their lives, changing the course of their evening. What they said and did would be different because I was there. I moved among them like a breeze, an unseen force. I felt I could have walked into people's houses or ridden in their cars without their noticing me. I caught a ferry back into downtown Sydney and watched as the city and its people moved from afternoon fun to the evening's more serious intentions.

As fortune had it, the Third Engineer on board was an Australian. His name was Clive Walker, although we'd rather predictably nicknamed him Skippy. He was born and raised in Sydney, and he told us that the place to be of a night was The Rocks. I gather things have changed a little in recent times, but then The Rocks was a bohemian quarter, lying between the Harbour Bridge and Circular Quay, and slightly off the beaten track for anyone who was not looking for it specifically. The Rocks was the unadvertised rendezvous for the young, trendy and musically adroit. This was a perfect description of me, so with the look of a man who knows what he wants out of life, I swaggered into coolsville.

No one noticed me even now that I wanted them to. The area hardly seemed very lively, and I could feel myself deflating by the second as the dark buildings and closed doors pointedly excluded me. From Skippy's description I had expected a sort of street party to be rocking along, and hordes of young people – recognising me as a kindred spirit – to rush up and ask me how I was doing and would I like to join them; but I could have found more life in a railway sandwich.

It was still only about nine o'clock, but I couldn't convince myself that there was any way this dull scene could ever explode into the hub of the universe. Then a door opened. Some people spilled into the street, and although they were not rushing up to welcome me personally, they were certainly young and good-looking, and the splash of light and the music that accompanied their departure indicated revelations within. As I stared at this door and listened to the music – trying to decide if I was brave enough to enter – another door opened further down and four or five more people moved into another splash of light with a rush of music. Now I was beginning to get it. I walked the length of the street and back. The buildings were old and imposing and the doors were faceless, but open almost any one and the chances were it would open onto a café or bar full of groovy groovers grooving. Some bars were hidden upstairs, some were underground. Some were forbidding, with bouncers blocking the entrance and high-fashion poseurs peering disapprovingly down their noses at you, others were enticing because tremendous live rock music flew down and roared at you as the door opened.

As a rock connoisseur, I chose the bar with the best live music and headed for the door. (Actually it was the door through which five short skirts had just disappeared, but the music sounded OK too.) More deep excitement. More butterflies. Behind the door were steps leading downwards. The throbbing party increased in volume with every step. I reached the bottom to be greeted by just the scene I wanted: a cookin' rock band, beers flowing and hundreds of people dancing, chatting and laughing.

I found a seat at the bar from where I could survey the scene, drink copious quantities of hideous cold, fizzy lager, watch the crowd and listen to the music. I smiled winningly at a few passers-by, but nobody stopped to talk. I could see them trying to work out if they knew me from somewhere because of the way I was smiling at them like one of Santa's helpers, but I didn't mind that nobody stopped to talk. I was once more enjoying my private excitement. I was in no hurry. Besides, I had been in a band at home and I knew there was absolutely no chance of a worthwhile conversation while the guitars were letting rip, so I sat back and satisfied myself with watching.

After a while some order began to emerge from the chaos before me. I began to recognise where the cliques were, and who was with whom. There were some stunningly attractive girls around, but I wouldn't dare talk to them. They could kill me with a single dismissal, and besides, they were never alone, not for a second.

When the band took a break I looked around. All the people I wanted to talk to were gathered into seated groups. Impossible to break into without the strong possibility of extreme embarrassment. Perhaps things were not going to be so much fun after all.

It's strange how hard it is to talk to someone who is with other people, isn't it? The Americans are best at it. Anywhere you meet strangers in the US – on a train, at a bus stop, in a queue – they will talk to you. If the lift is going more than three floors, like as not you'll make a friend for life. In England, if a stranger talks to you at a bus stop, you begin to shift uncomfortably and look for a policeman. In the US, it's the person who *won't* talk to you who arouses suspicion.

So here I was, being English and reserved. I had visions of drinking myself into a stupor until they threw me out at sunrise, and crawling defeated back to the ship. Then it hit me. The band! Of course! It *is* socially acceptable – even in England – to talk to members of the band without a formal introduction, and once you know *them*, you're in the top tier. Most of the band had already headed into the adoring crowd to accept their adulation, but the bass player was replacing a string and was alone on the stage. Perfect! I was a bass player myself. I strode right up there.

'S'cuse me, mate, is that an Alembic bass?' I knew it was, but an Alembic is an unusual, expensive and tremendous bass, so I reckoned on his having a lot to say about it. I smiled winningly for the four-hundredth time. He looked up, then jumped to his feet, threw his bass to the floor and started stomping towards me with his fists clenched.

'Will you FUCK OFF!' he shouted.

He was a big sod and I froze on the spot. My whole body had turned to stone. I became incapable of taking evasive action even though I fully realised that the stage placed his boots close to my face-level, and I was about to get the inside of my skull beautifully lined with steel-toe-capped leather. It's one of those situations you rehearse in your bathroom: yob coming at you full-tilt, you roll with his punch, grab his arm, sling him over the bar and put your arm round the nearest frightened maidens ('Evening, Ladies'). Any of the things James Bond does without ruffling his shirt. Then you find yourself in precisely those circumstances, and all you can do is stand there spoiling a perfectly good set of underwear.

To my utmost relief, however, he pushed past me and stormed across to one of the tables. A bloke there was evidently chatting up his girlfriend, and he did not like it. In broad and clear Australian terms he informed the gentleman that: (a) The young lady did not wish to receive his overtures; (b) The young gentleman had been putting him off his bass-playing by pressing his suit during the first half, and he would appreciate any effort the chap could make in desisting during the second set; and last, but by no means least, (c) If he did not piss off and leave her alone he (the party of the first part) would be left with no alternative but to fillet his (the party of the second part's) shins for him.

The low-life scuttled off to a dark corner to assimilate this information, and the bass player returned to the stage, this time grinning at me from ear to ear.

'It's relentless, mate. She gets that crap all the time.'

I was not surprised. She was, without any shadow of a doubt, one of the most beautiful girls I had ever laid eyes on, but I thought it prudent to keep that to myself. 'So, what were ya saying? You like the old axe, do ya?'

And with that we launched into a deep and meaningful discussion about pick-ups and string gauges, amps and effects, heroes and riffs. By the time Rip had to get back on to the stage we were male-bonding furiously. As he dressed himself with his bass and the band prepared to fire up again, he threw in just what I wanted to hear.

'Listen, mate. You doin' anything afterwards? We're having a bit of a jolly-up back at my place. You wanna come along?'

'Sure would,' I said. 'I'll help you load the gear up.'

'Tops, mate,' he replied, supplying me with a catchphrase I wouldn't shake off for years. Then he got out from behind his guitar, knelt down by the stage and spoke quietly to me. 'Tell yer what, mate. You wouldn't do me a favour, would ya?'

'Just name it, old friend. Your wish and all that.'

'Yeah, right. Well it's my little sister there. If you wouldn't mind sitting with her those other bastards would lay off. Mum gets real mad with me if I leave her alone, 'cos she gets a bit wild with a couple of vodkas in her. I'd be dead grateful. What do you say?'

I couldn't say anything at first. God may move in mysterious ways, but I never expected him to start a dating agency for me. 'Say, Lucy! Loose! This is a friend of mine, er . . . Windy. He's a Pom, and all that, but he's all right. Windy, this is 'Loose'. Windy, Loose, Loose, Windy.'

She was an absolute vision. And the vision was of a stockings commercial. She was tall and slim – probably only in her mid-teens – but with a certain surprising curviness easing out whenever she moved. Dangerous curves. There wasn't a man in the place who wasn't spending more time looking at her than at the band, and I had just been put in the chair beside her. I looked from her to the stage, where Rip was smiling at me as he put his bass back on, then back to her again.

'Er, I don't suppose,' I ventured innocently, 'I could get you a vodka, could I?'

Now life was beginning to look worthwhile. I was getting comfortably drunk and Loose matched each of my small beers with a large vodka. We chatted amiably and she laughed at my jokes. She really was very nice, and with a delightful weakness for vodka that I found quite irresistible. Each vodka made my next joke twice as funny as the last, and soon enough her eyes were full of admiration and various parts of my anatomy were clamouring to be released into the open, anxious to be admired too. She believed all the garbage I was spouting, and even laughed at dreadful chat-up lines like 'You're eyes are like spanners – they tighten my nuts.' Nothing seemed capable of failing and everything, as good old P. G. Wodehouse would have said, was for the best in the best of all possible worlds. Not only was I on course for a damn good rogering, but at the hands of a beautiful girl at optimum drunkenness. And, as if things were not perfect enough already, we were going back to her place for a party. Her parents must be out . . . she must have a bedroom . . .

'Another vodka?' I asked, my voice cracking as the butterflies that had been resident in my stomach all day now flitted away in my underpants.

After the gig, I helped Rip clear away his bass gear and we loaded up the truck. It was still only midnight and The Rocks was still rolling as we pulled away in a convoy of 4x4s. The three of us sat in the front seat with Rip driving, me in the middle and Loose beside me. All the way home she made advances towards me, and it was as much as I could do to avoid reciprocating, but I kept getting twinges in my shins when I thought about what Rip might do with his filleting knife if I touched her, so I kept backing off. This only served to encourage Loose to redouble her efforts to excite me. Once again I found myself in a car with a rampant young lady desperate to help me lose some weight, and circumstances forcing me to sit on my hands.

Rip chatted away, and thanked me for looking after Loose. I said it was nothing, but he must have been the stupidest guy on earth not to notice that I couldn't keep my mind on the conversation or my eyes off his sister. He was also too polite to ask what was wrong with my voice.

We got to their house, high up on the North Shore – and not a moment too soon as far as I was concerned. I was beginning to feel that to be put through a little shin-filleting would be a small price to pay for as much of a kiss as I could manage in the time it would take Rip to stop the car and set up his shin-filleting equipment. It was just as well nobody was interested in unloading gear, because I could only walk using a very restricted subset of my usual range of perambulatory powers. I desperately wanted to get Loose on her own, but had to be discreet for the sake of my shins.

Rip on the other hand, wanted beer. We wandered through the house to the back garden where the view across the bay to downtown Sydney was stunning. Within a couple of moments beers were fizzing open, music was in the air and we were all chilling nicely. Soon the warm night and cool beers began to weave their spell. People were interested in talking to me, the new kid on the block, and I looked about as far away from a session with Loose as I was from frenching a horse.

She kept brushing past me, and I got the occasional tantalising glimpse of the creamy bronzed thighs that lay beyond her short skirt. I became conscious that something else was going on in the world and dragged my senses back from my trousers to my brain. Rip was talking to me and, for about the fortieth time, he had received no response as I sat open-mouthed and bewitched by his sister.

'Oi, Windy! Windy? Come on, mate, you're losing the plot here. Your brain's gone up the pictures, eh? Tell you what. Why don't you go through that room, up the little stairs at the back and into the diner. There's some beer in the cupboard, get us one each and stick another dozen in the Esky, will ya?' I was pleased with the excuse to go. Even Rip, who seemed completely oblivious to what was going on right under his nose, was bound to notice sooner or later. 'Oh, and Loose,' he added, 'you go up there with him and give him one for Christ's sake, before the poor bastard cums in his pants. I knew the Pommies were reserved but you'll be all year if you wait for him to make a move!'

Uproarious laughter followed me as I walked across the living-room towards the diner. Of course they'd noticed! Good grief – how could they have failed to? I'd been sitting there all evening dribbling down my shirt. Fortunately, I didn't have time to dwell on the embarrassment of being the butt of the local humour, because no sooner was I into the diner than Loose was in after me. There was no lock – in fact there was no door, just a curtain pulled across – and I suppose we could have gone off to find a bedroom somewhere, but neither of us gave a fig. We tongue-wrestled one another to the floor and rolled around like fish on a line. Anyone peeping through the window would have thought a murder was going on. It was frantic stuff. Clothes were torn and furniture was knocked over. Suddenly the rolling stopped. She sat on top of me, pinning my arms to the floor, her hungry eyes looking at me as if I was a plate of sausages. She kissed my lips, then my chin, then my neck. She tore my shirt aside and kissed my chest, then slowly moved down to my stomach, then kissed her way ever so slowly towards my navel. She undid my fly and licked her lips, then . . . the curtain whipped back. We both shot up and stared at the imposing figure standing there. It was a policeman. A huge policeman.

'Daddy!' exclaimed Loose. 'What are you doing here?'

It was a huge policeman who was Lucy's father.

I looked at the gun on his belt and prepared to die. He surveyed the debauched scene and shook his head slowly. My testicles, sensing they might be unfairly blamed for all this, withdrew to a position behind my Adam's apple. He began to walk towards the fridge and I had visions of him force-feeding it to me. Then the most extraordinary thing happened. A smile grew across his face, and instead of the roars and limb-tearing activities of an outraged father about to commit justifiable homicide for the honour of his youngest daughter, he addressed us in dry, humorous tones.

'You been on the vodkas again, Loose? Who'd have bloody daughters, eh?' He lifted a box from the fridge and held it up. 'Forgot me sarnies,' he said, and disappeared.

I breathed for the first time since he had appeared on

the scene. Great laughter emanated from without. The boys had hugely enjoyed omitting to warn us of his approach. Good grief, this lot were worse than the bastards on the ship. But events had managed to dampen our ardour – cardiac arrest being somewhat unromantic – so we adjourned to the garden to grab a beer and to try and slow down our pulses.

We sat together with cold beers and laughed at the adventure of it all. We were young and rebellious. This was the kind of wacky event that happened to us dudes. I excused myself and went to the bathroom where I heaved a sigh of relief, splashed water on my face and tried to stop shaking. That was *too* close for comfort. No more sex for me. Beer is the thing. Beer and music. Sex is just not worth the accompanying aggravation.

Back outside I voiced this opinion to the lads and we sat around talking this point out. Apart from anything else, we agreed that we would all have been top session musicians were it not for the time and effort we wasted chasing girls. Any bloke who wants to make it in life should have his organ lopped off first. He'd be a millionaire within a year. A life without women suddenly made perfect sense.

Funny how these things work though, because before long I was looking at Lucy's lush pastures and quite fancying a private chat with her again. Strange thing really, because I couldn't so much as look at her a short while before, and now I couldn't for the life of me remember what the problem had been. Her dad was long gone and we knew that he didn't care anyway. Before you could say 'Who wants to be a millionaire anyway?' Loose and I were heading off for the diner once more.

Having checked the cupboards for members of the constabulary, we were soon at each other again like fighting dogs. This time I was domineering and masterful. I wanted no nonsense. Within seconds I was as naked as an Englishman gets, standing proudly in my watch and socks, and after a brief grapple her clothes were off and we were rolling around in demented lust. The moment of sweet surrender had arrived and I closed my eyes, prepared myself for heaven, and . . . the curtain whipped back. We both shot up and stared at the imposing figure standing there. It was a woman. A shocked and distraught woman.

'Mummy!' exclaimed Loose. 'What are you doing here?'

A shocked and distraught woman who was Lucy's mother.

'Oh my God!' I said, not wishing to be left out. At least she was not wearing a gun. But this time there was no wry smile. Quite the reverse. There was a fire of hatred burning in her eyes, an evil, crooked pointing finger, and fury in her quivering voice.

'YOU evil, EVIL girl . . . I warned you! I WARNED you. Well your day of reckoning is upon you. If Beelzebub is to have your soul, then now is his time. You must pay, wanton Jezebel! PAY!'

And with that she began to hurl things from the top of the dresser at her daughter. The air became thick with pictures, cutlery, vases and profanity. They were like some sort of flying gameshow prizes – for a moment I thought I ought to memorise them all.

I was rather hoping she would fling me my pants, which were hanging on the corner of the dresser just handy for her admirable pitching arm, but she seemed to be giving preference to heavier objects. I weighed up my options and being an astute sort of chap, deduced that the atmosphere was no longer conducive to an easy life, and more importantly, that my chances of intercourse with young Loose had taken something of a knock, so while ducking and weaving to avoid the continuous stream of household items as they traversed the room at high speed, I occupied myself with hopping around on one foot trying to put my jeans on. It was every man for himself, so I abandoned my underpants to whatever hideous fate awaited them, left headfirst through the window, and accepted an invitation to join a departing vehicle full of retreating musicians.

I sat in the open back of the 4x4 as it bounced away from the house and watched two silhouettes inside fighting behind the curtains, framed by the clear night sky and the distant city skyline. My weeks of freedom in Sydney had begun.

Chapter 15

The Grass

An agreeable life. Giewy is a party-pooper. Windy begins a relationship – but neglects to terminate the one he already has. The bizarre world of drunken reprisals. Poachers and gamekeepers. The tables turn.

Following my rapid exodus from Lucy's house, I stayed the night at the flat of the guitarist in the band. Steve lived alone and was the serious musician in the crowd so there were no girls in his life and I could crash on his sofa. Thus the pattern was set for the next week or so. I went out with the band to their gigs and social events, woke late, spent all day on the beach, had a couple of great nights out with Loose, grew slovenly and unkempt, drank more than is generally accepted as polite, and settled snugly into a lifestyle which can only be recommended. I can think of nothing which it does not have in its favour and can't understand why anybody in the world would live any other way. All I needed to do was find a way of jumping ship without the authorities cutting off my pay cheque and my goolies, and I would be set. So it was particularly nauseating when Grim Reality came swaggering back into my life.

We were playing soccer on the beach in the boiling sun. Everybody for a hundred miles in every direction was in beach gear, except Grim Reality. Grim Reality was walking towards us in black Oxford bags (with a three-inch belt), stacked black and red shoes, a jumbo-collared nylon shirt (unbuttoned to the waist) and a face like a smashed crab. The soccer game fell apart as one by one, the footballers stopped to stare at this apparition.

'What in the name of sweet Jesus is *that*?' asked Steve.

I knew what it was, and it did not bode well.

'Hello Giewy,' I sighed. 'You cannot be here for any good reason.'

He was smiling in a weird, twitchy sort of way, as if he was trying to keep a family of live fish contained in his mouth against their will.

'Giew,' he said, predictably, 'a quick end to *your* games, Windy. Harry Tate says you gotta come back. There's work to do and he didn't mean you to bugger off all month. I'm to bring you back to the ship.'

He was *so* pleased with himself. I rolled my eyes to the heavens.

'Why *did* you go back to the ship? You *knew* this would happen if you did.' The idea of going back to the ship was repulsive enough, but the thought of doing what bloody Giewy told me to do was against everything I stood for in my hedonistic new life. He waved his head around as if the wind had suddenly got up and smiled the weaselly smile of the school grass. The football had stopped completely now, and my new-found friends were gathering round to see what the trouble was. They had never seen a specimen like Giewy before and were curious to know what it was.

'Jeez, Windy, who's yer friend? Did he just crawl out of the sea?'

Giewy ignored them studiously. He was enjoying watching me squirm. He put his hand on his hip and gave me his ultimatum.

'You coming or what?' he smarmed. Rip noticed the spiteful edge to his voice.

'You all right here, Windy? Is this geek giving you strife?'

'Strife like you wouldn't believe, Rip. Listen, Giewy. See these boys, here? They are only out of the prison hospital for the day, and would take great pride in rearranging your face for you given the slightest provocation – wouldn't you, lads?' The boys duly pulled the wild, psychotic faces of a group of unstable men close to the edge. 'So you would be well advised to pretend you couldn't find me today. What you are going to do is be a good friend and tell Harry Tate that you think I went to Willigolonga to visit my dying grandmother, aren't you? You're going to pretend this meeting never happened. You never saw me today, did you? Now off you go, and do the right thing, there's a good lad.'

I could tell by the blank look on what passed for his face that the threat of violence was completely wasted on Giewy. *Actual* violence might penetrate to his decision-making processes, but I was being way too subtle. What he did manage to divine was that I didn't intend to go back to the ship.

'Ooooo! Are you ever gonna be in trouble when the Mate hears about *this*!' He laughed through his nose and snorted like a pig.

'Listen Giewy, if the Mate gets to hear about this, then I promise – absolutely PROMISE – that you will be caused physical and mental torture worth at least double that which you cause me, OK? That's a promise. Now get yourself a life and stop spoiling other people's.'

'That's you done,' he said ignoring my remarks entirely, 'now I've got to find NotNorman.' And off he waddled, walking like a contraption that a mad professor might have built to wash the car. Talking to him was as pointless as talking to a plant. At least I knew he wouldn't be able to find NotNorman. I was due to meet him for lunch so I'd be able to warn him of his pursuer.

Some thirty minutes later I was aboard the hydrofoil as it rounded the Opera House and pulled into Circular Quay. NotNorman waved happily from behind his drink as he awaited my arrival. There were tables and chairs on the peninsula behind the Opera House where tea and cakes were served, and from where it was possible to pass a happy hour or two looking out across that magnificent harbour. NotNorman was looking particularly pleased with himself, possibly because he was now sporting two young ladies instead of the usual one.

'Hi man!' he cheered as I rolled up. 'You've met Cindy,' I recognised her as the love of his life, 'and this is her friend, Jackie.'

He wiggled his eyebrows up and down and hung out his tongue in a way I took to mean that she was my blind date. Normally, I would be way too cool to face a member of the opposite sex in broad daylight without the aid of alcohol, but having scored with a girl as beautiful as Lucy, I felt almost happy at the arrangement. Besides, she was smiling cheerfully and looked civilised enough. The kind of girl whose parents don't wear guns or drop in suddenly during the night.

The four of us chatted away over lunch and three fundamental truths began to emerge. One was that as a foursome, we could certainly have some fun together, two was that Cindy and NotNorman were utterly in love, and three was that although Lucy and I were kind-of-sort-of-maybe an item, I felt a strange and powerful compulsion to do sordid, filthy, despicably rude things with young Jackie.

We spent the afternoon at Taronga Zoo, and the evening watching another band. Then it was back to the flat the girls shared (and that NotNorman had adopted) in Vaucluse. I saw NotNorman as a completely changed character. He was almost Norman. He had found the girl of his dreams and he didn't care who knew about it. As far as he was concerned macho values were ridiculous, and love and trust were the food and drink of a rich and happy life. And she was equally dippy about him. They were quite pathetic to watch. They didn't stop touching all day – it was as if they were joined at the hip – and they didn't stop touching all night because they *were* joined at the hip. They couldn't see past each other for the multitude of blue lovebirds flitting around their heads, and they could hardly hear anything for the violins playing everywhere they went. They didn't get a moment's sleep (as proven by the creaking bed all night) and yet were as fresh as daisies all day. They were running on pure love.

So my highly agreeable life was augmented by the occasional foursome, and the addition of Jackie to the daily roster of sexual bouts with Lucy. The only dog-ends in the beer glass of my life were the nagging irritation of Giewy tracking us on behalf of the Mate, and the disgusting spectacle of watching NotNorman and Cindy licking each other. Jackie and I began to feel somewhat inadequate in the face of the Olympian standards being set by the competition, but we persevered admirably. So life was about perfect. I had a dozen activities to choose from every hour, and none of them could remotely be described as unpleasant.

One night, I met Skippy in town. Having grown up in Sydney, he too was well pleased with the enforced sabbatical here. His parents lived on the river a few miles inland, in a superb house with a boat at the bottom of the garden. This was magic. Whizzing into the city centre on a speedboat is something people in Huddersfield and Croydon rarely get to do, and it's quite a buzz.

Skippy and I found ourselves together late one night, roaring drunk and wandering the streets trying to get a cab. The drivers took one look at us staggering about and zoomed off, so we started walking. He told me that the Mate knew I wasn't visiting my gran in Willigolonga, and suspected I was roaming the town and living it up at the company's expense. I told him that the Mate would have been blissfully unaware of my antics were it not for that stoolie, Kevin-bloody-Giew. Skippy – who also had painful experience of Giewy's smarmy ability to irritate – ever resourceful and with local knowledge, had a cunning plan.

'You wanna do him?' he asked, beaming with evil intent. I nodded emphatically. 'Right. Giewy drinks at Leemo's Bar, just over Pyrmont Bridge. Everyone's a defect in there, so he feels at home. It'll be shutting pretty soon, and he'll be coming out, so let's go and steal a car.'

And with that he strode off, a man with a mission.

'Steal a CAR?' I cried, running to catch up with the striding Skippy. 'You have GOT to be joking!'

'No worries, mate. Don't panic. We are gonna *borrow* a car. *Giewy* is gonna steal a car.'

I expressed doubts that this subtle distinction would wash with the authorities. I could clearly envisage us running fruitlessly in mid-air, subtle distinctions lost on the large policemen holding us up by our collars. Skippy cheerfully ignored me and I was none the wiser when we got back to his house where all was quiet. His parents were already asleep. We slid silently along the side of the house and in through the back door. I've always fancied myself as a burglar – one of those stylish, classy ones, dressed all in black who leaves a calling card and drives Inspector Grinder of the Yard mad by always keeping one step ahead – and it was a powerful feeling as we stole noiselessly through the house like shadows. I could definitely do well at this game. The newspapers would call me The Cat and women would feel a powerful thrill – a mixture of fear and excitement – anticipating that The Cat might visit *their* boudoir in the night and . . .

Once Skippy had helped me up and fetched me a plaster for the bump on my head where I'd cracked it against a beam, we found the car keys and ghosted through to the garage where we pushed his dad's Volvo estate out into the road. Once we were well clear of the house, Skippy started her up and we beetled back, drunk as proverbial skunks, towards the city centre.

At Leemo's Bar, I confirmed Giewy's presence by pulling myself up at a window. He was indeed inside, so I crossed the road back to the car to find Skippy hotwiring it.

'Aha!' I exclaimed. 'I geddit! Giewy's going to steal *this* car!'

'Well done, Bullet. You're on the case. I always said you were more than just an ugly wanker. Now, here's the technique. You drive up to Giewy as he's walking back to the ship and offer him a lift. You tell him it's my car, and that it has to go to the ship anyway. Then you say that you're too drunk to drive, and that he can keep the car and take it back for you if he drops you off at your bird's house first. While you're doing that, I'll call the police and tell 'em my car's been nicked by a sailor. They'll be waiting to pick Giewy up when he gets back to the docks on his own. See? Piece of cake. Giewy gets thrown in the chokey, and the police will want to know if I want to press charges against the bastard who stole my car. I get Giewy to promise us the world before I get him out. Pretty smart, eh?'

Now if there's one thing anyone who knows me will tell you, it's that if you want to expose the weaknesses in a plan, then I'm your man.

'If there's a hole in it, Windy will find it,' they'll tell you. 'It looks all right to us,' they'll shrug, 'but you'd better take it to Windy if you want to be really sure.'

And I have to admit that this little scheme had all the makings of a rock solid, watertight, belt-and-braces, safe-as-houses, dead cert. Flawless is the word. A peach. And Giewy the victim. Perfect.

So with the project passing all stringent assessment tests with top marks, I enthused warmly and we moved swiftly on to phase two: swift and clinical implementation. I began to think that maybe I'd missed my vocation. Perhaps burglary was not my calling after all. A career in undercover work seemed more 'me'. As Giewy emerged from the pub, passers-by could have been forgiven for thinking he was being trailed by Dirty Harry. I let him stagger a hundred yards, then slid up beside him in the car.

'Giewy, my old mate! D'you fancy a lift? I've got Skippy's car.'

'Giew!' he said, trying to focus events. 'Yeah, all right.'

This was like shelling peas.

'Great! Hop in this side. You can drive – I'm too drunk. Just drop me up the road here, then you can take the car back to the ship for Skippy.'

'No way, pal. You can fockin' drive. I'm too drunk to fockin' walk, sod alone drive.'

This was not in the plan.

'Oh for God's sake, Giewy! Why does everything have to be so difficult with you? I'm way drunker than you are, so just drive the bloody car.'

'Are you as buggery as drunker as what I am,' he dribbled, 'I'm – *belch!* – I'm well wrecked, me.'

We stood outside the open door of the car for some time with the conversation continuing in this vein. Now, many a lesser mortal might have crumbled along with the plan at this point, and it is at times like these that the possession of the quick-wittedness for which we Baboulenes are so renowned gives us the edge over our adversaries. Despite the tide running against me, I swiftly devised a contingency plan that would allow me to slide out of the driving seat, and for Giewy to drop himself in it.

The crux of the matter was that we needed to establish who was the more drunk, so I suggested a simple test. Now those of you who are following closely will remember that

I was not as drunk as Giewy, and will worry that I might lose any test to establish degrees of drunkenness. Fear not. I knew what I was doing. You see, the master stroke in my devious-but-simple plan was to *deliberately* fail all the tests, thereby appearing the more drunk, thus forcing Giewy to drive the car. Always one jump ahead, us Baboulenes, that's the secret.

So, to the utmost astonishment of the two policemen watching us from the shadows across the road, we started going cross-eyed trying to touch the ends of our respective noses with an outstretched finger. I convincingly poked myself in the eye, shrugged sadly and looked at Giewy. I was amazed at just how incompetent the bloke was. He missed his nose by a mile, insisted on a second attempt, and then missed again! He could hardly locate his whole head, let alone his nose. I wanted to locate his head with a baseball bat. We argued for a time, then decided the test had been inconclusive. We would try another one.

Across the road, the policemen were mystified. They had received news of a stolen car over the radio, and here it was, as large as life, with the thieves performing some sort of street cabaret alongside it. They didn't want to move in and make an arrest until they'd seen us more obviously involved with the car, which presently seemed to be playing nothing more than a cameo role in the proceedings. They looked at each other and shrugged as we put our right hand by our respective right ears, balanced ten coins on our elbows, then attempted to catch them all with the same hand. I lunged at the coins, spreading them impressively across the road. I knew there must have been a couple of dollars on my elbow, but it would be worth losing the money to get this farce over with. I failed to catch any of them. I shook my head at Giewy.

'Sorry, mate. I'm too drunk for all this. You have a go.'

THE GRASS

He balanced ten coins on his elbow, and, with his mouth wide open and his tongue sticking out with concentration, watched helplessly as they fell sideways before he'd even tried to catch them. Most went down a drain, so we had to spend a minute or two crawling in the road and accosting passers-by to get ten more coins for Giewy to fail to balance on his elbow once more. He couldn't even manage the balancing bit, let alone the catching. He was utterly pathetic. Had he no co-ordination whatsoever? Soon he had lost all the coins, so I declared the test null and void, and we began arguing again. I was now ready for a straightforward fight, but with so much to gain from getting my way, I kept control and suggested one last test: who could do the longest handstand.

People walked around us on the pavement, and the car ticked over patiently as I made my attempt. Up I went, did a fine job of pretending I couldn't hold it, and collapsed in a heap. I insisted on a second attempt, but with a convincing cry, toppled sideways into the car. I shook my head sadly and passed the floor to Giewy.

Giewy took a couple of exaggerated breaths, then went for it. He had barely touched the pavement with his hands when he stacked his entire weight on to his face and concertinaed his body into the back of his head. This was accompanied by a totally unconvincing animal cry of 'Giew!', and the penny dropped. This cheating bastard was not making any effort whatsoever to beat me at these tests! He was failing on purpose! Good grief! Was there no depth to which this dirty dog would not sink? What was the point in having these tests if he wasn't even going to make a proper attempt? I put my accusations squarely to him, and a raucous argument developed.

I was rolling up my sleeves and flexing my fingers as Giewy frantically explained that we were going about the thing all wrong. The answer was to do the same tests again, but giving the trophy to the demonstrably more *sober* of us. Whoever could do *best* at the tests would be deemed the winner, and the drunker of us, being the loser, would have to drive. This policy seemed perfect. A solution would certainly be achieved, and I knew I was more sober than Giewy, so the thing was as good as in the bag.

With a laughable improvement in co-ordination, Giewy touched the end of his nose with equal dexterity to me, so – being fresh out of loose change – we moved directly on to the handstands. The policemen in the shadows were treated to the spectacle of the two of us standing on our hands on the pavement beside a stolen car, arguing furiously. I knew I could stand on my hands for ages, but thought it a bit of a farce that Giewy, who had just a few minutes earlier collapsed like a house of cards, was standing on his hands arguing back at me. The bloke had no shame. I decided I would hit him. I padded across on my hands, then discovered the flaw. I was standing on the equipment I wanted to employ in punching. Giewy was equally ready for fisticuffs, but neither of us was prepared to lose the test by coming down before the other one, so, as passers-by passed by with question marks over their heads, we stood upside-down and back-to-back, with our heads arched round trying to look at each other, flailing our legs around in a scorpion-like effort at having a fight. The policemen decided that enough was enough, and moved in.

Two hours later, Giewy and I were woken in our cell by one of the screws (as we hardened crims call them).

'Wakey, wakey, boys. Got a visitor for you.'

In waltzed a beaming Skippy.

'Yip, these are the ones, Constable. Can I have a moment alone with them, please?'

The screw left and Giewy and I both started talking at once. I was wondering how Skippy was going to get me out and leave Giewy in.

'OK, boys. This is the deal. I have some disappointing news for you. I'm only here to pick up the car. Neither of you is getting out now.' Giewy and I what'ed and why'd in high-pitched voices. He calmed us once more. 'I'm sorry lads, but you have both been duped – by ME! I've put you inside, Windy, because the Mate promised me six cases of beer if I could catch you. I put you inside, Giewy, because you're a complete wanker. I want you to use your time in here to think about how you might become a better person in life and find a way of resisting telling people's wives about their girlfriends. I left a note on the Mate's door telling him there was a surprise awaiting him in the cells. He'll be here first thing in the morning to pick you both up.'

Skippy smiled the smile of a good night's work, rubbed his hands together, and got up, ready to leave. This was a disaster – and not just for me. There were two girls out there who needed my body, I had a starring role to play in a beach football match in a couple of hours' time, and I was working with the band that night. I had a life! The Mate would be down to pick me up shortly, and if he got hold of me I'd be grounded for sure. This was catastrophic.

'Skippy,' I said urgently, 'I will give you TEN cases of beer to let me go. Tell the Mate you couldn't find us. Tell him –'

'Sorry, Windy. Can't be done,' he replied, heading for the door. 'A deal's a deal and all that. Take comfort in the knowledge that if you ever do a deal with me, I won't do the dirty on you. See you back at the ship tomorrow!'

'You snake!' I called cuttingly. 'Filthy, miserable impostor!' I can be pretty direct when the need demands.

Just then, two screws came back through the door and blocked Skippy's exit.

'Impostor, eh? Sounds about right to us,' said one to the other as they took Skippy by an elbow each and invited him to take a seat. 'We want a word with you. We've just had a phone call from another Clive Walker, claiming *he* is the owner of that Volvo, and that it has been stolen from *him*. Now you told us *you* are Clive Walker, and that the car belongs to you.'

'Ah,' said Skippy, smiling as ingratiatingly as he could. 'I can explain that. Ha, ha! Er . . . *that* Clive Walker is my father – we have the same name.'

'Right. So you are *not* the owner of the car?'

'Oh. Er, strictly speaking, no, I suppose not. But he's my dad! I may not be the owner, but I'm his representative. He would –'

'Oh, really? Then why, may I ask, does he seem to think it's been stolen?'

'Oh, well. I took it without his knowledge. No, that sounds worse than it really is. What I mean is –'

'And why did you hotwire it if you are his representative?'

'Ah. Well. What we were doing was er . . . Windy! Yes! Windy here. He knows what we were doing! We were just having a bit of fun, that's all! Ha, ha, ha! Explain to the officers what we were doing, Windy.'

He turned to me with the most imploring of faces. I looked honestly into the faces of the men in blue and shook my head slowly.

'I've never seen this man before in my life. He seems hell bent on getting me and my friend here into trouble, and we never even touched his car. Ask the arresting officers. We were larking about on the pavement beside it.'

'That's right,' confirmed Giewy. 'We never even touched the bloody car.'

This interpretation was born out by the arresting officers, and the screws were definitely tiring of Skippy.

'OK,' said screw A, 'time for some musical chairs.' And with that he unlocked the cell door and the incoming Skippy hung his head as he took over from us beaming pair of departing inmates.

'You lads can go,' said screw B. 'You may be a pair of tossers, but if that was against the law we'd be well fucked on space around here, that's for sure. You want a lift home?'

We accepted a lift, and much to Giewy's surprise, I came back to the ship with him. No, I had not gone soft. I had a job to do before heading off to Jackie's house.

When he awoke, the Mate found a note on his door. A handwriting expert could have told him that although it was signed by Skippy, it wasn't written by him. It said:

'Windy is in New Zealand visiting his cousins. He knows nothing of your desire for him to return to the ship. I suggest you call off the hunt. You'd better keep your beers.

Lots of love,

Skippy.'

Chapter 16

Meat and Two Veg

Emotional departure from Sydney. Run for your wife! The stowaway. An evening with Big Phil. A narrow squeak.

After 32 days – and nights – I left Sydney with a tear of sadness in my eye, vowing to apply for Australian citizenship and immigrate to Sydney as soon as possible. I'd spent my last evening with Jackie a night earlier than the ship was due to depart. I'd lied to her, saying that it was going the next morning. The coast was then clear for Lucy to stay on the ship for our actual last night in Sydney which I enjoyed happy in the knowledge that Jackie thought I was at sea by then. However, Jackie heard on the grapevine that the ship was in port another night, and thinking an overrun of cargo was causing the delay, she popped down to give me a nice surprise in the morning . . .

I was sleeping soundly in my cabin when there was a frantic knocking on the door. Loose and I sat up a-who-ing and a-what-ing, trying to get our bearings as Gonad stuck his head in.

'Windy! Quick! We need you urgently on the bridge!' He was winking and twitching like he had a toad in his pants.

'Are you all right, Gonad?' I asked. 'What's the matter with you?'

'There's a problem with the, er, fitting-limitation squadron-linkage frig-monitor . . . valve . . . oil . . . persecutor.'

'Eh?'

'You know, the wobble-mayhem wop-lolly cat-winkler has gone again. The . . . oh, just come ON, you tosser!'

'Ah. Right.' I looked at Loose, who looked baffled. 'Shan't be a mo'.'

I leapt out of bed and hopped out into the corridor on one leg with the other trying to find its way into a pair of shorts. It sounded quite urgent and important, and the poor chap clearly thought I could help, but to be honest, I didn't know exactly what a fitting-limitation frig wobble thingy was. He grabbed me by the elbow and lifted me round the corridor as he gave me the news: 'Jackie's here! She's waiting at the gangway!'

'Jackie? Jeeeeez, no! Why do people always arrive when we have problems? We'll never get that . . . whatsit oil persecutor thing fixed. Listen, Gonad. Do you mind sorting it out by yourself while I deal with Jackie? I don't want her to meet Lucy.'

He looked at me with exasperation. I hate to be tough on people, but I had problems of my own. He would just have to fix his wobble-mayhem without me on the bridge.

'OK, Windy, forget the doodah. We'll do it later. Let's take Jackie to the bar. I'll try to distract her while you tell Loose the boat is leaving and she has to go. Once Loose is off the ship, you're in the clear. Oh! Here's Jackie.'

I put on a big smile and opened my arms to her at the top of the gangway. 'Hiiiiii, Jackie! You cheeky thing, surprising me like that!'

'I heard that the ship was still around,' said Jackie, 'and you left a shirt at my house, so I thought I'd drop in on you for a quick goodbye shag, and if you do a good enough job I'll give you your shirt back.'

To be honest, I was looking forward to getting away from all this physical stuff for a week or two. Both Jackie and Loose liked to ensure they got their fair allocation of time and effort, and I wasn't sure I could muster yet another grand finale of the type worthy of winning a shirt. I decided to try to keep Gonad around me at all times as a chaperon.

We led Jackie round to the bar. NotNorman and the Chief Engineer were already in there. Notters was looking a little strange and the Chief was reading a book. It was certainly an unusual atmosphere, particularly so early in the morning – there was usually nobody in the bar at this time of day – but we had a problem. The ship was due to leave in a couple of hours, and there were strict instructions that all 'friends' should have left the ship before midnight the previous night. The Chief was not at all strict, but he was top brass and would certainly not sit by while we broke the rules.

'Ah. Morning Chief! This is Jackie. She's, er, she's, er –'

'From the agents,' interrupted Gonad, 'she's here to . . . to clean the bar.'

'What?' said Jackie. 'Clean the – ?'

'There you go,' said Gonad, grabbing a cloth and some cleaning fluid from behind the bar and shoving them into her midriff. She was mortified, but the Chief was looking at her over his book so she began to play along, cleaning the bar with the exaggerated acting skill of a cheap television commercial.

'Right,' I said, 'see you later,' and before Jackie could complain Gonad and I made a run for the door. As soon as we opened it, our way was blocked by the imposing figure of the Mate. He looked down at us as we cowered in the doorway. His suspicious nose smelt the heady pong of rat, and his lips twitched at the edges as he scoured the scene for information.

'Why are you lot all in the bar at this time of day, eh? What's going on, then?' He grabbed my shirt and began to lift me up. 'You bastards are up to someth – oops! S'cuse the language, Miss. Didn't see you there.' He smiled uncomfortably at Jackie. He wanted to set about us with his standard, undiluted brutality, but he didn't know who she was.

'Can't a bloke get ten minutes with a book?' said the

Chief spreading his arms to the heavens. 'I might as well go and sit in the road.'

'You're right,' said NotNorman getting up. 'C'mon everybody, let's leave the Chief in peace. Off we go!' He headed for the door making ushering movements, but the Mate wasn't budging, so there were now four of us in an awkward scrum, bunched in the doorway.

'The Captain was looking for you,' I said to the Mate. 'I came here to find you and tell you. He's out on the foredeck. Says it's important.'

'Well, why didn't you look in my cabin, yer fool? What would I be doing in the bar at this time of day?'

'Exactly,' I said, 'but I *did* find you here, didn't I?'

The Mate furrowed his brow. 'But . . . you weren't looking for me – I just came to you.'

'Yes, you're right, I did,' I said cryptically, keeping him from comprehension.

'It was the same for me,' said Gonad, nodding enthusiastically.

'I wasn't looking for him either,' said NotNorman, 'and I found him here too.'

'Will you lot stop talking shite?' implored the Chief. 'I'm trying to read my book.'

'The Captain's out there. Now. Waiting for you.' I did my best to coax the Mate out. He was very suspicious, but began to leave. I knew if he went that I would only have about one minute before he would be back to torture me for sending him on a wild goose chase, but I had to distract him somehow. He turned and left, looking back at us as he did. Gonad and I gave him a little wave, shut the door, gave him a few seconds then opened it again to leave. There in the doorway was – Loose. I let out a little scream as she came in, and dived behind the door. The thought of Jackie and Loose finding out about each other turned my bowels

183

to water as I bravely hid in the corner. Jackie could see me and was about to ask an awkward question, but Loose couldn't, so I tried to pretend to Jackie that I wasn't hiding while, well, hiding from Loose. Loose looked puzzled.

'NotNorman, what's going on? Windy seems to have –'

'Darling!' gushed Gonad. Sensing Jackie's rising interest at a half-dressed girl mentioning my name, he dived across the room and put his arm around Loose. 'How great to see you!' He kissed her on the lips. Loose had only met Gonad a couple of times, so this was a little unexpected. She spluttered as she got her mouth free from his.

'What the bloody hell do you think you're –'

I knew about her temper, so I had to stop her or the Chief would go crackers, so I jumped out from behind the door. 'There, fixed it! Oh, hi there! You're . . . Lucy, wasn't it? Pleased to meet you. Nice, er, night-dress. Now then, I'll only be a second. Lovely day. What's for breakfast? It's done, lads. I fixed the mayhem wobble. Let's go and report to the Mate!'

'Ten minutes with a book, that's all I wanted.'

'Who is this, Windy?' said Jackie. 'Aren't you going to introduce us?'

NotNorman, seeing the look in Lucy's eye, suddenly dived over and put his arm around Jackie. 'Darling!' he pronounced. 'Didn't I introduce you?'

'Ten bloody minutes, that's all. Not a lot to ask, is it?'

'NotNorman!' shouted a new and unexpected voice from behind the sofa. We all looked around as Cindy popped up angrily from behind the sofa. 'Get your hands off her!'

'Whoa!' exclaimed the Chief jumping two feet in the air as Cindy appeared behind him. 'What the – ?'

'Ah! Hi Cindy!' said NotNorman weakly. 'You remember Jackie?'

Cindy was half-dressed. She and NotNorman had

obviously been interrupted by the Chief as they were saying a spicy goodbye in the privacy of the ship's bar when the Chief had come in for ten minutes' peace.

Loose was puzzled. 'Why were you hiding behind the door, Windy? And why was that girl hiding behind the sofa? And why was *that* cleaning girl asking you –'

'Ah, now Lucy, this is Jackie, she's from the agent and she's cleaning the ship. I was just fixing the persecution monitor behind the door here, and this is Cindy – pest control. How's it all going under the sofa there, Cindy?'

The Chief stood up. He had had enough. 'Persecution monitor? What on earth are you talking about? I don't know what sort of madness is going on here, but –'

'Ah-HAAA!' The Mate shoved his head through the porthole from the deck, right behind the Chief, who hit the ceiling. 'Try to get rid of me, would you, Baboulene? You're going to suffer like never before, you –' he looked around at the assembled troupe of cadets and half-dressed girls. 'You bastards stay right where you are. I'm coming round now!'

His head disappeared and we all dashed about frantically, trying to escape.

The Mate came piling in. 'Right, you bastards! What's going on?'

I answered as clearly as I could:

'This is Jackie, she's my cousin from New Zealand who has lost some money; this is Cindy, her mentally unstable lesbian girlfriend, and we're having a tea party in order to . . .'

Whatever I said was simply a desperate attempt to keep talking on the basis that it prevented the Mate from getting his turn. And in a way, it worked, because I genuinely believe he didn't quite know what to do. In the end he simply ignored me.

'YOU,' he shouted, pointing a shaking finger at Lucy, 'should have left the ship last night! Get your things and GO!

The rest of you, I want to see ID, or you leave too! Windy, get these people off the ship then report to me in my cabin in ten minutes.' But his heart wasn't in it. We were finally beginning to get to him. He wiped the spittle from his mouth and left, head bowed. He was utterly at a loss. He wasn't even able to rant effectively.

I led Lucy back to the cabin, made another set of excuses and headed back to the bar. Eventually I managed to get Jackie on her own. I began to explain but Jackie just laughed at me. I had forgotten that Cindy was her best friend. Her NotNormie had told her – Cindy – my adulterous secrets, and Cindy had, of course, grassed me up to Jackie, who told me not to 'sweat it'. 'You and I both knew you'd have to leave,' she said, 'but I didn't see a problem with me using you while you were here. Did you? You blokes are so ridiculous, you know, thinking you have a monopoly on straightforward sex.'

And she gave me the shirt she had brought me, and we said goodbye again, this time with added respect from me. Loose never knew any different.

Great sentiment also flowed between the band and me as the goodbyes rang out. I had found soul mates here; kindred spirits who lived life as it should be lived. I couldn't wait for the day we would be reunited. But, like true teenagers, we didn't exchange addresses, we simply agreed to 'see ya round' on the beach one day. We didn't consider for a moment the possibility that things might be different in years to come. I would miss everything about Sydney.

However, you will raise your eyebrows to learn that NotNorman and Cindy had no trouble with their goodbyes at all. But before you throw the book on the fire in disbelief, let me reveal all: they did not say goodbye.

As the gangway was swung aboard and the ropes released

us from Sydney's loving embrace, Cindy (and a good deal of luggage) had neglected to leave the vessel. She was stowing away in the ship's hospital. The Steward had been handsomely bribed, and the young lovers could see no problems with this course of action. They were together, so the world was as full of blue lovebirds and violins as it was before they'd become Mrs Fugitive and Mr Harbouring-Illegal-Immigrant. Any fool could see that it was all bound to end in tears, but they were in love, and, remarkably enough, as the ship puffed into Melbourne a few days later, she had not been discovered, and was able to rejoin society as the girlfriend who'd flown down from Sydney. The inseparable pair's great love story chuntered on.

For me, Melbourne meant many things. Looming largest, however, was not the city or the trams, the rain or the tennis, but a chap called 'Big Phil'. Big Phil had been synonymous with Melbourne throughout the trip – he was to provide the highlight of our Australian adventure, maybe even of our entire trip, and one of the first items of news to circulate now that we were alongside was that he would indeed be gracing us with his presence. So on the second night we did not go up the road. We were to have a quiet night in with Big Phil and see his amazing show.

The drink flowed freely as the evening built up, and I must admit that the unusually good spirits of my colleagues were a refreshing change. They were obviously looking forward to Big Phil's show, whatever it was.

Eventually the word went out that Big Phil had arrived and a buzz ran through the gathering. The double doors to the bar were opened, and by golly, when BP arrived at the threshold it was just as well both of them were open! P was indeed B. What was more of a shock though, was to find out that P was not a Phillip, but a Phillipa. A strapping,

187

cheerful woman of high tonnage, broad beam and lustful eyes.

Most of the older lads had met her before. She was greeted with unbridled enthusiasm and there was an air of camaraderie and expectation that was unsettling. I started to become conscious of a little alarm bell ringing away at the back of my mind. Now I noticed it, I realised it had been madly trying to get my attention for some time.

Big Phil had a wit and a charm that was quite disarming, and her weight became a decidedly secondary issue as her personality shone through. Nobody could call her a classically beautiful woman – and in an ideal world I suppose it wouldn't matter as her character was so special – but as a spectacular presence, and what with boys being boys and an ideal world being unachievable, her physical size mattered a great deal, especially when we found out why she was on board.

Once the formalities of arranging drinks and re-establishing long-lost links were over, Jinx took charge. Heavies were placed on the doors and we first-trippers were invited to sit on a line of barstools carefully prepared centre stage. I was conscious of a hollow pit in my stomach as I realised we were, once again, to be the night's entertainment. We sat as bidden on the barstools, and my mind was working overtime trying to imagine what horrors awaited us that could so excite a baying mob and involve an industrial-sized woman. Only one possibility entered my mind. It could not be . . . Surely, surely not . . . They could not possibly intend . . .

Jinx stood up and began his speech.

'In the grand traditions of the education and enlightenment of our younger colleagues, it is incumbent upon the elders amongst us to help these boys move from the uncertain deserts of boyish ineptitude to the flourishing gardens of confident manhood. We are gathered here this evening as further evidence that we will do everything in our power to help these young sparrows spread their sexual wings in a turbulent world.

'We will not shrink from the obligations we have to our seafaring traditions, and we will not fail in our duty to these lads, however ungrateful they may become. It is, therefore, my great pleasure to preside over this auspicious occasion, another grand example of the cementing of Anglo-Australian relationships, featuring, hhhhin the red corner, Biiiiiiig Phil! A tremendous performer with innumerable cherries already popped beneath her impressive undercarriage. Tonight, for your deee-lectation, she will subdue and roger – hhhhhhin the blue corner – these lucky young cherry-boys! Yes indeed! Here tonight, before our very eyes, these lucky lads will make the journey from boy to man. So without further ado, let us go straight over to the selection procedure!'

Can you imagine this? Can you even *begin* to imagine this? To put yourself in my place? I felt numb, pale, faint, weak, helpless and ill. The boys were like a fully-hyped gameshow crowd, all screaming and jeering their opinions as to which of us Big Phil should deflower first. In the bar. In front of everybody.

She paced back and forth in front of us rubbing her chins thoughtfully as the crowd went bananas in the background. She squeezed the odd thigh muscle and touched the odd cheek, like a shopper selecting groceries. I briefly caught her eye and withered under the strength of her worldliness. Like a mouse held firmly beneath the claw, I could see no escape. The fever built higher and higher as the crowd sensed the finger was ready to point. I knew she was going to choose me. It was absolutely inevitable. I rued my good looks, my boyish charm, my muscular forearms and sophisticated aura that . . . Gonad? She chose GONAD?

At first I was a little peeved at this. What was wrong

with the woman? She must have been bribed. Nobody in their right mind would choose Gonad if he was the last bloke on earth, let alone with *me* sitting there. Maybe she was saving me for pudding. I decided not to quibble, after all, Gonad was better than me at this sort of thing. He lacked my sensitivity and sense of timing. I would let it go this time.

Now call me a party-pooper if you will, but even as Gonad was struggling for his life and trousers, I was looking for an opportunity to escape, and – eventually – it appeared. In the mêlée and excitement of restraining Gonad there was, for the briefest of moments, a clear path between me and the bar doors.

Now I don't want you to infer from this that I'm the type of chap who would insult a young lady by legging it from her amorous attentions, but without so much as raising my hat I was out of my seat and through the doors before you could say 'meat and two veg'. A few of the boys – anxious that Anglo-Australian relations might become strained if a goodly portion of BP's dinner was allowed to run off – were hot on my heels. I made it to my cabin and slammed the door just as six hefty sailors hit it all at once. I leant back against the door and gasped a sigh of relief, but my problems were far from over. I heard shouts as they organised my retrieval. There was nowhere to run. I had the time it would take them to get the master-key to think of something brilliant. No point in blocking the lock – they would knock the door down if they had to. I was desperate. I unwound the lock on my porthole and peered out into the cool air. Freedom smelt good, but it didn't look as though I could get at it. It was a good 30-foot drop into the dark water. Besides, I could only just fit my head out and then only by catching my ears on the unyielding brass. I had heard tell that people on sinking ships had been known to escape through portholes. Frightened, panic-stricken people. I felt a curious kinship with them. The scramble outside my cabin was becoming more menacing, and I thought of my last view of Gonad, struggling like a desperate, hopeless fly in the web of a Greater Phillipa spider.

I gulped.

Next moment, I was falling through the air, watching the side of the ship flash by me. There was a splash, cold silence under the water, then air and noise again as I returned to the surface. I looked back up at the ship and could hear the distant sounds of the boys trying to find an answer. I turned away and swam – with the unique style you might expect of someone with two dislocated shoulders – across the dock to the steps on the opposite side and walked off into town. There was no way I would return to the ship that night.

Reliable reports from the lads themselves have it that Gonad, KiloWatt and NotNorman became bait for Big Phil's fish, and that a thoroughly enjoyable night was had by all (except two – KiloWatt loved every moment), but the fact that will pass down the generations into seafaring folklore was not Big Phil that night – she already has her place in the history books – but that a cadet was so desperately keen to spoil other people's fun that he managed to escape through a porthole. Any sailor will tell you that it is the action of a truly frenzied man. I have stood staring at that porthole many times since, and have hurt my ears trying to squeeze my head through it. It cannot be done. But there you have it. Necessity is indeed the mother of invention, and as far as I was concerned, it was an extreme necessity to invent a way of escaping that mother.

Chapter 17

Walkabout

A dart is thrown. Scurrilous remarks on Dunfermline. The train to Nowhere. A large Aborigine, a long way home and a re-evaluation of Dunfermline.

It is a great idea, leading to excitement and adventure who knows where, to throw a dart into a map and go wherever the Gods of Probability deem, but it can have its pitfalls in the hands of the unwary. Following the embarrassment of Big Phil, the Great Unwashed had an irresistible urge to get away for a day or two, so the dart was fetched, along with a map of Melbourne's hinterland, and we rubbed our hands in gleeful anticipation. The trouble was, we let Giewy throw the dart.

When we were on the induction course I'd been introduced to this game and heard many tales of legendary trips to all sorts of outlandish places. Before the dart flies, nobody knows where he is going, and once the destination has been established, nobody knows what adventures are in store when he arrives. It is as close as pioneering adventurers get to 'organising' spontaneity and chaos.

It sounds like the perfect recipe for excitement, but the reason I've neglected to mention this event so far was because the game did not live up to expectations. Some berk carefully avoided the promise of Newcastle, Glasgow, Leeds and Manchester, and threw the dart into Dunfermline for us. Despite the moans and groans, we had to go there. The chances were that we would have a far better time than we expected, but it was not to be. Dunfermline was crap. I suppose by rights, among all these stories of world travel and cosmopolitan excess, there ought to be a tedious monologue entitled 'A Crap Night in

192

Dunfermline.' I cannot say with absolute authority that Dunfermline is the most definitively dull spot on the planet, but it certainly reduced those old rascals Spontaneity and Chaos to a pair of snoring pussycats.

Maybe it's just me. I gather people live long and happy lives in Dunfermline; lives jammed to the rafters with laughter and contentment. Perhaps they do not wish for outsiders to discover their utopian haven, so they implement extravagant charades to convince dart-throwing visitors that Dunfermline is unspeakably pedestrian. They see people arriving over the hill and immediately stop the music, the laughter, the drinking and the making merry, turning it off like a tap. For the duration of our visit the pubs were shut, young girls an extinct species, and elderly locals wandered about in the drizzle yawning like hippos and staring longingly into the cemetery.

I suspect that the moment we had gone, the old folk tore off their masks and started dancing, the gravestones all turned back into jukeboxes, the tired old shop fronts spun round to reveal casinos, pubs, nightclubs and brothels and the town blazed once more into its 24-hour party of debauchery and excess.

Maybe.

So I feel sure you will appreciate how, when Giewy threw the dart into the Dandenong Ranges some 80 miles into the Australian outback, memories of my night trying to get to sleep on a bench in a rainy Dunfermline park came flooding back, as did the recollection of the subsequent fortnight's sensational and bubbly influenza and my recurrent desire to flush Giewy's head down a toilet. Every time Giewy did something pathetic, I imagined his head flushing down a toilet, and how the shape of his neck would fit exactly round the U-bend. I pray my day will come.

Upon seeing the location he had struck, there were cries of 'Bum deal!', 'No dice!' and 'Flush Giewy's head down the toilet!' but rules are rules, and we knew if we let ourselves off it would be the thin end of the wedge; the top of a slippery slope leading inevitably to anarchy, disorder and the breakdown of civilisation as we knew it. We didn't want that on our conscience, so a visit to one of the state of Victoria's more ticklish extremities was unavoidable.

One hour later, we were on the last train to Nowhere from Melbourne, and it was really quite exciting. The lads were in a buoyant mood and a good time seemed to be on the cards. Mind you, it was the same on the way to Dunfermline.

Soon the city levelled into suburbs with comforting English names like Blackburn, Canterbury, Box Hill and Camberwell, then suddenly civilisation *did* break down, and there were periods of awesome nothing. Just bush.

After a while we were in the middle of nowhere when the train hissed, squealed, farted, and stopped. We wondered what was wrong. The guard was passing so we asked him.

'Your stop, lads. Shake a leg!'

'What? *Here*? But there's no station or anything!'

'We put the steps out for you. Downtown is a couple of miles thataway.'

We looked at each other in disbelief, grabbed our stuff, and climbed down to the parched red sand at ground level. The steps climbed back on to the train, which hissed, squealed, farted and pulled away. NotNorman was looking around and shaking his head.

'How did the driver *know* this is a station?' he asked. I took his point. There was nothing to indicate the presence of anything at all, let alone a station or a town. No signs, no ticket office, no personnel. Mind you, I suppose all those things were unnecessary in the light of the other factor – no passengers. There were tracks and nothing else.

We looked around in deep, daunted silence. Someone

mentioned how neatly we were avoiding the excitement of Melbourne, and tried to recall how it was we came to be here. I remember the same comment outside a closed Indian restaurant in Dunfermline. Had a suitable public convenience been available, Giewy would most certainly have suffered a cranial indignity.

This was really wild. The odd bush, a murderous sun directly above us, and a shimmering heat haze in every direction. As my eyes tracked the horizon round, the diminishing train could be made out dimly to the east, and the merest break in the landscape, roughly where the guard had indicated, could be perceived to the north-west. We decided that, although somewhat less imposing than the Manhattan skyline, this must be 'downtown', so we wiped our foreheads, lifted our rucksacks, and began tramping towards it. Soon we fell into a hot, exhausted silence, our heads drooping. We were no longer fun-seekers – we were survivors.

After a while our dying minds were distracted from the fact that we were voluntarily being fried in the Australian bush by the tiniest hint of a distant hum. I ignored it at first, thinking it was just another of the many symptoms of slow death. Then Patch stopped, put his head on one side and said, 'Listen.'

We all held our breath and listened to the hot silence. Sure enough, the hum was becoming a drone, and it was coming from behind us. We turned to look, and the unmistakable shape of a van became visible through the heat haze. It took a full two minutes for the drone to become a growl to become a din to become a roar, then a Volkswagen campervan zoomed past in a noisy flurry of pink and white coach-work, full of music and cheering youth. Then the roar became a din became a growl became a drone became a hum, and the pink and white shimmer disappeared into the heat haze leaving us alone in the hot afternoon silence once more.

We shrugged our shoulders and carried on. Shortly, however, the same thing happened again. A hum on the horizon behind us materialised for a second into a large white convertible full of groovy kids and loud music. It roared past, and before that apparition had disappeared to the north-west, another was emerging from the south-east. There was obviously something happening in the bush that night, and somewhere near the Dandenongs was *the* place to be!

A couple of vehicles later, a drone had become a growl, but instead of the growl becoming a momentary cacophony of teenagers and music, the growl became pacific, and we looked around to see an open-backed truck pulling up beside us.

'You boys going to the concert?' said the large and friendly looking Aborigine in the driving seat, his silver beard filling the entire cabin.

'Yes!' I said, as Giewy said, 'No!' and Gonad said, 'What concert?'

He looked confused by our lack of harmony. 'Well, you gotta be going to the Gulley whatever else you're doin'. There's no other friggin' place to go. Jump on!'

We leapt gratefully on to the back of the truck. I got the floor space shared with an over-friendly black Labrador sporting a silver beard eerily similar to that of its master, and the truck bumped its way off towards a place called Ferntree Gulley (a place we had already thundered through on the train an hour or two before).

Ferntree Gulley was less of an anticlimax than our railway station, in that it existed in some tangible sense. To us it was like an oasis in the outback. It was lush and green, with new houses and tended gardens, and a proud sign announcing the imposing presence of 'The Ferntree Gulley Hotel'. Below this sign was a poster featuring the legend:

'From England! In Concert! Lomax and Mellish Productions Proudly Presents: SQUEEZE!'

A strip was placed across the poster declaring that the concert was SOLD OUT, and the small print revealed that the event was for One Night Only. Now this was absolutely and totally incredible. If you've given me the benefit of the doubt regarding some of the things you've read so far, you need not feel ashamed if you find the presence of Squeeze at the Ferntree Gulley Hotel beyond the realms of possibility. I felt the same way, and I had the black and white evidence in front of me, and hordes of revellers arriving in their droves from all points of the compass. We counted the 'e's in 'Squeeze' (I've been caught out that way before – only 'The Beetles' play Dunfermline, never 'The Beatles') and the way the names of the band were spelled. There was no doubt about it, this was the genuine article.

What Mr Lomax must have done in order to secure a band like Squeeze – at the peak of their superstardom – to play the Ferntree Gulley Hotel will have to remain one of life's great unsolved mysteries. And what Mr Mellish must have said to Mr Lomax when he did it must remain similarly shrouded. Whatever was said or done, I should imagine that their negotiating skills have probably taken them to some elevated positions in the world. They certainly deserve it.

We went to the ticket window and got a shake of the head from a chalk-white woman with dyed black hair, red lipstick, and house-bricks for earrings. We searched for touts and were moved on by a pair of large policemen who could eat house-bricks along with any incidental black-haired, red-lipped, chalk-white women who might be attached to them. There seemed to be no way for us to get in at the front of the house, so we wandered around to the back of the hotel to try our luck there. Two huge trucks indicated the presence of the band and their entourage, and a large pair of closed double doors, labelled 'Artistes' proclaimed the stage door. Unfortunately there was nobody around to be badgered, implored and bribed so, because my southern accent was deemed to be the closest to that of a loveable Cockney, I was pushed forward to bang on the door.

'Yeah?' came the unwelcoming response to my rappings. The door stayed shut.

'Oh er, lissen, mush, weer from Deptford, int we,' I lied in an appalling South London accent. I sounded Pakistani. 'Can you geezers get us into –'

'Nah! Piss orf!' He'd heard it all before.

'Aw, cam on, cock! We've cam all the way from Landin! We've gorn 'arf across the poxy weld to be 'ere, and cor blimey! We carn't get no bladdy tickets! We got all yer albims. I gotta big poster of Jules 'olland, honest, and ma mate 'ere, he went an' –'

'You got any beer?' came the gruff reply.

'Er . . . no.'

'Well, like I said, PISS ORF, then.'

And that was roughly the size of it. The state laws and hotel policy had it that the gig featured soft drinks only. Gonad's excitement at the poster on the front door saying, 'Alcohol Free' was a misunderstanding on his part. The roadies were being denied their lifeblood, so it was hardly surprising that they were somewhat icy, even towards Pakistanis from Deptford.

I turned back to the lads just in time to see NotNorman heading off round the side of the hotel. I thought he must have been caught short or something, but as we walked around after him we saw what he was up to. Our Aborigine friend was still there. He'd been smoking a little and watching people since he'd dropped us off, and . . . was drinking a beer. Some swift negotiations from NotNorman brought forth a six-pack, and before you could tie your kangaroo down, sport, the artistes' entrance was banging in the breeze, and half a dozen roadies were falling on our necks and blessing us. Some money changed hands, palms were greased, winks and nudges abounded, and within half an hour a certain Aborigine had earned a month's money for a short drive and the supply of an unspecified quantity of – to use the local vernacular – the golden throat lubricant.

The term 'male bonding' is 50 per cent reliant upon men to make it male, and 50 per cent reliant upon a decent agent for the bonding. Beer is the ideal glue for male bonding, and to these roadies we were all the world's long-lost brothers rolled into five. We were taken backstage where we began male bonding ourselves into oblivion with both band and roadies before, during and after the gig. That particular drinking session was made all the sweeter by the knowledge that it was the only booze in town.

I'm not sure how, but I think I may have become somewhat intoxicated, because I don't remember much after the first couple of hours. The gig was terrific, and I can say without doubt that overall, it was a fast-moving evening involving a fair degree of uproar, the details of which conveniently escape me. Suffice to say I opened my eyes to find the sun twelve o'clock high, pounding into my unsteady pupils, a chicken on my chest, my hand in a pile of dung up to the wrist, and an Aborigine woman alongside me who made Big Phil look anorexic. I leapt up and stared at her, ignoring my throbbing head. I couldn't have. Surely there must be . . . I tried to remember the evening's proceedings.

I had a vague recollection of hanging on to the back of some sort of flatbed truck for grim death as it thundered through the hot night, my legs flailing like a flag. Then I was dancing in the bush with some extremely friendly Aborigines. I remember swirling stars above me, people leaping around and everybody laughing. I remember the strangeness of larking about hundreds of miles from anywhere. You could shout your heart out and there was nothing to reflect the sound, so there was no echo; the sound just kept going away. It was like having a party in deep space. Then I remembered nothing.

I certainly didn't remember arriving at this roofless chicken hut, or sleeping with this . . . Where the hell AM I? I stumbled out into the bright sunlight, the horizon shimmering alarmingly in all directions. There was nothing. Certainly no transport. No people. Just one shrub with someone having a crap behind it.

'Mornin'!' said NotNorman. 'Have a good evening did we?' NotNorman was blessed with the inability to suffer hangovers – he just got kind of taller for a while.

'Jeeezus! Where are we?' I was genuinely worried. 'People *die* out here, you know.'

'Yeah,' he said reflectively, 'bummer, eh?'

I laughed a mirthless laugh. 'How did we *get* here? More to the point, how are we going to get back?'

'Well, me old son. See that sand that's a slightly different colour from the rest? That's the road. The sun rose that way, so that must be east, so I suggest we start walking west and thumb down a lorry – unless you fancy waiting for a bus. The next one's due in the year 2012.'

I could see no other feasible course of action and I wanted to leave before *she* woke up, so we slung our shirts over our shoulders and headed off along the road like the heroes of some epic movie strolling off into the sunset.

Come back, Dunfermline, all is forgiven!

★ ★ ★

As I took up my usual departure position – leaning on the rail watching a much-loved country receding into the distance – with the customary tear in my eye, I could feel nothing but sadness. I had found paradise in Australia, and kindred spirits in the people. I loved the no-nonsense attitude of the Australians and the classless nature of the society.

One thing I found just brilliant about the Australians was their extremely high 'don't-give-a-shit' factor. Given an opportunity to establish great personal wealth and world superstardom, your average Australian would happily turn it down in favour of a cold beer if that was the way he felt at the time. Someone told me a story that perfectly exemplifies this Australian humour and attitude. I don't know if it's true or not, but if it isn't it should be.

A couple of Aussies were tracking their way across some uncharted area of Western Australia when they came across a new and undiscovered mountain. It was a very high, very prominent and obviously important landmark. Their discovery would be historic.

Down the centuries, whenever anybody has made a new and exciting discovery, they have naturally named it after themselves, thus ensuring their name is enshrined in the history books, maps and lecture theatres of the world for the rest of time. You or I would do the same, I'm sure. Hence we have Mount Cook, Halley's Comet, Fox Glacier and so on. And these Australians were no different. Their egos would have it no other way. Hence, on today's relief maps of Western Australia you can find a proud and steadfast landmark by the name of 'Me and Harry's Mountain'. Nobody knows who 'Me' or 'Harry' were, but they were 'Australian' enough to thumb their noses at tradition rather than have their names go down into history. Only an Australian could do that and really mean it.

Chapter 18

South Pacific

Surprising discoveries concerning the Solomon Islanders' coiffure, working practices and dancing expertise. The chill breeze of the Second World War.

The South Pacific contains countless small islands. Many are inhabited, with their own people and culture, many are deserted, but all are beautiful beyond belief, and each has its own distinctive character. Sailing through an idyllic, sparkling sea, with a cloudless sky and a huge orange sun shining on the palm-fringed coral sands is like sailing into some sort of Fairyland, a storybook wonder I am privileged to have witnessed.

We went to around eight of these islands, an experience that will remain with me for the rest of my life. As we weaved through the reefs and lagoons, flying fish skimmed the surface, multicoloured shoals darted and flashed in the clear water, and birds of every size and colour played the breeze with commanding grace. I've never seen such places. Rich and lush with towering coconut palms, flowers of the most vivid reds, yellows, mauves and greens, all set against the backdrop of a turquoise, jewelled sea and white coral sand. A visit to the South Pacific is as much of an experience for the nose as it is for the eyes as each flower competes for air-space. Early Polynesian sailors, lost in the Pacific, would detect the presence of land from the fragrance the islands gave off long before they could see them.

We began with a graceful flit from one minute island to the next – with names like Yandina and Tarawa – in the Solomon Islands. We would anchor in some idyllic lagoon and be serviced by a hundred noisy, chaotic 'bum boats', or we would come alongside a gloriously unsafe wooden jetty and deal with the chaos direct.

We were loading coconut husks, collectively known as copra. Back in the 'civilised' world (really, to label our culture as in any way more civilised than that of these island people is the work of grossly undernourished brains) this copra would be turned into perfume, soap, cleaning agents and other such items that didn't bear thinking about in this paradise.

The workforce was unconventional to say the least. Hundreds of stocky, chocolate-brown men with huge, broad smiles, wide, flared nostrils, the most laid-back attitudes of anyone on earth, and every last one of them adorned with a shocking mop of curly ginger-blond hair! Quite alarming at first. The place looked as though the world's best salesman had recently passed through the area with an unbeatable deal on peroxide. Not so, however – no *Candid Camera* here – every last one of them had his own completely natural orange afro!

They were also extraordinarily agile and athletic, particularly when it came to loading the cargo. Most stevedores are fat, lazy slobs, with about as much athletic ability as a plate of cold noodles, but here it was different. Each net of copra, swinging fast and hazardously from the shoreside to the hold, would also contain half a dozen black blonds, laughing, shouting and playing the goat. Quite the most dangerous working practice I've ever seen, but they were just enjoying the ride. Each net returning from the hold to the shoreside would be similarly overloaded – I don't think I ever saw a worker use the gangway! They were such lovely people, so full of life and laughter. Every now and then, as boredom with the work began to set in (which it regularly did) a shout would go up, a song would start, and a dance would begin. The infectious rhythm would spread like wildfire and before you knew it, as far as the eye could see and on every surface that could support a man everyone would be dancing and singing their hearts out without a care in the world. The ship would be instantly converted into Carnival Central – afire with joy and happiness – and in the middle somewhere would be the Cargo Officer. Reduced from a smart, dignified official to a red-faced, rhythmless white bloke, hopping awkwardly from one foot to the other, while the dancers around him fell about laughing and stole his cap. I was so jealous of their ability to immerse themselves completely in a mood and a moment, and to love life so freely. It would take six hours, an ill-advised quantity of drugs and five pints of ale to get me that relaxed, and even then I would still have the capacity to worry about tomorrow.

Their happiness was all the more poignant after a walk around the island. These people had lived the same way for thousands of years, and as the industrial world developed elsewhere they neither knew nor cared. They certainly had no need of it, and there was precious little they could be taught about values; but inevitably, the cancerous spread of 'civilisation' found its way here, and their fragile utopia became a pivotal spot during World War II.

As the Japanese and the Allies began throwing things at each other, these islands became logistically important. They provided vital refuelling posts for men and aircraft that couldn't make the distance to the battlefield in one jump and meant superior positioning of supplies and equipment. Controlling the islands would have been a huge advantage. So all of a sudden these quiet, peaceful islands learned about 'civilisation' as a desperate scramble for their control ensued.

The people were at best ignored, often abused, and

without exception trampled underfoot. The islands were torn apart to make runways and buildings, and were officially adopted as army property, irrespective of what the Islanders might think about what represented their best interests. The ripple effect of the war still haunts the islands decades later.

These islands are not just a natural wonder of the world, but also an eerie graveyard. Everywhere there were physical epitaphs to the dreadful rape of the islands and their people. There were army buildings, standing decrepit and empty, hastily-constructed aerodrome runways overgrown and silent, stark machine-gun posts sticking out like giant malignant pimples – some still equipped with rusted guns and mountings. Along the coral beach the odd truck or personnel carrier sank chillingly into the sand, gradually being sucked under over the years. You look from these instruments of destruction to the unparalleled beauty of the nature surrounding them and the incongruity is the starkest reminder of what parasites we humans are on this planet. The world would be a better place without us, and Mother Nature would definitely have a much easier time of it without people. The pointlessness of war and the depths of our depravity become an embarrassment. The occupiers' rapes left a legacy of children, some of whom were working our ship now in their middle age. What seems so needless when you look at these places is the war itself, especially a war between distant lands, and one in which these people so patently had no personal interest. They were caught in the global cross-fire.

It is quite an experience to visit these islands and in the tropical sun of an island paradise, to feel the chill breeze of the war years.

Chapter 19

A Sea of Balloons

Policemen in skirts. The Captain expresses his dissatisfaction. Windy battles valiantly against overwhelming odds. The Captain decides enough is enough.

Of the other islands we visited, it was nice to include a couple of well-known ones. Fiji was fascinating, the capital, Suva, being particularly cynical. Prices quadrupled as soon as the passenger liners arrived, and the local 'characters' lined up at the bottom of the gangway with their napkins tucked in, their knives and forks rampant, and slavered through their smiles as their prey descended. Fiji was memorable for two particular events. The second is a sticky subject I would rather put off until later. The first occurred at two in the morning in a Suva nightclub. I was awakened from my deep, hypnotic, personal boogie wonderland by a tap on the shoulder.

'Oi, oi, Windy. Plod's in!'

This was MegaWatt-speak for, 'I say, old boy, it appears the constabulary have arrived.' I looked towards the entrance and sure enough, there was a queue of bobbies lining up behind the counter remonstrating with the ticket girl. And in employing the very British term 'bobby' I do not stray from the straight and narrow. Because apart from being jet-black and seven feet tall, they looked precisely like British policemen. Same helmet, same jacket and shirt, same accessories – no difference at all. That is, from the waist up. But as they stepped out from behind the counter, I nearly pulled an eye muscle trying to comprehend what I saw. The size-twelve black boots were the same, but unlike

206

a British bobby, these coppers were wearing white skirts. Yes, skirts. No trousers at all.

A nervous smile crept across my face and I looked around to see what others were making of it, *Candid Camera* once more springing to mind. Everyone else was looking uncertainly at one another too, and the nervous smiles were turning into raucous laughter. I looked back at the rozzers. From the waist up they were indisputably mean-and-moody plods, but from the waist down they were Hawaiian dancers in combat boots. Then I saw people dancing around prodding them and laughing, and I cottoned on. The passenger ship! That was it! This was some sort of fancy dress to do with the passenger boat! I relaxed and joined in the laughter at the antics of these fun guys. We asked them to dance, blew their whistles, peeked up their skirts and made lewd jokes about truncheons and shiny helmets. And while the gang roared their approval at every new joke, the funniest thing of all was how the policemen kept stony straight faces. Had I not known they weren't *real* policemen, I could have got quite concerned at their granite features and mock sternness. It didn't matter how funny we were – poncing about with handbags and mincing around in front of them – they kept straight faces the whole time. The more we knocked their helmets off and pinched their bums when they picked them up, the angrier they appeared to be getting. They were priceless.

The next half-hour was a bit of a whirlwind in my memory. I just remember all hell breaking loose, have a faint recollection of being marched down a street with my feet off the ground, then waking up in a prison cell with my watch and money missing, and a Tom-and-Jerry-style lump on the top of my head that had combined with my alcohol intake to provide me with a unique headache. One look through the cell door confirmed the minor error that had led me to this predicament. All the policemen running the prison were exactly like normal British bobbies from the waist up, and from the boot-tops down, but with white skirts where the smart black strides should have been. This was their genuine uniform.

The Captain was waking me, although so far I hadn't managed to get my head on to the same wavelength as his words. When I did tune in, it didn't sound good.

'Before I bail you out, I have a few matters I wish to make clear to you,' he said pointedly. 'You have been in trouble too often. This trip has about eight more weeks to run, and if you come to my attention once more for ANY reason WHATSOEVER, I will be filing a report to the cadet training officer recommending an extra three months' sea-time on your cadetship. Understand? Right. So let's have less of it. More work, less horseplay.'

I tried to get myself together to explain that I didn't go out *looking* for trouble – it came bouncing up to me round every corner like an unwanted puppy. Not my fault. I was a victim of circumstances, me. But my voice wouldn't work. My words came out as a series of gurgles and belches, at which the Captain shook his head and tutted. He signed a couple of forms for my release and stalked out.

Keeping out of trouble was now a high priority as it carried a three-month extra sea-time penalty, which was to be avoided at all costs. I was determined to start afresh and keep way, way away from anything or anyone smelling remotely of trouble. The problem with this resolve was that ALL the lads on the ship ponged to high heaven, so my avoidance routine began that night.

There was a major drink-up going on in the bar, with a lot of very seedy people from Fiji's substantial low-life invited. I crept out nice and early and steered well clear. I went up the road for a blameless walk, then curled up in my bunk with an educational book at 10.30. I listened for a while to the whooping and hollering, and the cries of ladies of the night, but before long the book was over my face and I was snoring directly on to page four. The ship was on the home stretch now, so thoughts of England were looming large in everyday life, and it was not surprising to find my dreams full of the green and pleasant, the brown and frothy, and the nearest and dearest. The sweet, innocent dreams of a lad who didn't realise how hard people were working on his behalf as he slept . . .

You probably remember the fate of NotNorman, KiloWatt and Gonad in Melbourne when an alleged woman by the name of Phil forcibly introduced them to the delights of public sex in the ship's bar, while I, in stark contrast, squeezed myself through a hole that was too small for me. You may also remember that Big Phil's industry represented the first-trippers' cherry-popping, and that this inauguration, as *Sesame Street* would have put it, was generously brought to us by bar profits, the bonhomie of the lads, the colour red, and the words 'big', 'hideous' and 'all-consuming'. You do? Good. Then those of you who are particularly on the ball will also have thought 'Wait a minute, surely these highly responsible British officers are not going to let Windy get away with an entirely complete and untarnished cherry?' And you would be absolutely right. While the rest of the world slouched around enjoying itself that fine evening, those proud lads were putting in some extra hours with pride and dedication. They put themselves out to whatever extent was necessary to secure the services of six of the largest Fijian women the island had ever produced. They had spared no expense in getting them well tanked up in the bar, and had struck a simple but effective deal with them.

BLUE ROAD

In essence, the deal went like this: any of the aforementioned women (hereafter referred to as the parties of the first part) who could demonstrably extract spermatozoa from the party of the second part (that's me), would receive handsome remuneration for her efforts from the parties of the third part (the boys in the bar).

Once the parties of the first part were clear about the sums involved and the means of accessing these funds, they were keen to get on with the job, and it dawned upon each of the individual members of the party of the first part that the earliest to work over the party of the second part would have the easiest job squeezing out some remuneration. In fact, experienced girls that they were, the parties of the first part were concerned that the party of the second part might not be physically capable of providing enough deliveries for all six members of the party of the first part to get paid, so, working on the reasonable assumption that only the first of them to get busy could be sure of getting paid, the parties of the first part threw their drinks to one side and to roars of approval from the parties of the third part, began a thunderous stampede for the cabin of the party of the second part in order to get first bash at the party of the second part's parts.

Such was their enthusiasm for their work that they came through the door as if it wasn't there. I was actually thinking about my mother when the door was knocked down. After all, I was only seventeen, so a bit of homesickness was inevitable, and thoughts of my mum and crazy family were deep and frequent. So when the door hit the floor, my first thought was that this was mummy, rushing to bring me my early morning cup of tea. I reached out for it with sleep in my eyes. The next thing I knew my entire world consisted exclusively of Fijian womanhood. Folds and folds of it. An all-engulfing sea of blubber and lips was setting about me like a kid in a lollipop factory.

For the sake of decency, I shall not describe the ins and

outs, so to speak. A blow by blow account, if you will, would not advance our knowledge of the world, nor indeed would a description of what I looked like or how sore I was several hours later when the last one – after an epic battle – scuttled off to pick up her salary. What I will tell you, however, is that the Captain, returning during the height of my ordeal from a highly civilised shippers' dinner party in the town, was distinctly unimpressed. He became curious when he heard crowd scenes echoing round the corridor. As he walked on to my landing, he saw a splintered and damaged door torn from its hinges and cast aside like a used cadet, and as he approached the cabin from which the door had been torn he became anxious at the sounds of a desperate struggle, along with the unearthly squelching noises of a man with wet fingers drowning in a sea of balloons.

He stepped through into the cabin and switched on the light. In the two seconds that the light was on I saw – framed between the acres of black flesh around my head – his horrified countenance, quivering like an aspen, turn grey, then blue, then purple.

'I . . . I WARNED you, Mister Baboulene. This is THE LAST STRAW!' And with that, he stormed off.

Why was it that every time the Captain stumbled across me, he got the impression that my life was way more exciting and debauched than I could have ever managed through my own efforts? As it was, I had no choice but to stay where I was, which the Captain would surely read as a further example of my putting sinful pleasure before the needs of my career. Disgusting.

As we left Fiji and headed back out to sea, I carefully applied calamine lotion to my raisin-like testicles. I knew a report would soon be winging its way to London Office, and the party of the second part would be as severely dealt with as the party of the second part's parts.

Chapter 20

A Straight Bat

Windy volunteers for captaincy. Ships don't pass in the night for NotNorman. The battle to make leather meet willow.

There is a word that strikes at the very core of a true Englishman's being. It stirs his blood and inflames his passion. It rouses him to bid farewell to his family, link arms with his fellow countrymen, take up his weapons and fight the good fight to the bitter end for Queen and country. No other word in the English language is quite as powerful. And that word is . . .

'Cricket,' said Sparky. 'Does anyone here know anything about cricket?'

Now I happen to be rather good at cricket. To me, it is fire and brimstone, hope and glory, love and death all rolled into one. So it was to my utmost astonishment that everyone in the bar turned away from the man as if he'd asked whose round it was. They averted their eyes and tried to hide in their beer cans. I must have misheard. Surely the mere mention of the great game – one of the very pillars of the British Empire – should bring them out of their seats to a man, champing at the bit to get out there and teach the upstarts a lesson? I can only suppose that my shipmates were suffering a malaise in tune with our national team; despite the fact that only the English *truly* understand cricket, it seems that nowadays any tinpot country with a population greater than eleven can beat us at it.

Well, I am not one to shrink from matters of national pride, and, being duly inflamed by the use of the 'C' word, I stood up with my eyes aglow and my hand in the air.

'Did you say cricket? Why yes, you know what, I'm really rather good at cricket.'

Sparky's face lit up. He clasped his hands and looked on me proudly as if I was a gift from heaven.

'Windy!' he said with worship in his voice. 'Stand tall, my friend, for thou art at last useful.'

He was obviously pleased with me, but for some reason I didn't feel enriched by his pleasure. He took my beer and placed it on the bar, snaked his arm around my shoulder and, having attached himself firmly, led me to the door. 'The Captain would like to see you in his office immediately. And Windy – thank you. The world is indeed a strange place.'

He was a man for whom the clouds had lifted, and I appeared to be the reason. The laughter rising from the bar as I climbed towards the Captain did nothing to ease my puzzlement. Besides which, the Captain was the last person I wanted to see.

'Baboulene?' He spat as I stood meekly in his doorway. 'I thought I told you you aren't allowed above the boat-deck. There had better be an exceptionally good reason for you to be here, or I will arrange for you to be brutally beaten. Twice. What the hell do you want?'

'Sparky said you wanted to see me, sir.'

'I most certainly do not! Why? Do you think I've gone mad or something? All I want from you is –' He stopped in mid-sentence and his face crumbled like that of a snowman in the rain. 'Oh, good grief. You're not my cricket man, are you?'

In the time it took him to interpret my 'at-your-service, you-can-trust-me' wink, he went from an irritated but authoritative Captain, to a shattered shadow of a man. I was put out by his reaction. I didn't feel I was getting a fair trial.

'Actually, I'm really rather good at cricket,' I said indignantly.

The Captain sighed. 'Didn't anybody else volunteer? Nobody at all?'

As I shook my head he left his desk and went on his habitual circumnavigation of the day room (followed shortly by his clothes), holding a half-dozen of his pendulous chins in his hand while he tut-tutted his course around me. Suddenly, he came to a decision.

'All right, Baboulene. It seems you're my only hope. Let me explain. Global Link has had a presence in Tonga for over one hundred years. We own the land, the businesses and all the trade deals. Everyone works for Global Link. We brought cricket with us, and taught it to the locals. They now have three teams, all fed up with playing each other, so they challenge any Global ship that comes alongside to a game of cricket. And it's deadly serious. You are not a serious person, Baboulene, but cricket is a serious matter, and for a Global Link team to be beaten is unthinkable. They have just Morsed us across the challenge, and we must accept. You will organise a team and you will beat them. Now I realise you may be tempted to drop me in it by throwing the game because you are on a charge at present, so, to give you a little motivation I will do a deal with you. You win this game, and the report is forgotten. You lose, and it goes off to London the same day. Tell any man who refuses to participate that I wish to see him immediately. They might change their minds. Understand?'

I understood, all right. This was a great deal. I could beat these Tongan types standing on my head – knock up a century or two, then bowl them all out single-handed – *and* I was getting some power over the lads. This would be a cinch. An enjoyable way of showing some islanders how the game should be played, and getting off report! I agreed heartily, gave the Captain a broad grin to inspire him with my confidence, and – practising a cover drive every third step – strolled off to do some recruiting.

I was pleased to find that my fellow Englishmen were all properly impassioned by the idea of a game of cricket, (at least, they were after being asked to visit the Captain) and pretty soon I had a motley assortment asking me if I minded them taking beer with them to the long boundary, and if they could be excused if they had a note from their mums. I realised that this merry banter was all part of a positive team spirit, and chose not to discourage them. I may be a tough master, but I know when to give the lads their heads. My suggestion that we spend a degree of our spare time practising was met with the same levity, but I decided against forcing them. I didn't want to dampen their confidence. Besides, I only needed them to make up the numbers while I got on with the business of the day. I was as good as home free.

I won't bore you with the details regarding how beautiful Nuku'alofa, the capital of Tonga, is. You can take that as read, but I must impart to you the details of one prominent aspect of the view to the shoreside. I was on fo'c'sle stand-by (again), and as I admired the view, one particularly curvy topographical feature waved at me and smiled. I couldn't believe my eyes, but there was no mistake. As soon as I could get away, I legged it for the cadets' accommodation.

'NotNorman! NotNorman!' I burst into his room and woke him up. 'Guess who's on the quayside awaiting clearance to return to your loving arms?'

'Eh?' said NotNorman. He was never quite up to my pace. 'What are you prattling on about?'

'Cindy!' I said, shaking him. 'It's Cindy. She must have flown all the way here to be with lucky old you! HA!'

'Oh Christ,' he said flopping heavily back into his pillow. 'You are *joking*, aren't you?'

You may be surprised by this reaction because the last you heard of these two, they were slushing pathetically around the Australian coastline unable to bear being apart for as long as it took to get undressed again. I must apologise for not bringing you up to date on the latest gossip, but you understand, we were not expecting to see Cindy again. You see, sailors' romances tend to become very intense very quickly. Two people safe in the knowledge that they only have a limited time in which to run the full gamut of love's lifecycle before being torn apart forever, tend to fall more deeply in love more quickly than those who have to face practical realities – such as the prospect of being together till death do they part. So NotNorman had safely fallen as completely in love with Cindy as she had with him, and a deeper love (for one week only) you could not find.

The flaw, however, was that Cindy was not a sailor. She didn't realise that the ship's departure was traditionally the end of love's great journey, and she mourned NotNorman's leaving as the end of her life. She moped about, wringing her hands and imploring the moon like a tragic Shakespearian thesp. NotNorman on the other hand, was enjoying a little peace and quiet, and looking forward to another deep and meaningful three-day-forever in the next port. He was relieved to get away. He and Cindy had been together for weeks, which is really quite unnatural when one is seventeen, and he often spoke of this romantic experience in the grave tones of a man who has been to the brink.

So he'd hung in there for the last few days in Australia, safe in the knowledge that circumstances would sort out his problems for him. He'd been pleased to avoid the unpleasant task of splitting up with her, but we reap what we sow in this life, and now here she was, waiting on the quay for chapter three of their great love story in the full belief that her NotNormie would be as chuffed as a train that she had made such strenuous efforts to be with him again.

'So whatcha gonna do?' came the obvious question from Gonad as NotNorman paced the bar chewing his bottom lip.

'Well,' said Notters, working the thing through reasonably, 'I shall have to be honest with the poor girl. I must tell her it's all over, that I don't love her, and that she must go back to Australia. No point in any further deceit – it only causes grief and heartache. I shall bite the bullet and let her down gently. Cruel to be kind, and all that.'

'Definitely the right decision,' I said, and I admired his fortitude.

But once the customs procedures had been attended to and NotNorman got close enough to Cindy to see how happy her breasts were to see him, his resolve left him as if it was being physically drained from his feet. He wimped out of his 'cruel-to-be-kind' routine, and acted as if he was exceptionally pleased to see her. Nothing short of a rifle under the left ear could have got him to tell her the truth, so on the first night in Tonga, NotNorman and Cindy sucked each other's faces as if nothing had changed.

The next day I took him to one side.

'I thought you were going to knock her on the head?' I accused. '"Let her down gently" you said. "Cruel to be kind" you said. What you actually meant was you'd shag her for a couple more days, then send her a note from Panama, right?'

'Well, that's not exactly how I'd put it,' he replied sheepishly, 'but there's no point in spoiling her holiday, is there? I'll tell her just before we go.'

BLUE ROAD

I don't know. The youth of today have no moral fibre. You could tell NotNorman had never played cricket. Cricket engenders a more upstanding personality. Maybe the game would do him some good.

On the day of the cricket match we arrived at the ground – a tenderly manicured, pristine baize of grass overlooked by a pavilion that looked as if it had been airlifted from Surrey and placed untouched into this Pacific island – to find a fairly good crowd had gathered, mostly consisting of respectful Tongans eager to see an exhibition from representatives of a real live empire in full swing. We looked smart in our uniform whites and the pads supplied by our hosts, and once I'd seen the ramshackle bunch we were up against, I felt we were in for a pleasant afternoon. I smelt the air; it tasted of victory.

We won the toss, and I chose to bat first. Cricket is a game of psychology, you see; I was in at number one, so the impact of my knocking up a wholesome score would take the zing out of their best bowlers, frustrate them tactically, and demoralise them before they got into bat. You know, a five-day cricket match can be fundamentally all over within the first 20 minutes if you get the psychology right. I don't suppose they understood the subtlety of my approach, but we rarely appreciate how we are being manipulated by our superiors.

I strode out to the crease, swinging my bat and acknowledging the reverent ripple of applause from the gathered throng. The sun was high, the light was good, and I was looking forward to a bit of fun. I took up my position at the crease and was surprised that the opposition didn't immediately set about rearranging their field. I am left-handed, and normally, as I line up middle-and-off with the umpire, a certain degree of logistical shuffling takes place in the field. This lot either did not *know* what to do, or else they were not taking the game at all seriously. From the amount of unseemly merriment abroad, I assumed a bit of both. Either way, they were fielding in couples (presumably to facilitate a cosy chat), another sign that we were going to romp home.

A hush fell over the ground as the umpire indicated the first over. I locked horns with the bowler – a long, chocolate-brown figure – the classic shape of a pace bowler. He held eye contact and I nodded knowingly at him. They would certainly have pitched their best bowler in against me, and this was he. I knew what to expect here: it was definitely going to be pace. Pure speed. They were making the classic mistake; pace balls run straighter. I would use his pace against him, and was determined to be merciless from the first ball.

He turned at about thirty paces from the wicket, took six little pigeon steps as he curled his fingers about the ball, then dropped his nose to the ground and broke into a run like a bull charging a matador. It was definitely going to be pace. About halfway through his run-up his legs were a blur and his top half began to lean backwards until the back of his head was shaving the grass behind him. It was *definitely* going to be . . . the ball whistled past my ear, cleared the wicket-keeper and reached the boundary behind me with one bounce. A stunned silence fell over everyone in the ground. The only noise was a high-pitched whimpering sound (which people later claimed came from me), followed closely by a sickening thud and agonised cries from the spectator who had just taken 200 miles an hour off the pace of a cricket ball using only his kneecap. I couldn't make out words from his howls, but as he hopped around hugging his knee to his chest, the gist of it got across and the group of spectators positioned around him were quick to respond. Working on the basis that future bombshells of this ferocity would be manifesting themselves in the neighbourhood, they gathered up their blankets, picnics, kneecaps and children and hurried off to safer vantage points.

I looked at the bowler, whose run-up had brought him to within a foot of me. He chewed his tongue with a vulgarity I did not care for and snorted through flared nostrils. I had to keep calm. Cricket is a game of psychology; it was imperative at this point that I didn't show any fear to this bowler. It may have been a devilishly fast delivery, but he'd just given us four runs, so to some extent honours were even. I got up, dusted off my trousers, looked around for my bat and retrieved it with a nonchalant air from over near the umpire at square. I eyed the man again. He licked his finger and rubbed it on the ball with lewd deliberation before turning and heading off once more towards his launch pad.

I didn't expect any variation – this man clearly had only one gear – and I didn't get any. He motored into the stumps, leant back and released the pin. I didn't see the ball at all, but the smell of sulphur in the air told me it had been in the vicinity, and the dull thud as the ball found a weak point in the sight screens behind me told me we were a further four runs to the good. It was a scary place to be standing, but at this rate, as long as I could keep my head on my shoulders, we would win without playing a ball.

My memories of cricket at school – where my bat flashed like a scythe in the sunlight, and fielders became exhausted as I distributed them to all points of the compass – were now but a distant fantasy. This guy might only have one delivery, but I wasn't sure that I even wanted to connect with one of these rockets. I needn't have worried. On his third delivery I saw a patch of turf explode about four feet in front of me and then a cloudburst of matchsticks rained about my head. He'd caught a criminally jammy bounce outside the off stump and what should have been another four runs to me cut back viciously and uprooted all of my stumps. I was out. I had been responsible for eight runs (though I had yet to see the ball) and my bat remained a pure and unsullied virgin.

I walked off in disgust. This wasn't cricket. What is the point in pure pace? Bloody foreigners will never understand cricket. I mean, anyone can just bowl *pace*, but that's not *cricket*, is it?

The home team reorganised their approach for our next three batsmen. They kept the same unsporting bowling technique, but repositioned the fielders. Working on the sad basis that we were highly unlikely ever to make a stroke, and in order to try and prevent the bowler from directly bowling us a winning score, they scattered half a dozen secondary wicket-keepers in the area behind the unfortunate guy in the traditional location. So the script took on a new predictability: bowler fires off another cannon, batsman hides his face behind raised thigh and forearm, if the stumps don't fly and the keeper with the gloves on misses it, then the line of extra keepers leap for cover too, and we are another four runs to the good.

By the time Giewy came in to bat at number six, we were 28 for 4, with all our runs scored by their bowler. None of our team had yet made contact with the ball, and all ten of the opposition fielders were now queued up in the area behind the wickets. I looked at Giewy and felt pangs of guilt and sorrow. The poor goon was grinning inanely, and didn't appear to have any idea what he was letting himself in for. Admittedly, the bowling looked calmer from the sidelines than it did looking down the barrel, but surely he had some idea of the dangers involved?

As the bowler's nose lifted off from the ground once

more and he began steaming in I could barely watch. Giewy was standing there as if he was waiting for a bus. I shut my eyes as their loose cannon shot off again. There was a spark like lightning from just outside off stump, a cry of 'GIEW!' and the sound of leather on willow for the first time that day.

Giewy had hit the ball!

I stared in disbelief as the ball rolled off gently across the uninhabited grasslands around mid-off and over the rope for four runs. Giewy looked as shocked as anybody. It must have been a fluke. The law of averages must have stepped in: if you leave a bat hanging around in that general locality for long enough, the ball must hit it sometime. You could hear the buzz ripple through the crowd. This guy could hit the ball!

The bowler prepared again – looking angrier than ever – and Giewy took up his stance. Another delivery cannonballed in . . . and once again, Giewy did a little fishing movement outside the off stump, and cracked the ball off for another four runs.

To cut a long story short – and I don't wish to dwell on this – Giewy was a revelation. He stood there for half an hour scoring heavily as the sweaty paceman worked his way through a steady stream of Giewy's partners. We were all out for 60. Giewy was undefeated on 24, the rest were scored by their bowler.

As Giewy came off, he was surrounded by admirers from all sides. The lad was hailed as a sporting genius. They wanted to know why he'd never turned professional, how old he was when he started, who his heroes were, how he contrived his unorthodox grip, and how often he practised. He laughed falsely and said he didn't ever practise, he'd never played the game before and that he'd always thought it looked a bit simple. Lying dog. I couldn't explain what I'd seen, but one thing was for sure, it had nothing to do with skill on Giewy's part. Bastard. But now it was MY turn to be the hero. It was our turn to bowl.

Now if there's one thing I *can* do, it's bowl a cricket ball. Cricket is a game of psychology, you see. A battle of wits. A duel between great minds. It's all well and good to be able to sling the thing at 200 miles an hour, but to play at the top level requires strategy and subtlety. A truly great bowler takes men out by monkeying with their minds and egos. Sure, a pace-ball is good to have in the armoury, but it is a *complete* player who can use a combination of several balls to confuse and disorientate before delivering the *coup de grâce*. *That* is what real cricket is all about. So as I arranged an attacking field (it's always good to start aggressively) I was more than happy to see that the first batsman up was my talentless, flukey adversary – the opposition fast-bowler. Our eyes locked once more, but this time, I was in the driving seat and he was my helpless victim. He tried to look casual, spitting beetle-nut and rubbing his crotch, but I knew he would be worried deep down.

I've always fancied that receiving a ball from me must be akin to unexpectedly receiving a World War II Spitfire over the garden fence. Descending out of the sun with speed, skill, control and deadly accuracy – one bad decision and you're dead. Nobody has ever told me any different, so I suppose this is probably a fair assessment. I bowl left arm round the wicket off a short run-up that begins from a concealed position. I crouch down entirely behind the umpire before every delivery. Cricket is a game of psychology, you see, and a batsman always feels less sure if he can't see your grip on the ball. In my case, he couldn't see any of me at all. I then strike quickly. Two paces and I am up to speed. I leap high above the ground, coiling into a power-packed time-bomb hanging ten feet in the air. I then uncurl in a single lightning movement, and unleash a ball that is turning in the air like a jet-propelled butterfly. It is virtually unplayable.

Many batsmen freeze in horror, and even the best can see that this is a fearsome delivery. They know it is fast, but they also know it is spinning furiously. I pitch it short, so they have no chance on the front foot. A stroke player with any knowledge of cricket drops on to the back foot to give himself as much time as possible to adjust to the effects of the spin. I usually deliver two which cut back, and occasionally get lucky with an LBW, then I bowl the third out of the back of my hand so it whips through dead ahead off the bounce. It's a certainty for an off stump or a thick edge and a catch in the slips.

From my first delivery it was immediately apparent that my adversary was not worthy of the contest. I was playing on a totally different plane to him, and he stood there as naive and innocent as a newborn babe. He didn't *know* how good my delivery was. He didn't *know* that the most effective response was to drop on to the back foot and play a defensive shot as best he could. Out of sheer lack of knowledge he came galloping down the wicket, caught my ball on the full toss and walloped it for six over mid-on. He had no clue whatsoever.

He came running down the wicket on the second ball too, and got four through extra cover. The man was unbearable. He obviously hadn't the first idea how to play cricket. I had to drop to his level and rethink. I pitched the third one even shorter, in order to trap him on his ridiculous gallop up the wicket, but he must have run out of puff, because this time, he stayed back. This gave him an age to watch my delivery sit up nicely before cracking it off for a six. It was pathetic. The crowd were applauding warmly, but anyone with any knowledge would have known that were he playing properly, he would have been out by now.

I outsmarted him with the fourth ball. My class shone through. I hid behind the umpire, danced out, coiled and sprang. He ran down the wicket, caught the ball on the full toss and gave it 500 miles an hour towards square leg. I looked towards square leg hopefully – and there was Giewy, staring gormlessly off into space as the fireball flew into his midriff. His cheeks ballooned and he doubled up on to the deck, motionless with his head between his feet, ten yards back from where he'd been standing. A worried crowd rushed over to him. They rolled him over and were horrified at the appalling sight that met their eyes. They gasped and turned away, unable to look at the carnage before them. But he was fine. He looked like that all the time. Soon enough he was up again, posing around like a twat and saying how he was happy to play on. He plucked the ball from his belly-button and the penny dropped. It was a clean catch! Using only his belly, Giewy had caught the man out!

The next few overs featured me from one end and Patch (displaying a laughable style) from the other. They reached 40 for the loss of only the one wicket. The crowd was beginning to get behind them, a carnival atmosphere developing around the ground, and things were looking bleak. I decided a change was in order and thought it best to swap Patch for someone fresh. I pointed past Giewy to Cranners who was from Surrey – surely *he* had picked up something from growing up in the spiritual home of cricket. But Giewy thought I had pointed to him, and trotted across, wagging his tail. He picked up the ball and gangled off to bowl. I tried to call him off, but he couldn't hear me over the frenzied crowd cheering his name. Patch stopped me from running after him. 'Aw, let the guy have a bowl. He looks pretty stylish!'

It was too late anyway. Giewy was scuffing his feet like an impatient bull (whose mother was a vulture). He was already into his preparations, and 'stylish' was not the word that immediately sprang to mind. He rubbed the ball against his crotch for a while – with a crooked look on his face and no idea of the purpose of this technique – then gave a snorting laugh like a dastardly villain. If cricket was a game of psychology, Giewy was the patient. He didn't commence his delivery with the mandatory half-dozen pigeon steps, in the style of Botham, Snow and Lilley. He commenced with an effort reminiscent of a pregnant woman running for a bus. His face, pointing skyward, puffed and grimaced with the effort of it all, and before long the entire Giewy contraption was up to its hectic maximum speed of around two miles per hour – markedly slower than the pace at which a pregnant woman could have walked it.

As Giewy puffed and grunted his way feverishly towards the crease the batsman couldn't believe his eyes. He rose from his preparation and looked around for support, but all eyes were on Giewy's inexorable advance. The sound of children crying reached my ears as Giewy's shirt buttons gave up the unequal struggle and his belly broke free to express itself. And he was still only halfway there. As Giewy entered his final approach he began to spin both his arms in great windmill circles. Faster and faster they spun, like propeller engines starting up. And as his arms swung, his head wobbled from side to side to prevent his ears getting caught.

His arms were a whirling blur, his head was an oscillating haze, his legs pumped and jolted and his face was contorted with effort. Women covered their eyes and strong men comforted the elderly as he approached the line. From somewhere in the stroboscopic mass of Giewy the ball emerged. All heads turned skyward as it shot 100 feet in the air. It was what we used to call a 'donkey drop' at school. The batsman would have to contrive something like a tennis player's overhead smash to sort this one out, but he was finding it hard to take his eyes off Giewy, who remained out of control and was heading his way, so he was not concentrating when the ball bounced two feet in front of him, beat his feeble defensive stroke, and sailed through to take out his centre stump. Giewy had clean bowled him!

Now I don't wish to bore you with the details of the next 30 minutes, and I hesitate to dwell on the fact, but Giewy was a revelation. Every delivery was different – although they all featured the same alarmingly bizarre twin-armed, windmill-wobble run-up – and by the time he got the last man out they had only reached 54. Incredibly, we had WON! We left the opposition crying and complaining and consulting the rule books, but it was fair and square, and we headed back victoriously to the ship to celebrate another foe vanquished in the name of Great Britain.

'Well, well, well,' said the Captain, 'so we won, did we?'

What was he talking about, 'we'? He didn't even turn up to watch.

'Yes, sir. A tough tactical battle, but the best team won through in the end.'

'Indeed? I'm sorry I couldn't make it. I hear young Giewy was our star man. Is that right?'

I curled my lip.

'I can't take anything away from the lad, sir. He did exactly as I told him, and it paid off. For a time I think he got a little uncertain, but I stood firm and he believed in me, and between us we carried it off, sir.'

'Indeed. So, Giewy's a cricketer, is he?'

I gritted my teeth.

'He, er, he had a good day, sir, but no man is an island. There's more than one link in a chain and all that. Teamwork did it, sir. It's what I always say: an army is only as good as its general, sir.'

He stopped and looked at me.

'Do you really think so, Baboulene? Do you really think that?'

Now we were getting somewhere. I puffed my chest out proudly.

'Indeed I do, sir. A group of the finest individuals are as useless as tripe unless a strong man is at the helm. A team has to be guided from the front by a man they believe in, and I firmly believe that is the case here, sir.'

He looked kind of weird and sat down again, looking at me all the while.

'Well, that's awfully kind of you to say so, Baboulene. I'm really touched. I thought we had a real problem with you, but this is marvellous. I'm pleased this game of cricket has caused you to see the sense in a rigid adherence to rank and discipline. I never thought I would see the day when a game of cricket could get through to the soul of an ignoramus such as yourself. Cricket's all about psychology, you know, and now you've seen the light, you'll find tremendous depths in such things. Cricket engenders a more upstanding personality, Baboulene, and I hope this little episode has gone some way towards maturing you. I'll put this report in the bin, and I hope to see you flower into officer material in what remains of this trip. Go and talk to Giewy about the lessons you've learned today. I feel sure he'll be able to help you up on to the new moral plane you've discovered.'

Good grief. The people I had to work with. I didn't

know whether to laugh or cry, but with the report in the bin, at least there was one monkey off my back.

Now, after such cheering events, I would like to be able to tell you that we all lived happily ever after. But it is my unpleasant duty to tell you that this was not the case. As we left Tonga some four days later, we still had the sticky matter of Cindy's unrequited love and the heavy weight of deceit upon NotNorman's droopy shoulders. He had not found it too hard playing the loving partner, and they were having such a lovely time that he couldn't bring himself to drop the bomb. I had to admit that it would take a tough man to top off a few days like those with the summary dismissal of a beautiful, loving, smiling, humorous young lady, so as the ship pulled out, nothing had changed.

'You *promised*,' I said, rebuking the deceitful chap. 'That poor girl is going to hold a candle for you until you get back to Australia, and did you shake the head and wave the finger? You did not! You said you'd tattoo her name on your forehead and request another ship to Oz as soon as we get home!'

'I know what I said. I just couldn't do it! We'll go straight to my cabin now and compose a letter and send a telegram and some flowers or something. I've got to get this sorted. I know it's cowardly, but there's no other way now.'

So as our mighty vessel headed for Samoa, NotNorman and I sat down and composed a letter and a telegram to send to Australia for poor Cindy to receive upon her return. The telegram and flowers were dispatched immediately, and the letter was sealed up, ready to send from Samoa. Then the dirty deed would be done and NotNorman would be free to continue his rotten, cowardly existence once more.

Chapter 21

Western Samoa

The officers murder motorbikes. Windy behaves illegally and finds a beautiful girl. Windy, International Spy, is caught in the act. Phillips crosshead jungle biking.

Western Samoa was a new style of island. It was large with a sizeable population, a beautiful capital called Apia, a mountainous central region, large areas of impenetrable jungle, and a motorbike rental agency – called 'Apia Bike Higher' – containing a cheerful, round-faced man who was smiley, helpful and genuine, and whom we instantly liked very much indeed. The price was very reasonable, although we each had to put down a $500 deposit, but we would get that back at the end – wouldn't we?

In no time at all we were a chapter of Hell's Angels. We were untamed and free. A pack of wild kids living close to the edge (on 50cc Hondas). We were rebels without a cause. Well, nearly. A couple of the lads had some shopping to do, and two needed to get back to the ship, so like children who would leave home if only they were allowed to cross the road, we put off our rebellion until later. We agreed to meet in a couple of hours for a beast-machine cruise jam that would seriously wake this island up.

A couple of hours suited me fine because I had a little personal business to attend to myself before I could pull on my leathers and Peter Fonda sneer. In Melbourne we had loaded a large and interesting wooden crate into one of the now-empty deep-tanks. The tank was then bolted back down, so whatever was inside was clearly top security. A conspicuously rich sleaze wearing a broad-rimmed black hat, sunglasses and a black trench-coat worn as a cloak had overseen the loading while sucking a large cigar. During the latter stages of securing the special consignment, he sleazed up to me. He spoke in a conspiratorial undertone and a false Italian accent.

'You wanna get yourself a liddle Christmas money, my friend?' he asked, relighting his cigar.

I narrowed my eyes. I knew the game.

'Maybe I do – and maybe I don't,' I looked to the left and right for earwigs. 'What's the blag, then, John?'

He stared straight ahead and spoke out of the corner of his mouth. He looked like one of the Ant Hill Mob.

'I'd like you to make a leedle delivery for me when you arrive in Western Samoa.' He handed me a piece of paper with a hand-drawn map, a convoluted address and the name 'Roly' on it. 'I want you to take ten bottles of whisky from that cargo we just loaded, and deliver them to Roly. He'll be expecting you.'

He slipped me a hundred dollars – a hundred dollars! – and said Roly would do the same upon successful delivery. I looked at the readies and decided that I was more than delighted to help this honest fellow out, and as he slunk off the ship like syrup down the side of the pot, I had the spring in my step of a man who is up on the day.

And now I was in Western Samoa with a motorbike and an attitude, it was a simple matter. I visited the cargo in deep-tank three with a spanner for the manhole cover – yes *that* manhole cover – but this time there were only four bolts as there was no need for a watertight seal. Some minor implements of destruction made short work of the wooden crate, I slipped the booty into a haversack, and walked blithely from the ship, whistling a cheery tune and smiling at everyone as if I'd be giving a sermon later that day. Soon enough I was riding high and fast into the outskirts of Apia with the haversack on my back, the warm wind in my hair and thoughts of a career in international espionage filling my mind once more.

The tarmac of Apia soon gave way to an unsealed track, and I climbed steeply for some time. Then I found the correct turning and eventually a sign indicating that the residence I was looking for was down a long driveway hacked out of the jungle to my right. When I say 'residence' I may be misleading you slightly. The address I had was:

'Seventh window along on the right-hand side of Temperance House. If there is a cross in the window, knock three times. If not, come back later.'

The unusual directions to the window had distracted me from the name of the place, but now as I approached it, I could see it was some sort of institution. If I had any idea what 'temperance' was, I might have understood entirely. It was not big and imposing as an English residential institution might be, it was modern and spread out like a giant bungalow, with carefully tended lawns fighting back the surrounding jungle.

I decided not to park the bike, but to ride directly round the side to facilitate a quick getaway, but as I rounded the side of the building – too fast – I had to swerve suddenly to miss someone, or to be more accurate, to miss an angelic vision of feminine excellence directly in my path. She had her hand to her mouth and was frozen in horror at the dangerous approach of a James Dean look-alike on a speeding motorbike. As I ploughed my bike into a bush and somersaulted over the handlebars I didn't take my eyes off her for a second. I was utterly in love, and the somersaults and airborne nature of my physical demeanour merely served to match my emotions. Her big eyes and open mouth – registering surprise and fear for my well-being in equal measure – and her long blonde hair flowed into every corner of my consciousness.

Fear not, my love, I thought as I flew through the air, *once I have landed, I'll be by your side to soothe the dread that hath seized thy troubled mind. I shalt mop thy brow and pat thy hand. I shalt – Ooof!*

I landed on my back – on a haversack full of bottles. I was winded like never before, and although physically unable to move, I was determined that the angel would meet a serious guy, on a secret mission, on a motorbike – not a chicken on a moped whining about how his bum hurt. I wanted to tell her I was Mr 'X' from British Intelligence – in Apia only for a few hours, but that I could just fit her in for one fiery lifetime of unceasing passion. The trouble was, I couldn't breathe.

She came running over and looked into my eyes. Good grief, she was beautiful. My first thought was to go for the old kiss-of-life routine by feigning unconsciousness. It would have been worth stopping my heart with a spanner for resuscitation from her. One kiss would jump start the oldest corpse on the planet, but my image as a rugged international spy would be shot so I thought I'd go for, 'Hi, my name's Bond. James Bond. You must be Heavenly Boobies.' I don't know why, but these words emerged into the open air as, 'Eeeaargh! Oh, bollocks!'

'Are you OK?' she purred, running her hand over my brow. Her touch fizzed on my forehead and shimmered through my entire body.

I was cured.

'Oh, er, yes, yes. Nothing really. Happens all the time.' I tried to get up but just wobbled about on the floor.

'What are all those bottles?' she asked. Her huge, enquiring eyes were full of innocence. She looked like a lamb asking the wolf what the shiny knife was for. I looked around me. The treacherous haversack had forsaken its load and the lawn of Temperance House was strewn with whisky bottles.

'Ah,' I said, 'special delivery. A kind of international deal. This kind of thing goes on all the time in the Secret Service. All very hush-hush, you know.'

I gave her a wink and nodded slowly. I was amazed to see that she was genuinely impressed. Her childlike expression gave away her age as about the same as mine rather than the early twenties that she looked.

'Wow!' she said. 'You were on a secret mission, and now I've ruined everything for you! Whatever can I do to put things right?'

My mind flooded with good ideas, but I kept my dignity.

'Well, I'm here for a couple of nights. You could let me take you out somewhere?'

Her eyes lit up. I could not believe her reaction.

'Oh yes! That *would* be exciting. We could go to Jazzies on your motorbike. Let's do your mission, then we can go to the beach on your hog!'

I felt it might be pushing my disguise a little far to pick her up on the fact that a spy like me does not 'do' a mission, and that a Honda 50 hardly represents a 'hog'. I also wanted to tell her that I didn't give a fig for the mission and that the trip to the beach should begin immediately, but for the sake of continuity, I simply stammered out some sort of agreement and began picking up bottles.

'What do we do now?' she said. 'You're the spy.'

I looked at her. Beauty with innocence. I was, to say the least, distracted.

'Oh, yes. We er . . . we knock on the window. Yes. That's it. Knock. Seventh window along, and there should be a cleavage in the . . . CROSS! I meant cross. There should be a CROSS in the window. Yip, this is the one, I'll give the secret knockers. KNOCK! Yes. That's it. Knock.'

I gave the knock, then stood staring at her like a rabbit in the headlights. Her eyes were mesmerising. I hadn't seen such a fascinatingly beautiful girl since . . .

'Yes? Hello? Can I help you?'

The window had opened and a myopic gentleman was disturbing our perfect relationship. I snapped back to international spy.

'Oh! Are you the man they call Kissy? ROLY! I mean Roly!'

He looked puzzled for a moment, but recovered fast.

'Yes, yes. Have you got the stuff?'

'Sure have – ten bottles! You got the money?'

'Too right I have! Pass that stuff in here quick-smart my beauty! I have *got* to get a snifter down me or I will *die*! And listen here, mate. There's forty bucks a bottle for each one on top of this lot you can get us. Here, love, cop this.' As I passed the bottles through the window (and calculated that I could retire on the proceeds if I could get the entire hold-full up here) he passed the money to my fiancée. I could see the excitement on her face as she joined in with our illegal activity, and I felt a definite bonding as she moved from being an incidental girl to an accomplice. Things were going extremely well.

'You've got a deal,' I said through the window. 'I'll try to get back up here with some more lovely big lips – BOTTLES – in the next day or two. I've only –'

'What in the blue BLAZES is going on round here?'

A new voice roared into the arena, and not one I particularly liked the sound of. The girl spun on her heel, then burst into fits of giggles with her hand in front of her mouth. She was not put off by this blot on the landscape, so I assumed he was one of the inmates. I thought it would be most impressive if I came down hard on him.

'Quiet!' I said. 'If you want some too, you'll have to get your money out. Place your order with the girl, here, and I'll see what I can do.'

He turned purple and shook like a space rocket just before take off.

'I don't know who you are, my lad, but let me tell you: many others have tried to gain financially through the illegal transfer of smuggled alcohol into my sanatorium, and all have ended up in the prison, but none of them went so far as to try and embroil my daughter in their sordid affairs! I shall track you to the ends of the earth, my boy, and shall mete out the fiercest punishment the name of God will allow!' As he said these words, he picked up a stick and started towards me. 'And for starters, I shall flay you to within an inch of your life!' He was shaking all over and screaming his head off.

Despite this unnerving outburst, it was still vitally important for me to look cool in front of this girl. He was not a young man, so I felt confident that I could keep out of his reach. I leapt on the bike and set off down the drive with the old buzzard in stick-waving pursuit. Once I had led him about 20 yards, I doubled back past him and headed for his daughter. I circled round her three or four times.

'I'll be in touch,' I said, 'as soon as I can. I don't know where and I don't know when, but I'll be back.' I picked a flower from a passing bush and delivered it to her as a romantic touch. She clutched the flower to her bosom and swooned as I blew her a kiss, narrowly dodged the wheezing stick-waver, and with a dismissive, 'Up yours, Grandad!' I disappeared up the drive.

I had never been so callous to anybody in my entire life, but he was old enough for it not to require an act of great bravery and I didn't care what I had to do to impress this girl. And she had been so impressed! That was probably why I liked her so much. No girl knows from where her prince will come, but when he turns up on a motorbike with a sack of goodies for the needy like some sort of latter-day Robin Hood, she knows she's got a good 'un. It was this thought that made me realise just what a great guy I was, and I could see that now I had a slightly mean streak, I was going to have even more problems with girls swooning around me. I vowed to put up with it.

This said, I hadn't laid a finger on her and didn't even know her name, or how to contact her. How could I get back to her? There was no way I was going to knock on the door of Temperance House – something told me I'd get a frostier reception than a pair of pants in a nudist colony. I thought about the impression the stick-waver must have of me. I'd propositioned his daughter, corrupted her into illegal dealings and sold illicit whisky to the inmates of his health farm. I liked the image, and made a mental note to buy a studded leather jacket at the next possible opportunity.

I agonised over what to do about my blonde bombshell for over an hour, and rode back up to the entrance of Temperance House four times. The demonic threats of the stick-waver had obviously hit home to some extent – even now I was a tough guy – because I couldn't bring myself to ride in. I resigned myself to a strategic retreat. It was almost one o'clock, and we were supposed to be meeting back at the ship to go off on our motorbike tour of the island, so I headed for home trying to ride a bike in the pose of *The Thinker*.

I have no idea how many lives I was dealt when Saint Peter put me in to bat, but I knocked a good half-dozen off the tally during the afternoon's biking. There were nine of us, on six extremely unsafe mopeds, and none of the six – or the nine – was roadworthy. The competitive spirit began on the very first gravel road, and we lost two bikes at the first corner. They went through a hedge into a field and we spent 20 minutes trying to get them back through. At 30 miles an hour the bikes and their incumbents had ghosted through the hedge like it wasn't there and – but for a few leaves floating serenely to the road – there was no evidence of the visitation in the composition of the hedge, but now, without the benefit of momentum, neither bikes nor personnel could find their way back again.

Sparky, NotNorman and Benny the Dog decided in the end that they did not *need* to come back through the hedge, and that the rest of us – having the road at our disposal in order to get up the necessary speed – should imitate their actions and pass through to their side. We told them not to be so ridiculous, but they told us that it was fun; a bit like a fairground ride. We couldn't see each other, so an argument developed with Sparky, NotNorman and Benny the Dog jumping up and down in order to harangue us over the hedge, and the rest of us standing on our bikes, peering back over the hedge shaking our fists and ranting back at them.

Eventually a coin was tossed, and despite the inverted logic, we were honour-bound to attain the appropriate velocity and ride our bikes through the hedge to their side. As I approached the barrier at 30 miles an hour, I remember trying to figure out how we'd arrived at the belief that this was a sensible course of action, but we all piled our bikes into the hedge nevertheless, and reappeared on the far side.

So we were half an hour into our motorbike tour, still in sight of the ship, standing around like sheep in a field unable to get out. Only half the bikes would start, and we all looked as if we'd been dragged through a hedge forwards. Eventually, we got all the bikes going again, and bumped off unsteadily round the field looking for a gate. It transpired that there was a bumpy jungle track leading up into the mountains, and we took to it at ill-advised speed.

It became obligatory, if you came close enough to one of the other bikes (usually during suicidal overtaking expeditions) to attempt to knock its rider into the thick jungle on either side, so after a further ten minutes of quite ludicrously dangerous malarkey we stopped once more by the side of the track. We'd each come off once or twice, and now we'd lost Giewy. He'd last been seen doing a handstand. On the handlebars of his bike. At 30 miles an hour. On a machine that was already eight feet off the ground and heading off at right-angles to the track.

'Giiiieeeeeeeeeeeeeeeewwwhhhhhaaaaaaaaaa!'

BOOF! He disappeared through the thick foliage into the jungle and all went eerily quiet. Search as we might, we couldn't find him. I was in pain with a mixture of injuries and laughter at the antics of the ride thus far, and when the bedraggled Giewy emerged wobbly-kneed from the undergrowth clutching nothing but a set of handlebars I just about keeled over. His motorbike was a complete write-off, partly because it had wrapped itself round a tree like a frightened child clinging to its father's leg, and partly because it could not be extricated from the tangle of plant-life that had adopted it forever. That was Giewy's $500 down the drain.

All was not lost for him, however, because NotNorman – who had sustained impressive injuries during a piked, double-back-somersault with three-and-a-half twists earlier on the track – no longer had the stomach for the ride and was going to walk back to the ship. He was more than happy to hand over his death-trap to Giewy.

Soon the eight of us were bouncing along through thick

jungle on narrow, uneven paths. Bushes swiped at my steering arm and overhanging branches thumped me in the chest as we flew through the air after hitting stumps and roots on the jungle floor. It was lethal.

Before long the novelty of multiple injuries began to wear a little thin, and the bikes, as we steered them from one crushing disaster to the next, were beginning to wise up and think twice about doing their masters' bidding. But spirits were still high because it was principally Giewy who continued to suffer above all others. This time the bike had flung him skyward, waited patiently for him to return to earth, then jumped on his head. Giewy got up, cut to ribbons but unbowed as ever by his umpteenth injury. The bike, however, had more sense than Giewy and, having failed to murder him, no longer saw any purpose in life.

We tried kind words and we tried shaking it ferociously. Then we tried wiggling wires around and switching switches on and off, but all to no avail. This would need some real engineering. Benny the Dog, as the senior engineer present, took charge. He was a man from a long line of engineers, with a formal degree in electrical engineering and eight years' shipboard engine-room experience. He took a good run-up and kicked it in the vitals. The bike immediately leapt into life and promised never to fail us again. Unfortunately, as we turned to congratulate Benny on his engineering prowess, the engine noise didn't level off and calm to idling speed, but built and built until it was roaring at the absolute top of its range, and would have committed suicide if Gonad hadn't had the good sense to cut off the petrol. The throttle was stuck open. Benny the Dog tinkered around for a while before announcing, 'Well, the good news is, I know how to fix it. The bad news is, I need a Phillips crosshead screwdriver.'

'Good grief,' said Patch, 'I thought your toolbox contained nothing but different-sized hammers!'

'Aye, well. If I had a hammer I might easily find a use for it, but the thing we need to fix this bike is a Phillips crosshead screwdriver, and we've as much chance of finding one here as we have of finding Giewy's brain.'

This analogy allowed us all to fully appreciate the gravity of the situation. We stood around the toppled charger proposing and rejecting creative but unworkable plans. We were, in the eloquent words of the Mancunian Benny, 'boggered'.

The best plan put forward was to tear further bits from the bike and try to cobble together some sort of tool from these amputations that *might* do the job of a Phillips crosshead screwdriver. Gonad and Benny the Dog set about this task, and the rest of us stood around pointing and giving them advice, until all of a sudden, a distraction was discovered.

'Giew!' cried Giewy, pointing up the jungle track. 'Gie-ew-ew!'

And there, about 30 yards away up the path, crouching behind suspicious eyes in the jungle undergrowth was some sort of pygmy. He was short and brown, carried a stick and was completely naked but for some kind of loincloth. A pucker, genuine, 24-carat pygmy, of just the specification Doctor Livingstone mixed with. I was amazed, but the others thought he was hilarious.

'HOW!' boomed Patch in his best Red Indian voice, saluting like an Indian chief. 'We come in peace!' Everybody laughed and I could see the pygmy tense up.

'Shut up, you lot,' I said firmly, 'or he'll bugger off. Let's take it nice and slowly.'

We quietened down and made smiling, friendly-type gestures. I was utterly fascinated, so I have to admit I was less than chuffed when Benny the Dog screwed the whole thing up just for the sake of a cheap joke. He stomped off up the path towards the little chap, waddling like a chimpanzee, and in a deep, patronising, Tonto-like voice called, 'Kemosabe, YOU HAVE PHILLIPS CROSSHEAD SCREWDRIVER?'

The laughter from the lads and the preposterous figure of Benny bearing down on him proved too much, and he disappeared instantly into the deep undergrowth, leaving not a speck of evidence that he'd ever been there at all. The fun was all over, so we returned to watching Gonad and the Dog and the ritual humiliation of the motorbike.

I was really angry with Benny for what he'd done – he was indeed a Dog, but, being the kind of international spy who had others do his fighting for him, I just laughed vigorously at his superb sense of humour and boiled up inside instead.

Eventually Benny the Dog had managed to fashion a sort of Phillips crosshead daffodil from the torn metal. He held it up proudly, then set about the bike with it. It was all very pretty, but didn't seem to help in any way when it came to undoing screws. Benny was sweating profusely and becoming steadily more brutal with both the tool he'd crafted and the patient. Suddenly he rose from his task, held his daffodil high in the air like a sacred object, gnashed his teeth and questioned its parenthood, then drop-kicked it deep into the undergrowth. This caused a good deal of unrest both amongst those present and apparently amongst his toes. It had taken some time to create this daffodil, and great hopes were resting on its utilisation. Now, in a moment of enraged impetuosity, it was gone forever. Then, over the noise of the ensuing row, Giewy's whining voice could be heard once more.

'Giew!'

And sure enough, back in his place up the path, was the

pygmy. This time, however, he strode confidently down the path towards us. I thought he was going to produce a blowpipe and kill us all for being so obnoxious, but as he drew closer, we could see he was proffering . . . a Phillips crosshead screwdriver.

During the minute it took Benny to fix the bike, the pygmy didn't talk to us. We knew he could speak English because he'd understood Benny the Dog's request for a screwdriver, but he stood inscrutably quiet, ignoring our questions and simply waited. We felt fairly embarrassed because we'd been rude and patronising, and he'd still lent us the tool. As he walked back up the path, I called after him.

'Why – why won't you talk to us?'

'Because,' he said, turning and staring back down the path at us, 'you are only dreaming.' Then he disappeared forever.

Chapter 22

A Watery Grave

Notes on picking up girls in church. How to drown rather than be called names. Adventures underground. The Ascension: Windy rises from the dead. A new career as a mantelpiece ornament?

That evening we were counting the cost. Major surgery was going on in both the ship's hospital (to rescue survivors from the *Global Wanderer*'s motorbike display team) and in the engine-room (to rescue $500 deposits).

I was working the evening, which disturbed me immensely. Apart from the fact that it was Christmas Eve, I wanted to get out there and retrieve my fair maiden from the clutches of her evil father. It would probably be difficult to prize her out on Christmas Day, so time was running short. I could only hope she would see my non-appearance as supreme coolness and fancy me all the more by Boxing Day.

Even for the lads who didn't have to work Christmas Eve, it didn't feel very seasonal. Not so much as a steady drizzle or a massive credit card bill for a true festive atmosphere, and with temperatures soaring, the bookies were offering long odds on a white Christmas. Even so, the lads were becoming hyped up like five-year-olds at the prospect of Santa delivering a few beers, but were all agreed that the resource distinctly noticeable by its absence was – women.

Jinx was summoned and a strategy for integration with the local concubinary was demanded. A wry smile emerged, and the ends of his twirly moustache twitched promisingly. The signs were all there that a plan would shortly emerge.

'OK, lads!' he cheered rubbing his hands. We leant

forwards expectantly. 'It's Christmas Day tomorrow, so we're all going to church!'

A stunned silence fell over us. This was not what we wanted to hear at all. Jinx could usually be relied upon to come up with unbeatable schemes for meeting young ladies, but this time he had definitely failed to cut the mustard. Church did not equate to sex to my way of thinking, and besides, it was Christmas, a time for excess and debauchery.

NotNorman put the thing in a nutshell. 'Who the hell goes to *church* on Christmas Day?' he asked puzzled, and we all nodded our agreement. The scheme was a loser. It had no redeeming features whatsoever for anyone who was not a lover of cassocks and abstinence.

Jinx must be losing his touch, we thought, and he confirmed it by adding, 'And full uniforms, lads. Full uniforms,' as he left the bar.

A discussion ensued during which Jinx was accused of being (among other things) a fink, a charlatan and a miserable impostor. I agreed heartily. The last place I wanted to go was church. We were generally agreed that a new plan would have to be thrashed out. But then Benny the Dog piped up. He was a devotee of Jinx, having recently benefited to the tune of one legal secretary on the Australian coast, and what he referred to as a 'deep and meaningful bath' in a nurses' home in America, all as a direct result of Jinx's 'cocktail parties'. Benny stood alone but defiant in Jinx's defence. He reminded us of the great man's performance to date. He spoke enthusiastically of the Australian parties, the strip-poker night with those girls on holiday in Barbados, of the 15-girl dance troupe he'd managed to coax back to the ship in New Orleans. All around the room, resolute hearts began to weaken as each man remembered the fantasies that Jinx's enterprise had transformed into full-breasted reality. All those extremely fit dancers running, giggling and half-naked, around the ship; drunk, screaming girls losing heavily at cards in Barbados as they turned up yet *another* ace from a totally rigged pack – they were a memory for life. Australian nurses partying the night away as only Australian nurses can – I would never forget them.

People rarely saw Jinx in action. He generally disappeared up the road and returned like the Pied Piper with a bevy of lovely ladies. And they were always 'nice' girls, such as nurses or British workers overseas. This led to a greatly improved demeanour on the part of the lads. Shavers were employed, clean shirts found and swearing was – at least initially – kept to a minimum. Jinx's parties always went extremely well for all concerned. Deeper, longer-lasting relationships were established (relatively speaking) and the compliment was often returned with interest as invitations into town and to private parties and family homes came back to us. Jinx always found it quite touching when there was a small group of broken hearts waving white hankies from the dockside as we left a port, and he must have heard more promises to write than you could shake a stick at.

Now, however, I had to be firm. I dismissed the curvy, pouting images from my mind and took stock of the cold hard facts.

'Let's face it,' I said, 'firstly, I do not wish to waste a pressed uniform on a visit to a blooming church, and secondly, I think there's a trick here. I'm dead suspicious of this one. There's *definitely* a practical joke behind this somewhere. I mean, who goes to church to meet girls? I recommend we beat him at his own game and nip off swimming, eating, sunbathing and drinking somewhere as ungodly as we can find.'

Despite my logic, most of the lads didn't have the strength of character that I'd shown in shaking off the images of dancers, drunk bikini-clad strippers, and Australian nurses partying the night away as only Australian nurses can. There was a degree of dispute and eventually all but two wandered off to apply their weak minds to sorting out their uniforms and stumbling haplessly into Jinx's trap. I was convinced there was a hidden agenda to the plan, and stood firm. NotNorman and Gonad – the other two main sufferers on the trip to date – also showing a healthy degree of suspicion about a plan that involved uniforms and a church. Which is how I came to find myself swimming in a tropical lagoon on Christmas Day, and how I nearly managed to kill myself without the aid of a single shark.

It's rather strange to put on your trunks on Christmas Day and go swimming in a tropical lagoon, although I must say, it was preferable to my usual December fare of a walk on Brighton seafront. I think this was a lagoon; it may have been a fresh water spring, but whatever it was, it was idyllic. Fresh water emanated from a huge cave at the base of a cliff to the landward end. The lagoon therefore comprised clear, cold, fresh water. Then the tide would come in and flush out the lagoon with warm seawater. Above the cave entrance were steep cliffs rising high and out of sight, and all sorts of wildlife trotted and flew about the place enjoying the festive day off. NotNorman, Gonad and I peacefully wished the world a happy Christmas.

The cave fascinated us. It was possible to swim deep inside until it became too dark for our nerves. We decided to return with torches and head into the dark inner sanctum to explore on another day. Our exploration, however, was to come sooner than we expected, because as we swam into the cave for another chicken-hearted sortie, we were given the fright of our lives by two divers emerging from the half-light like the Loch Ness monster looking for cadet pie. We were pretty sure they hadn't entered the cave from our end, so the obvious conclusion was that it must lead somewhere.

'Sorry, mate,' said one of them looking at my face. 'Did we give you a fright?' They were New Zealanders.

'Oh, wow!' I said. 'We were just talking about getting some gear down here and checking out these caves! Must be magic in there.' I neglected to tell him that my 'gear' consisted of a bucket, a spade and a rubber duck.

'Sure is!' said the first one, adjusting some valves and straps. 'But you don't need all this gear to check out the best bit. It's just here.' He indicated the water under his feet. 'There's a hole about eight feet down, goes along about eight feet, then you pop up in this massive grotto. They used to hide in it during the war, so it's all kitted out. There's a big long ladder to the roof with a hatchway.'

My mouth was open. Underwater tunnel? Grotto? Ladder and hatchway? The other diver picked up the story.

'We guess it must come out in the town somewhere. During the war, the locals would open the hatch in town, climb down the ladder, then dive out through the hole here and into this cave. They'd have boats hidden out there in the lagoon and escape anything. How cool is that?'

It would have been pretty obvious that I thought it was waaaay cool. I love things like this, and my jaw had dropped so much as they were talking that they must have thought I was dredging for plankton. 'You are joking,' I gabbled eventually. 'You have *got* to be joking. The town must be about five miles away from here!'

'Maybe it is if you go round the road, but you go straight up, and the town's just up there. We're gonna go through now. We want to find out where the hatch opens up. Nobody's used it since the war. You can swim it dead easy and come with us if you like. Nothing to it. Just follow us!' And with that, they duck-dived and disappeared into the dark rock about eight feet down.

Instead of asking them why, if you don't need any gear to get through to the grotto, they were laden down with enough life-support equipment to start a farm on the sea-bed, I strained my eyes underwater and watched their flippers disappear into the hole. NotNorman, Gonad and I were fascinated, curious . . . and cowards.

We spent a good ten minutes diving down the eight feet and staring into the deep, forbidding hole. None of us had the guts to commit ourselves to swimming in. I wanted desperately to see inside the grotto, but didn't want to take the risks involved in getting there. I was frustrated by my own lack of bravery. Each of us in turn dived down, took one look and returned to the surface.

'It's pitch black in there. It's got to be more than eight feet to the grotto once you're in. You can't see any sort of light at all,' said NotNorman, shaking his head in despair.

'That's 'cos it's dark in there, Spanner-brain! The exit's in sight, you just can't see it,' replied Gonad logically.

I was at the end of my tether. I was spellbound by the prospect of this grotto and the secret passage from the town, I was determined to find a way of getting in. 'We've *got* to do it, lads,' I said. 'This is a once in a lifetime opportunity! After the first time through, it'll be a piece of cake. We'll wonder why we were so soppy about it!'

But after another half-dozen cheek-expanding, goggle-eyed dives, neither of them had fallen for my master plan and gone first.

'Tell you what,' suggested Gonad, 'why don't we go into town and climb down through the hatch?'

That sealed it for me. I realised that we had no idea where in town the hatch might be found, and that we might never see the Kiwis again. The only way into this adventure was through the tunnel and I, Windy Baboulene, was man enough for the task.

'Right. I've had it with you carpets! I can't float around here with you yellow-bellies any longer. Am I the only one with any balls around here? You two have a nice day – I'm going through.'

I took a deep breath and disappeared beneath the waves. I sunk down to the hole, gripped the sides and stared into the darkness. It was jet-black and forbidding. My head shouted at me to swim in – 'Eight feet, for God's sake. It's only eight feet!' – but my arms stayed rigid and my hands gripped the sides more firmly than ever. I looked up at the legs of my scorned shipmates at the surface and imagined the ridicule I would receive if I wimped out after what I'd said. I was far too egotistical to go through that, so my head told my arms that there was no way we could go back to the surface, and I was amazed to find the rest of my body agreeing that drowning was better than facing humiliation. My grip on the sides relented, my whole self worked as one for once, and I began to swim into the hole. I was BRAVE! 'OK body, let's go for it!' I shouted, and in we went.

As soon as I entered the hole I regretted it. Humiliation suddenly seemed the preferable option. The passage was shaped like a teardrop; as I floated higher, it became increasingly narrow and restrictive. I couldn't move my arms properly to swim or even to 'climb' along the walls. I considered going back, but found that reversing was even harder than going forwards. I didn't wish to die of indecision, so I scolded myself to keep calm and keep going. 'Just keep a grip,' I told myself, 'it's only eight feet.'

I felt my way ahead with my arms outstretched in front and kicked as hard as I could, but things quickly went from bad to worse. Not only could I not use my arms, but I was now scraping my back and head painfully against the sharp, abrasive coral roof of the tunnel. The roof also served to greatly restrict my legwork as the backs of my feet and calves suffered similar agonies against the brittle, unforgiving coral. 'KEEP CALM!' I insisted to myself. 'PANIC AND ALL IS LOST. It's only eight feet, KEEP CALM!'

'But we must have swum twenty feet already!' screamed my nerve-endings, 'And we need oxygen to survive, and there isn't any down here! And the blood we are losing from scraping along the coral will attract sharks and piranha! And we need to see light to know which way is up. And we're running out of air, and its dark and we're going to die! PANIC! PANIIIIIIIIIC!'

With a massive effort I held on to my breath, dribbling the remaining air from my mouth in a controlled fashion. Meanwhile my legs flailed painfully against the rock, my arms groped desperately into the black void ahead, and my head and back scraped agonisingly against the cheesegrater coral. I continued, getting steadily less and less effective for what seemed like an age, while my bodily panic and my mental calm were both reducing as hope of survival slipped into the fog of my oxygen-starved brain. The road ahead promised nothing but more of the same, and there seemed no prospect of any change in the texture of the ceiling. There was no point in turning back (impossible anyway) and the last of my air was dribbling from my blue lips. I remember very clearly thinking about what the next 20 seconds held for me; my last 20 seconds of consciousness. My lungs were empty and every reflex in my respiratory system was triggering frantically, trying to get me to breathe in. I knew I couldn't resist the urge for much longer, but that my next intake would not be life-giving, fresh cool air, but a thick, choking, soupy ingestion of cold, dark water. The water would rush in, pushing down my throat and filling my lungs, but my brain would continue to function long enough for me to experience all the horror, and I would beg for death to take me from this nightmare. As my head knocked feebly against the coral roof, and the water pressed coldly against my tongue, I found myself recalling a distant memory.

I'd nearly drowned once before, back when I was about seven. I was diving for coins in a swimming bath and, while I was upside-down and underwater, I got my foot caught in the ladder. I became aware of this as I floated towards the surface. I simply bent my knee so that I could float upwards, but about six inches from the surface, I found I couldn't get any higher without breaking my leg. This I would gladly have done had I the physical strength or leverage, but underwater, I was simply stuck. I flailed wildly trying to make it the few inches to the air, but getting nowhere because of the ladder, and I was in too much of a panic to go back down and release my leg. A lifeguard rescued me that day, and now my life passed before me from that moment onwards. It was as if everyone I'd ever known had made a slideshow of all the significant events in my childhood and presented all five thousand snapshots to me in a split second. The house where I was born, primary school teachers – Miss White, Mrs Foreguard – playing football on the recreation ground, old Doctor Beeston with his stethoscope, my first bicycle (with white tyres), climbing trees in Wolf's Wood, playing with a hose in the back garden, my happy face at the far end of a birthday cake shaped like a football pitch, building a snowman with my sisters and sledging into it, Mum's Morris Minor, riding on Dad's shoulders, getting chased for pinching golf balls, Grandma cooking, our Collie dog jumping for a stick, the day I cut my own hair – thousands and thousands of snapshot images; absolutely vivid, and quite incredible. I know it sounds clichéd, but it's true what they say: your life passes before you as you drown.

My family and friends were just saying goodbye and powering down the slide-projector to go home, and I was about to sleep forever when I became aware of a jolt. I coughed and spluttered and the world whirled around me as I tried to focus on the face of Saint Peter leaning over me. Saint Peter was wearing a wet suit, and was pushing hard on my chest. It was one of the New Zealanders. I finished coughing and my entire body gasped, tearing at the precious oxygen, sucking like a black hole until all the rocks in the grotto began to move towards me. I then began a record-breaking exhale.

'OOOH, MY GOD!' I rasped, putting all the rocks back in place again.

'You made it, then,' said the Kiwi glibly.

Once I had recovered a little, we inspected my wounds. Apparently they were fairly serious, but because they were *behind* me I was able once more to give the impression of admirable bravery. Had I been able to see the state of my back and head, I may well have passed out, but they were out of sight and merely smarted at the time. To the Kiwis, I was impressively brave. And I was about to impress them again.

'Right, let's explore the old grotto then,' I enthused from the prostrate position, dismissing concerns for my mental condition and the state of my back and lungs.

'Are you kidding, mate? We should be getting you to the doc's.'

'Sure I'm sure! And I want to climb the ladder and

emerge in the town. I didn't suffer all this just to go back. Let's rock and roll!'

The Kiwis looked at each other in amazement. I had now been brave twice in succession, something noticeably without precedent in the life that had just passed before me. They must have thought I was quite a guy. However, following my harrowing experience they decided to nip back through the hole and collect NotNorman and Gonad before they too injured themselves horribly trying to follow me. They were led through like girlies by the Kiwis, and I made as much out of the fact as I could.

While the others were thus engaged, I reflected on the look on the Kiwis' faces. They were genuinely impressed with me. What I had omitted to tell them was that the only reason I was looking so brave now was because of simple and abject terror at the prospect of getting back into the water and going back through the dreaded tunnel.

Eventually, the others arrived and they ooh'd and aah'd around the grotto while I pretended I was absolutely fine. Were I in a calmer frame of mind, I think the grotto would easily have lived up to expectation. As it was, I needed urgent medical assistance and there was no easy way out. It felt like a prison.

Soon we decided to climb the ladder. Heights don't usually bother me up to about four feet, and I had grudgingly got used to the 30-foot ladders in the holds on the ship, but this was a whole new ball game. This was an extremely old and unsafe ladder, towering up into the blackness. We shone the torches up into the void and still couldn't see the top. The ladder just disappeared into the darkness.

When we were about halfway up, I couldn't see either the top or the bottom. This was a weird experience. I began to feel hypnotised by the height and had a tremendous urge to jump off. I wisely managed to resist the temptation as a conversation began on the subject of the reactions of the townsfolk as a hatch lifted up and five lads appeared as if by magic from the middle of the road. All our clothes and shoes were on the beach back outside the cave.

Eventually we reached the top of the ladder. We were immersed in an eerie blackness that the torches cut through like lasers. The bottomless void beneath us was overwhelming. One of the Kiwis pushed at the hatch. Nothing happened. He pushed again. Not a sausage. Here we were, five little dots in the top corner of an underground cavern, with every prospect of having to return to the real world via a murderous underwater tunnel. I channelled my panic into assertiveness.

'Come ON!' I said, as a return down the ladder was mooted. 'Great adventurers do not turn back simply because of a sticky hatch. Put your back into it!'

The Kiwis obviously thought that bravery such as mine must also be accompanied by a fearsome temper, so they jumped to it. They contrived to get next to each other at the top of the ladder and brought their combined strength to bear on the recalcitrant hatch. Still no luck, so they gave up with their arms, stood two rungs further up the ladder, braced their backs against the hatchway and bent their knees.

'One, two, three – HEEEEAAAAVE!'

In the church on the edge of town the Christmas service was in full swing. Jinx and his flock, putting heart and soul into 'Good King Wenceslas', were looking very smart in their uniform whites and, despite the sobriety of the church, they were in thoroughly cheerful spirits and were contributing heartily to the proceedings. A look around the congregation revealed the reason for their good mood, because as the congregation had arrived for the service, it became clear that they were predominantly British and that there was no shortage of what employers of the vernacular might refer to as 'crumpet' amongst their number. For their part, the resident folk were impressed by the attendance of smart, religious British officers, and introductions to daughters and invitations to homespun Christmas celebrations had been readily forthcoming. Jinx had done it again. His plan was showing its substance, and although it would be a couple more hours before it bore fruit, the lads were salivating at the peaches and pairs that were ripening before their very eyes.

So you will understand that it was something of a distraction for all present when, as they split into descant and congregation for the line 'When a poor man came in sight', a large floorstone in the middle of the church began to join in the chorus. It scraped a bit, then it roared like two scuba divers contracting a hernia each before finally throwing itself up in the air and plonking itself down to one side. And as if this wasn't enough, a pair of heads popped up through the resulting hole like nervous chipmunks checking to see if the wolf had gone. The resounding carol tailed off into silence.

'Good heavens!' said the vicar, never one to mince his words, 'I shat m'cassocks!' (Well, that's what he should have said.) He had been at the church for 20 years and had no knowledge of the hatch. For all he knew this was Beelzebub himself, coming up from Hell to question the validity of his theological standpoint personally. The assembled gathering was now sharing a stunned silence.

I was stuck ten rungs down the ladder behind the other lads. I couldn't see past them, and could feel panic welling up. The exit was finally in sight and I wanted it badly. I decided that the silence and the lack of activity above could benefit from a little more of my new-found authority.

'Come on, you wankers! Get a wiggle on up there! Jesus H. Christ, we'll be here all day if you don't shift your arses!'

My shouts filled the church as roundly as if God himself had spoken and the poor congregation, assembled choir and clergy were offended not just the once, but every second for the next minute or two as the church's superb acoustics echoed my profanity a thousand times into each sensitive ear. 'WANKERS, wankers, wanke . . . JESUS H. CHRIST, Jesus H. Christ Jesus.. ARSES, arses, arses . . .'

Despite my encouragement there was still no motion above me on the ladder. It was as if they'd seen a ghost, so I batted on with more of the same as one by one, the lads above me slowly trickled out and stood sheepishly by the hole. I continued to rant as I followed them out, swearing vigorously the whole time. The lads smiled wanly at the masses as my words filled the church.

When I emerged and saw where we were, I was completely lost for words – although some of my old ones were more than happy to fill in for a while in the absence of anything new. I gulped, shut myself up, and stood half-dressed and bleeding with my latest profanity reverberating like Christmas bells around the throng; every echo another kick in the shins of decency for these highly principled churchgoers.

The five of us stood in a line and stared bashfully at the floor like naughty schoolboys in the headmaster's office, shifting awkwardly from one foot to the other. Had we pockets, we would undoubtedly have thrust our hands deep into the bottom of them, and had cans been available we would certainly have kicked them coyly.

And as if things weren't tough enough, a new horror was about to befall me. As I caught the vicar's eye, the slow light of recognition dawned on his greying countenance – he knew me from somewhere. I recognised him too, and the presence of his beautiful blonde daughter in the front row confirmed my worst fear.

'Y-Y-YOU!' he cried, pointing a shaking finger at me and searching his congregation for support. 'This! This man is a criminal! Call the police immediately!'

A great gasp went up from the congregation and the ladies pulled their jackets protectively over their peaches and pairs in horror while the men jumped up and rounded on us. Never one to miss an opportunity, Jinx leapt from his pew and raised his clenched fist high in the air.

'Stand back, everyone! Let us handle this! You lads, get the ruffians!'

And like a well-oiled crack troop of SAS, our own shipmates leapt on us from all sides and began pummelling us impressively.

'It's for your own good,' whispered Jinx and as if I wasn't suffering enough physical pain, he held me prostrate on the floor and squeezed my throat through a half-inch gap in his hands. 'They'll hand you over to the police if we don't make it look realistic.' Then he turned to catch the eye of his intended and posed, smiling for a photograph as I turned purple from the neck up. For some reason, I found it hard to feel grateful as they practised their best wrestling moves on us. I guess I just wasn't in the mood. On the other hand, the lads loved every minute and you could sense the entire female population swooning with admiration at the swift actions of those smart British officers. They were well in.

We picked ourselves up from the dusty road outside and brushed ourselves off. I was still choking from the impressive throttling Jinx had so generously given, still dazed from the drowning and still losing blood at a dangerous pace from my back, head and legs. And no, that wasn't all. We had no money, no clothes, no shoes, and a nice long walk ahead of us.

It took several hours of trudging and moping to get back to the ship, but only a minute or two for the Second Mate – in his capacity as Medical Officer – to take one look at the state of my aft, turn me round and rush me off to hospital.

I awoke on Boxing Day to a spinning head and vague dreams involving my spine being worked over by a combine harvester. Apparently, if coral gets into a person's blood stream, for instance mine, it can grow and spread like a cancer, turning the victim into a brittle blue and red mantelpiece ornament within a month. Death may also figure in the process. Not that I cared, really. The chances of my ever running into my loved one were now as remote as winning the Best Kept Spine Award for 1977. I was in hospital for the rest of the day for sure, and the ship was due to leave the next day. I had also lost a $500 deposit on my moped, despite Gonad's best efforts at emergency surgery. I supposed I should look on the bright side, at least it was the moped that had passed on, and not me.

The burning issue was the girl. I was seriously considering jumping ship for this girl. I had planned a small wedding and a long and happy life spent staring into the oceans of her wide blue eyes, but apart from the practical stuff – such as finding her and guessing her name right – she had not, so far, been given too good an impression of my net worth. She had seen me impersonate an MI5 agent, handle stolen goods, exploit alcoholics, damage hired goods and private property, appear half-naked and bleeding through a church floor, marched off and thrown out of said sacred premises, take the Lord's name in vain, shout 'wankers' and 'arse' during a religious ceremony, and lie blatantly to her and her father. Her tall mysterious spy, sweeping her off her feet on a white charger had turned out to be a skinny vulgar cadet on a moped.

I pictured her standing next to me at the altar, and when asked, 'Do you take this man?' instead of saying, 'I do,' she laughs a hollow laugh and – to roars of approval from the congregation – spits roundly on my shoes. It was becoming a definite possibility that the marriage might be off. If my life couldn't include this girl, then passing it as a rather sad mantelpiece ornament somehow seemed a fitting finale.

So, having had the doctors save my broken-hearted life against my will, the last thing I felt like doing was socialising. Have you ever noticed that whenever you are in pain, everybody and everything conspires to aggravate your injury? If you have a sore throat, it's salty, overcooked chips for dinner. If you have a headache, it's on the night you have highly expensive front row tickets to see Motorhead. If you have coral growing in the wounds in every part of behind you, everyone wants to pat you on the back for emerging so spectacularly through a church floor. It's always the same. Then they want to tell you how successful *they* were in impressing parents and daughters alike with the swift and clinical suppression and ejection of bleeding swimmers from places of worship, and they insist on boring you with the vital statistics of the girl they have coming to the ship's barbecue that night and what they intend to do to them. Disgusting, depraved, immoral, unprincipled and childish in the extreme. They have no idea of true love, and not so much as an ounce of sensitivity between them. Most of them have barely emerged from the primordial soup. They should be strangled at birth for the benefit of womankind and the planet. I was blowed if I was going to go to any poxy barbecue with a bunch of bottom feeders. They could stuff it.

I lay on my bunk for an hour and listened to the sounds of the party getting underway on the boat-deck. The distinctive barbecue aroma floated to my nostrils, and the sounds of glasses chinking and laughter jangling regaled my ears. I could hear Benny the Dog holding forth on the story of the Phillips crosshead screwdriver – he even did the Tonto voice – and the happy sound of awestruck ladies' laughter rang out. I put my pillow over my ears and harrumphed miserably. I couldn't even lie on my back. I was starving and uncomfortable – and I could tell that story WAY better than Benny the blooming Dog. A ring-pull fizzed. I imagined a cold beer washing its way around my dry mouth and I cracked. I decided to throw on some shorts and sit in a corner of the barbecue getting hideously drunk.

I limped onto the boat-deck and grabbed a beer from the Esky. I then turned to look for a quiet corner in which I could fester, but a splash of a very distinctive colour took me flashing back in time to the one moment in my life I had seen that particular colour before. Now as then, my mind was swamped with blonde hair and the sensation of falling through space in slow motion. She was leaning over me at Temperance House. I felt her hand on my brow and a tingle rushed through my entire body just as it had then. I blinked and shook my head back to the present. There she was – walking towards me – here on the boat-deck of the *Global Wanderer* – with smiling eyes and laughing lips.

'Hiii!' she sang, 'I thought I'd never see you again!' Was she pleased to see me? I couldn't believe it. Why wasn't she bombarding me with unprintable adjectives? Why wasn't I wearing her drink? 'When they said you weren't coming tonight, I thought I'd never get the chance to thank you.'

I didn't understand. Not at all.

'So . . . you know who I really am, then?' I hazarded.

'Oh, yes. One of the other lads here was trying to chat me up after church and he told me. He got pretty mad when all I wanted to talk about was you, but what you did was *so* funny! My dad absolutely wet himself when you came up through the floor! I've never laughed so much in all my life! He's been banging on since the beginning of time about religion and his abstinence. Then *you* come along and break every one of his top one hundred rules in two thirty-second bursts! He's shut himself away in his own temperance home for a week to recover, and I AM FREE! So where are you taking me, then? Bearing in mind that I owe you!'

I didn't need asking twice. The poet in me sprang to the fore.

'What would you say if I were to sweep you away from all this, to my castle nestling in the hills of a South Pacific island,' I grabbed a bottle of wine and a six-pack, 'where we could slide away to a warm moonlit beach and . . .'

She interrupted doubtfully. 'Can you guarantee that this beach will be completely clear of fathers?'

'Now there's a piece of luck – I happen to know *just* the place. May I escort you to a perfect sunrise?'

'But the sun won't be up for hours! Whatever will we do all night?'

'Well now, I'm sure we'll think of something, won't we?'

And we strolled off hand in hand.

Chapter 23

Copra Bugs

Homeward bound. Setting up home with several million others.

As we left Western Samoa it struck us like a frying pan in the face that the next port was effectively Liverpool. Apart from the briefest kiss with Panama, and a whistle-stop in the Azores, we were nearly home.

As the islands disappeared over the horizon behind us and the sun set behind them, I was sad to see once more the retreating silhouette of a wonderful place, and once more I vowed to return. My advice is to do whatever you must in life to visit the South Pacific islands. They are a magical part of the world. Skip Clacton-on-Sea this year and go to Rarotonga.

The outstanding feature of the crossing to Panama was the population of copra bugs that had booked up to make the journey with us. Copra bugs live on, in and because of coconut husks. They are oily-black beetleish chappies that can fly. They are also incalculably numerous. For each coconut piece there must have been eight copra bugs. That's roughly 32 to each complete coconut shell. We had thousands of tons of coconut husks. That's MILLIONS of copra bugs, and they get *everywhere*. Absolutely everywhere. They appear from the shower head instead of water, they get behind the screen and feature strongly in every television show. Clouds of them accompany you to bed, they crunch underfoot with every step you take (both inside and outside your boots), families of them swim happily in your beer, they break every mechanical entity on board through mass suicides in the workings, they share your tea and render every meal, snack and lick of toothpaste crunchy with copra bug. One is never alone with copra bugs.

Jinx had a nest of them set up home in his left ear (he eventually had to be hospitalised) and Crate – who discovered an unfortunate phobia for them – went seriously barmy trying to escape their omnipresence.

They were also incredibly resistant to attempts at murdering them either individually or en masse. It was nigh on impossible to kill them without endangering the lives of any humans in the vicinity, and their massacre quickly became the principal source of entertainment on board. They had the most astounding ability to accept a total flattening as if it was a dinner invitation, then bounce back into shape and continue about their business as if nothing had happened. If you stamped on a copra bug or smashed it on a tabletop with a clenched fist, it would squash, flat and round as would a baked bean. You looked on, taking pride in a job well done as it remained squashed flat for a few satisfying seconds. Then, just when you were shaping up to bean the next one, ping! Up it pops, back into fit and healthy mode once more and beetles off as good as new! I think it actually did them good to get bashed about in this way – they queued up and begged to be next. It seemed to invigorate them and set them up for the day.

Numerous experiments were set up in the bar as copra bugs were subjected to all sorts of torture and bets were placed on how they would fare. The ones left to swim in vodka didn't drown or sink. They adapted to the conditions, had a family and grew old gracefully. The ones placed next to the diesel generator exhaust outlet grew bigger, bent the bars and escaped. They all lived long and happy lives irrespective of our actions and we just had to learn to live with it. When copra bugs take over the planet, remember, you heard it here first! The only clue I can provide for a future generation vainly fighting back on The Day of the Copra Bug, is that we put one in a jamjar with one of MegaWatt's famous farts. It died horribly in three unspeakably painful minutes.

The return through Panama was a very routine transit. Everybody was too tied up with thoughts of England to bother with practical jokes, and there was no cargo to deal with so we shot through. The Atlantic looked, smelled and felt different. We were getting close to Europe, and the focus of my attention – and everybody else's – swung like the ship to face north-east: home. Nobody could talk of anything else. Every effort was made to get the ship aquaplaning towards payoff, and everyone on board was preoccupied with plans for the ensuing three months' leave which would begin the moment we hit Liverpool. But first, we had one final port of call. A swift cargo stop in Ponta Delgada in the Azores. Nothing of any import could possibly happen in this windswept corner of the Atlantic, now could it?

Chapter 24

A Class Act

A lady of great repute is taken to a restaurant. Everybody is ready for her. Windy takes her home. Everybody is ready for him.

I swaggered into the bar. All eyes were on me, as I knew they would be.

'Baboulene! There you are at last. Well? Did you give her one?'

I shut my eyes and turned my face away, shunning the uncouth questioner. I then gave one of those smiles that turns down at one side – the side opposite the raised eyebrow – for the fans, and sauntered towards the bar. I removed a beer from the fridge, signed for it and turned back to my adoring public.

'Well, come on, Windy! There's a lot of money riding on this! Did you give her one or not?'

I looked down on the poor fools – all wide-eyed and drooling like seals awaiting fish – and took a long, slow slug on the beer. It was going to be pleasant enough taking all that lovely money from them, but I would have gladly forgone the cash just for the pleasure of telling them all about it. In fact, just to prolong their agony, let me tell *you* all about it, starting two days previously.

The Azores are a beautiful, if exposed, group of islands belonging to Portugal and stuck way out in the middle of nowhere. This was much nearer home, and although the weather was still warm, the wind was up and the general flavour was definitely Northern Hemisphere once more.

Shortly after the ship came alongside, we'd gathered in

the bar to discuss the forthcoming evening when the shipping agent entered.

He said something along the lines of, 'Hi guys! I'm Bob Rumsby from Barrion's Shipping Agency. I know you're only here for a few days, but if you need anything I'm your man . . .' He petered out to nothing as he realised that nobody had heard a word he'd said. Not a syllable. Because behind him was the most astoundingly beautiful woman I had ever laid eyes on. And 'woman' was the operative word. A curvaceous thirty-something in a very expensive, very full suit. Bob was sharp. He noticed a room full of tongues and eyes-on-stalks and turned his sentence round to make it worth bothering with. 'And this is Michelle. She works for Turbo TV in the UK. They're filming a movie here in the Azores and they need some shipboard stuff. Michelle is the assistant director so you'll be seeing her around the ship a fair bit. I'm sure you'll all make her feel at home.'

'Good afternoon, boys,' she purred, her voice licking the inside of my ears and rummaging in my underwear. Very business-like and upper class, she was clearly the kind of woman who could hold her own in the movie industry, but simply oozing sex whether she wanted to or not. I noticed people around me were breathing again. She was gone. There was a fair amount of collar-loosening and brow-wiping before Sparky – who was in charge of such things – announced, 'Bar profits are proud to announce SIX cases of beer to any man who can assist the assistant director out of her panties! NO! Make that TEN! Bar profits are safe as houses with a class act like her and a barfull of prime-time tossers like you! Any takers?'

It's at times like these, a wise man keeps his mouth shut, has a drink and looks around for the idiots, but then

I noticed it was me shouting, 'I'll take your profits off you, Sparks!'

Sparks looked at me in disbelief and a general buzz ran round the bar. Not laughter as such, more a murmur. OK, giggling. Sparky did some sums in his head and never took his eye off me as he chanted:

'Bar profits are proud to announce a book on the chances of Windy shagging the director! Starting at fifty-to-one against!'

Silence.

'OK, SIXTY-to-one! Who can resist odds like that? Come along now gentlemen!'

Nothing.

I held my head up high. 'I will offer ten-to-one against me failing – that should finance your book for you,' I said. And with that, Sparks was besieged by frantic crowds waving money at him. It looked like the dealer floor of the Bombay Stock Exchange. Nobody wanted to put money on my being successful. Then, amidst phenomenal derisive laughter, I put a tenner on myself. It occurred to me that I was not a wise man.

Gambling was taken very seriously on board, and the perceived likely outcome made this particular wager more extreme than the usual couple of quid. As the odds settled, the people who eventually placed money on me would be extremely miffed were I to come away empty-handed. Those who'd placed money against me would be equally miffed were I successful. Either way, I would be unpopular with most people for a long time. And I'd be skint myself if I didn't manage to seduce the lovely Michelle.

I got up and headed for the door, a man with a mission.

I left in a storm of heckling and laughter, but I wasn't interested. I had to get to this woman at all costs or my life wouldn't be worth living. I ran up to my cabin and threw on my uniform whites. Then I dashed out on to the foredeck. Michelle and a small entourage were surveying the scene, planning angles, lights and backgrounds for filming to come. I swanned up to her all business-like, set my cap at a jaunty angle, and offered her my hand.

'Hi, Michelle. My name is Windy Baboulene. I'm the officer in charge of, er . . . (Seduction? Orgasms? Filming? Good grief! Why didn't I *think* before I opened my mouth?) in charge of . . . well, I'm in charge, and I've been asked by the Captain to look after you while you're on board. Your wish is my command!'

I bowed with a musketeer's flourish and beamed at her. She looked me up and down. She was old enough to be my mother, and here I stood, feeling like a ridiculous child. Then she smiled back.

'Well, thanks very much, Windy. I appreciate that. Would we have to open the hatch to get into the cargo from here?'

Great! I knew the answer!

I leapt into action, tripping over a stray foot that was hanging around the bottom of my other leg and banging my nose horrifically on the corner of the hatch. I bounced back up as if nothing had happened.

'Doe, doe, dot ad all. Der is a dadder dowd into de 'tween deck from dat masd-house over dere.'

I was carrying a clipboard in order to enhance my (admittedly excellent) look of authority, but as I swung it out to indicate the masthouse, it left my hand and flew gracefully over the side of the ship into the sea. I looked at Michelle and could see she was having trouble suppressing her laughter at this, at my nose – which was now throbbing like a distant lighthouse – and at my voice squeakily trying to force its way out through the right-angle halfway along my poor old hooter. I composed myself and went to speak just as my clipboard splashed rudely in the water. Michelle was close to bursting. She put a handkerchief to her nose to cover her laughter. I straightened my own nose with a crack, and tried to keep the mood up.

'Come on! Let's do it now. We'll need some lights in the 'tween deck. I'll take them down for you.' She honked with laughter in a way I found disappointing in a lady of such class. Then I realised my double entendre. 'NO! No! What I meant was . . . the lights. I'll take THEM down for you. I wasn't talking about anything else. For taking down, I mean. I wouldn't want to take anything else down for you . . . I don't mean to be rude by that. I mean, don't get me wrong, it's not that I don't find you attractive or anything, I mean, I don't mean that if you *wanted* me to take something down for you – even it is was rude – that I wouldn't because of course I would – if you wanted me to, that is – just not now, of course, because we are talking about lights. Not pants. Or anything . . .'

Michelle was laughing so loud people thought another ship was passing. But the damage was already done. I was a plonker and had walked up and proven it to her in under a minute. What a genius. I picked up a cluster lamp, dropped it into the 'tween deck, plugged it in, climbed down the ladder and set it up. Fortunately there were a couple more lights down there already, so I nipped back up to get Michelle. When I got back out on deck she was nowhere to be seen.

I trudged off sadly towards the accommodation to get something for my pulsating nose and bruised ego.

The next day I was on cargo watch. Cargo was being loaded at hatches one and two, and Michelle and her team were filming at hatch three. I didn't intend to look for her again. I felt that a lifetime's worth of uselessness had already been imparted to her the like of which I couldn't match if I spent all day trying. I didn't care if I never saw the silly cow again. She obviously wasn't my type of woman if she laughed at people's misfortune. Obviously bossy, too. That's how she got to be an assistant director. I wouldn't cross the road to spit on her if she was on fire.

Then one of her lackeys came up to me and said, 'Michelle was wondering if you could help us at all?'

'What? Me? Of course! I'd be delighted!' and like a white knight recently released from a dungeon, I sprang – carefully – across to hatch three.

'Hi, Windy!' she cooed, smiling broadly. 'Can you work this winch for us? We need a shot of all these wires moving.'

She gave the international hand gesture to indicate wires moving. I gave her my reassuring 'leave-everything-to-me' smile – the one that so excited the Captain – and swaggered across to the controls. It wasn't a winch, it was a derrick, and getting the wires to roll was simply a matter of pulling out the safety switch and turning the lever. I knew I wasn't supposed to be doing this alone and unsupervised, but there was no way I was going to let Michelle know that, and besides, what could go wrong? I wasn't even lifting anything.

'What, like this?' I said triumphantly, and whacked the lever over. I then stood proudly awaiting my applause. Instead, there was a creak. Then a LOUD creak. Then a whip-crack. I opened my eyes to see tripods, cameras and lights being knocked over as the camera crew dived for cover. The cargo hook on the end of the wire was still stowed in the traditional fashion. In other words, it was hooked over the topmost railing at the ship's side. I was now applying a steadily increasing degree of tension to the wire, hook and railing, and the noises we could hear were nature's way of indicating that something was about to give. The creaking was the railing bending upwards, and the whip-crack was the wire straining before it reached breaking point. I hit the emergency stop just in time, then put it back on again, whacked the lever the other way and released the tension. Thank God nothing went – although I had a rather obvious problem with the upper railing on the port side, which was now eight feet long instead of three, and pointing towards the sky. People began to emerge from their shelters and mop the sweat from their brows.

'Jesus! If that wire had gone, someone could have been killed!' pointed out the cameraman, quite unnecessarily I thought.

'Sorry? Oh. Didn't you want any tension on it? My fault. Let's try it again.'

Half of them dived for cover once more, the other half gave the international sign for 'Please for Christ's sakes leave that thing alone', but I insisted with chivalry. I nipped down, unshipped the hook and reeled the wire in and out as required. Anything to help.

Much to everyone's relief, the shot of the running wires went smoothly this time, and they moved on to some long shots of the real cargo work going on at the next hatch. I replaced the cargo hook on the bent railing and hoped no one would notice it.

Having succeeded in my mission, I felt rejuvenated. I was once again confident that Michelle would be swooning with desire, so I trotted across to her with the loping self-assurance of a tennis star about to jump the net. Fortunately, she was on her own, looking down on the hatches, mapping out some future scene in her mind while the others set up the next shot. I was also mapping out a future scene, but I doubt it was the same one as her.

'Was that OK? Did you get your shot?'

'Yes, Windy. Er . . . Thank you.'

'Not at all, not at all,' I said, sweeping her gratitude away with a magnanimous gesture.

'Sorry about your railing.'

'Oh. You noticed that did you?'

'Couldn't really miss it! Another second and that railing would have been on the moon! Are you always this accident prone?'

'Not at all! It's just that I am so nervous when I'm . . . when I'm around you. I can't seem to do a thing right!'

She took this in her stride.

'Really? Well I'd better leave you in peace while you still have a ship that can float.'

'No, no, no. That's the last thing I want. In fact, I want to see *more* of you. Any chance I could take you out for dinner?'

She gave me that maternal look again and shook her head.

'Windy, I'm very flattered, but really I don't think it's on, is it?'

'Why not? You've gotta eat, haven't you?'

'Well, yes, of course, but –'

'And you must like a good French restaurant?'

'Well, yes, of course, but –'

'So what's the problem then?'

She laughed and I could see she was going to give in.

'OK, OK. I'll risk it! But only if you promise me you won't touch any railings or wires.'

'I promise.'

'Or hooks?'

'I promise.'

'OK. Pick me up at the Hotel Flores at eight.' And she walked off. I was so blown away, I dropped the spanner I was carrying, and spent a constructive minute hopping around holding my foot.

Two hours later I had tracked down the most expensive

French restaurant in the Azores. Le Restaurant D'Amore was absolutely perfect, with intimate, romantic tables amongst plants and water sculptures. It was just right. I called the waiters, the manager, the wine waiter, the maître d', the chef, old Uncle Tom Cobbly and all into a huddle, handed them a handsome bribe, and outlined the importance of the situation. They all grasped the thing readily – as Frenchmen are apt to do in affairs of the heart – and we agreed our strategy. We pulled out of our huddle, slapped our high fives and looked forward to the evening's teamwork. I might have struggled to seduce Michelle on my own, but having secured the services of half a dozen Frenchmen, she wouldn't stand a chance. I looked at my watch. It was two o'clock. I had to get back to the ship. I only had six hours to prepare my body.

As it was such a special evening I even found my toothbrush and employed it in the traditional fashion. This may not seem like much to you, but when a toothbrush has been down behind a toilet for a couple of months it takes quite a man to use it for the first few minutes, I can tell you. Mind you, it didn't seem to do my teeth a whole lot of good. Anyway, I borrowed some soap and got someone to show me how it worked. I used one of those girly, lavender-scented soaps – didn't half pong! – and a shampoo that allegedly brought to me 'The Fresh Austrian Atmosphere of Old Pine'. I then used a pre-shave cologne, a lemon-scented shaving foam, and a traditional 'manly musk' aftershave. I was definitely going to knock her dead. But, looking at the range of aromas I had employed, I began to doubt that the whole effect was masculine enough, so not wishing to give Michelle any chance of escaping me, I added an aerosol can full of Sea Spray deodorant to the mushrooms under my arms, half a bottle of Old Spice to my chest (including a good splash of it on my shirt and jacket – a trick I learned from one of the lads) a light splash of Brut all over my neck and a subtle dab of Men's 'eau de' behind each ear. I felt a little woozy for some reason – for a place set in mid-ocean, the Azores had pretty poor air quality – but I felt good. However, I didn't seem able to smell too much considering the work I'd put in, so I added a four-year-old bottle of Denim – with an octane rating along the lines of rocket fuel – to my crotch, feet and trousers, and hoped nobody was going to put a match too near me. By 7.30 I was all ready, so I set off for the hotel.

It was a most peculiar journey marked by the problem with air quality I mentioned earlier. At one point I had to stop before crossing the road, and was completely enveloped in a fuggy cloud. It was good to get moving again. It was also on the journey to the hotel that I noticed another problem peculiar to the Azores. Apart from the air quality, it seemed their dog population was inexhaustible. Every time I looked around, the motley gang of mongrels lolloping along behind me was growing in size. I don't know how the locals put up with it. Between the dogs and the smell, a walk was almost unbearable. Funny I hadn't noticed it earlier in the day. It was good to escape through the revolving doors into the hotel.

The receptionist called up to Michelle and shortly she emerged from the lift like a blooming flower. Her image shimmered a little through the cloud, so I kept moving from side to side to keep my vision clear. She tacked her way across to me, a little confused by my side-stepping, but we joined hands in the end and I reached up to kiss her. She held up a wagging finger.

'Ah, ah. None of that. I agreed to go for dinner with you, but no more than that. I'm old enough to be – ahem! – to be – aHEM!' she went into a small coughing fit.

'Goodness me!' she said, screwing up her nose. 'They've overdone it a bit with the cleaning fluids in this reception, haven't they? I can hardly breathe!'

I helped her to a seat where she had another coughing fit, produced a handkerchief and made a noise into it like an engine with no oil. She nipped back upstairs and took a couple of hits of Ventolin, and returned looking better. She said she would be all right and that she needed some air, so I helped her to the door where the doorman was struggling with a couple of dozen dogs that had gathered outside. Really, I was amazed that the authorities didn't do something.

The air outside was only marginally better than that in the foyer of the hotel, but once we got moving, the dogs took her mind off the whiff, and she began to pick up. I said I supposed the smell might be the processing plant in the middle of town, but I was only being polite: for all Michelle's obvious class, she had definitely overdone it with the old eau de Cologne this evening. A lesser gentleman might have made an issue of it, even a joke, but I *knew* women and decided to let it go. I was probably making her feel all young and girlish again by asking her out, and she had overdone it out of nervousness. All rather cute really. And she was certainly turning heads! As I walked along with my head held high and this wonderful woman on my arm, everybody was looking, and even making way for us. It was as if we were royalty, the space we were being given. You could see the jealousy in their faces too.

The dogs caused a small incident outside the restaurant. Having been tracked by a particularly persistent Irish setter, I decided at the entrance to give it a parting gift; but I needed a moment when Michelle wasn't watching (cruelty to animals is not recommended as a romantic aid). One of the Frenchmen in my pay met us at the door and beamed dutifully as we arrived.

'Bonsoir, Madam. Welcome to D'Amore,' he drawled, clasping his hands together with reverence and half-bowing to the lovely Michelle. And while she looked the other way, I took the opportunity to offer the dog a swift one in the ribs. This involved letting go of the door – which I thought Francois was holding anyway – and going for the horizon with my left boot. The door jammed on Michelle's fingers. She yelped (in a way that did nothing to help disperse the dog population), bent double and placed her fingers under her arm at precisely the same time as the dog, having the benefit of a lifetime of people trying to kick it, ducked my kick with the subtlest of feints. My boot, up to full speed and unstoppable, continued along its parabolic course, landing Michelle a juicy one in the backside. It looked awfully deliberate to the other people on the street.

She spun round in amazement. I had to act quickly. I grabbed the nearest Frenchman by the lapels and shouted, 'What the bloody hell do you think you're doing? Do that again, and you'll have me to answer to!' And I threw him down like a used rag. Either through the forcefulness of my masculine power, or maybe because I'd slung him a bribe earlier on, he bowed and scraped and apologised profusely for kicking Michelle up the arse. He didn't know what came over him. He just saw it there as she bent over and couldn't contain himself. Michelle and I straightened our clothes indignantly and stalked into the restaurant.

We sat down at the table and, with a lot of surreptitious nudging and winking from my Gallic partners, I set about parting Michelle from her sensibilities. Alcoholic cocktails arrived instantly, and the wine waiter and I decided on a good fruity red in seconds. Michelle was taken aback.

'Wow! They don't mess about in here, do they?'

'Cheers!' I said, raising my glass. 'To your very good health!' and we both disappeared into the foliage and umbrellas of our extravagant cocktails (one of which was highly intoxicating).

Soon the conversation was flowing as quickly as the aperitifs, and the team was attacking Michelle along two main avenues. The obvious one was the alcohol. There is nothing like a few drinks to lower the inhibitions of a lady who is on her guard, and Michelle had such a terrific sparkle in her eye I couldn't believe she was anything but an unbridled nymphomaniac once tanked up. The second – and less obvious – line of attack was the food. Men often ignore this important source of success. Lots of food. Piles and piles of heavy, rich food. It makes girls feel lethargic and easygoing. It means they can't be bothered to fight you off if it comes down to a bit of a struggle. I'm a great believer in packing them to the gills with big dinners.

So within a mere 20 minutes Michelle had succumbed to two cocktails, a Dubonnet, and was well into her second glass of wine (each wine containing an extra shot of something a little lively to fortify it). She'd lowered a good big starter (some red meaty thing in a rich, brandy sauce) and the maître d' was just explaining to us how it had happened that we now had coq au vin for four instead of for two, and that we could eat as much as we wanted for the same price. I thanked him warmly, invited him to serve it up and raised my glass to Michelle once more. She was looking very happy. She seemed to have forgotten what an inept young boy her suitor was, and was chatting about her childhood and laughing at her inability to say 'Welwyn Garden City' – the place where she'd grown up – and when it came out as 'Willy Garden City' the image of a Willy garden got her laughing like a drain. I winked at the wine waiter as he brought her another 'vodka Côte du Rhône' and she grasped at it like it was a life-preserver.

And she proved no slacker when it came to putting the food away. I lowered a biggish single portion of the coq au vin, and felt I was doing well, but she worked her way through two of the other three portions like some sort of earth-mover, and was licking her lips at the prospect of the third. This also meant she'd taken aboard a fair bit more vin with the coq, and I watched her jaws and oily red lips working with great satisfaction.

When she wasn't eating, she was now talking in a very, very loud voice, and her accent had taken a surprising journey from the posh suburbs of Welwyn Garden City, down the A1 to somewhere out behind Arsenal Football Club. I was amazed. She cackled like a gossip, swore like a fishwife and laughed like a hyena at anything I said. She reached across and touched me during her conversation, and I felt the time was getting ripe for my organised highlight.

Michelle was still talking away nineteen-to-the-dozen, her words fighting their way past her full mouth, when I signalled to the waiter. The strolling musician sauntered over and launched into playing his violin. The dulcet tones filled the air and the moment was perfect for me to strike to her heart. The violin had sounded to her more like an air-raid warning than Mozart, but she looked at me, a stray giblet hanging from the corner of her mouth. I looked longingly back into the one of her eyes that was looking at me – the other finding an involuntary interest in the ceiling fittings.

'Michelle,' I said, reaching across for her hand. 'I just wanted you to know,' she belched roundly, holding the air in her cheeks and releasing it under pressure, 'that meeting you has been the most incredible experience for me,' I moved closer, holding her other hand too. 'I can't bear the thought that we may be parted in the next day or two,' she was still blowing a bit, but I decided to go for the biggie, 'and, well, I think I love you.'

The violin swelled dramatically in time with my declaration. As did Michelle's cheeks. She threw her chair away and ran to the toilet with her hand over her mouth.

To give her her due, she was a tough one. When she came back, I thought she'd want to go home to her sick bed, but she was apologetic and didn't wish to spoil the evening, so she sat down, and after only one Perrier, set about not only the coq as if she hadn't eaten in a month, but also the vin once more with a vengeance. Within half an hour the party was up to speed again. Her stamina in the food and drink department was unparalleled. Our meal for four was reduced to a large, empty pot containing only the least digestible bones and the bouquet garni (which was only there because Michelle, at the height of her energies, had spat it back out with a screech of uncontrollable laughter).

She topped herself up with a family selection of cheese and biscuits (tastefully accompanied by a Napoleon liqueur), followed by an industrial caterer's delivery of tiramisu (tastefully accompanied by a bottle of dessert wine) and a plate of chocolates.

With no space left for so much as a cappuccino, I suggested we adjourn to her hotel room for coffee and 'afters', and we left amidst much curious gesturing from the French contingent. Despite now having the limpest Visa card in the North Atlantic, I felt things were definitely going my way, so I got a taxi to speed the prey to the lair, and within a trice we were shutting her penthouse door on the outside world and I was rubbing my hands for the ensuing festivities.

And that has brought you up to date with my awestruck audience in the bar. Michelle and I had been spotted entering the hotel, so they knew I'd got as far as her room, and as outlined, they were now keen to know how their investment was doing on the final leg.

'Well, come on, Windy! Stop standing there like a prize prat! Did you give her one or not?'

'Lads, lads, lads. Calm yourselves and I shall tell all,' I took another long swig on my beer. 'I didn't "give her one", as you so crudely put it,' I waited for the furore following this statement to die down. 'Easy lads, easy. I haven't finished yet. I didn't "give her one" – but we did make wild and passionate love ALL night!' Another furore, then they wanted to know the details. I eventually gave in to their clamourings. 'All right, all right. I am not usually one to kiss and tell, but as this is a business matter, she was like a tiger! All over me, all night long. I didn't get a moment's rest! And so skilled was she with her tongue, so insatiable, curvaceous and passionate, that each time I thought I could give no more, she got me going again. It was unbelievable! That woman was a sex goddess! She nearly killed me with sheer, undiluted, continuous SEX!'

This was all going over very well. I was playing my audience like a master. All that is, but Sparky, who, having organised a book on the basis that I couldn't possibly get my hands on Michelle, stood to lose out big time. He stood up and calmed the madding crowd.

'Wait a minute lads, wait a minute. We all know Windy and how full of shit he is. We bookies can't possibly be expected to pay out purely on his word. We need proof!'

'Hang on!' I interjected. 'You can't go moving the goalposts around now just 'cos you lost. I give you my word as an officer and a gentleman, and I'm afraid that will have to suffice! The only witness was Michelle, and I don't think you can go and ask her to tell you all about her earth-shattering multiple orgasms. You have no witnesses, and that's just your tough luck!'

I know how to put someone in his place when the time is ripe. I may run for government one day.

Sparky held up a videotape.

'I don't think you're quite right, there, Windy.' There were big, alarming smiles on the faces of all the lads. 'You remember she's doing some filming here, right?'

I didn't like this direction.

'Well they were filming some panoramic views across the bay. From her hotel balcony.'

Not one little bit.

'We thought it might make the bet a bit fairer if we asked the cameraman to turn the camera round a tiny bit, so instead of looking out across the town, we might all get a look at Michelle's bedroom!'

My bowels turned to water. They could NOT have filmed last night. THEY COULD NOT!

'So when you arrived back in reception, the cameraman started the camera and left the bedroom. He then nipped into Michelle's room this morning, retrieved the footage and made a tape. We have now got a copy – there are plenty more if you want to buy a few – and I think it's time for your finest moment to have its world premiere! Patch! The television, please!' And Sparky set off across the room towards the video player with the dreaded tape in his hand.

My mind was sand, my legs jelly, and my bowels had turned to ice. I rushed over to intercept Sparky in a flat panic. I grabbed the tape and we wrestled for a while. Eventually Sparky, giving in to my desperation, shouted, 'All right! All right, Windy. We have plenty of other copies.

Gentlemen, I believe Windy wants to make a short introductory speech before the performance!'

I stood there. There was no way out. I'd lied my way into the lads' admiration, and now I was about to be shown up in the most embarrassing way possible. All I was doing was playing for time. But what could I say? What *really* happened was terrible. This was the worst – the very, very worst – moment of my entire life.

But I had no choice. I hung my head in shame and explained to the lads what had really happened. I figured it would soften the impact of the video if I provided a context. This is what actually took place in the hotel room.

I made some coffee, found an old movie on the television, and sat down beside Michelle on the sofa. Before long I snaked an arm round behind her, leant over and kissed her softly.

'No, Windy. I said no!' she said weakly. I sensed her resistance was low so I pushed on, hoping to raise her excitement level enough to dispel any reluctance. She didn't object too strongly, so I leant across and kissed her on the lips. It was like kissing an ashtray into which someone had thrown up, but I wasn't going to let this one go. I moved on, employing my tongue, gentle words and hot breath expertly in her ear. I then moved down and began snarling away at her neck – always a winner. I looked for signs of arousal and was disappointed to find them few and far between even though she looked every inch the sexpot. Finding her less responsive than the promise in her eyes would be a dreadful disappointment. I increased the tempo and bit hard at her neck. Ah! There was more response! A low moan. She was coming round to my way of thinking! I bit her again – the idea of Michelle sporting a lovebite on deck the following day was appealing. Another long moan. No, no. Not a moan. More of a . . . oh.

A snore.

I pulled away and looked at her. Her mouth was open, her tongue halfway out, and a highly unattractive grinding noise emanated from the back of her throat.

To my credit, I ended up doing nothing to the poor girl. Whether the seediness of it all got to me, or the pointlessness, or simply the flatulence, I cannot tell, but I gave it up as a washout and went to sleep in her bed. When I awoke she was gone. My embarrassment in the bar was much more due to my having lied so extravagantly than due to Michelle going to sleep during my amorous advances. The video would be unimpressive stuff.

The lads took my story with a childish lack of dignity and absolutely no self-control. I'd decided to tell them the tale so that the video could remain unseen, but that was short-sighted of me. They were laughing and shouting – it was like a chimps' tea-party – and they wanted to see the video more than ever.

And I feel sure you can appreciate that I felt that the video must not be played at any cost.

I gulped.

'Listen lads, give me a break. I've come clean. I . . . I didn't sleep with Michelle last night, and I –'

'Ahaaaa!' laughed Sparky. 'So what's all this sex-mad tiger stuff?'

'Well, that's what I was about to explain, you see –'

'Shut up, Windy, and stick the video on!'

'Hold on, let me explain, you see the thing was –'

'You've got three seconds to put it on Windy, then we're going to do it for you!'

I looked up and noticed they were not actually guarding

the door, and although they could get further copies, it would at least give me some time. Escape was my only chance. I tucked the video under my arm, dropped my shoulder and headed for the door like a wing three-quarter.

Eleven men jumped on top of me. The Windy lungs became winded and the video was removed from my possession.

'OK, lads! Take your seats for the show! Windy, you sit there in the middle where we can watch your face.'

'But lads, what I –'

'And SHUT UP! God, you do go on, don't you? Welcome everyone to the world premiere of "Windy Lust: One Man and his Sex Goddess"!'

He fumbled with the video player, and I freely admit that I was praying for a war, an earthquake, everyone to be gassed, anything at all to head off what these bastards were about to see. I would never, NEVER live it down. Even my explanation was a complementary version of the truth, and now they were going to get the full unexpurgated, technicolor version. Truly and definitely the very worst moment of my entire life was about to get worse.

The picture came on with an intro screen. More eyes were on me than were on the video. I wanted the world to swallow me up. Then the music started. The piss-taking sods had even edited on jokes – it was the music to *Match of the Day*. Good grief, Michelle's entire post-production team must have seen it. Then the music ended and Des Lynam came on the screen introducing football league action from the previous week. I looked around at the faces grinning back at me. I couldn't bear it.

'What's going on? This . . . this is football!'

'Well, you like football don't you, Windy?'

'Er . . . yes, but, what about the film of me and Michelle?'

'Eh? Sorry? Film of you and Michelle? Oh. There is no

film of you and Michelle. I'm afraid we made the whole thing up as a sort of joke. Good of you to tell us the truth though. A lot of people might have lied about last night!'

And the laughter rang out all over the Azores as I tramped off to kill myself.

About an hour later I was lying in my bunk. I was actually worrying about my financial situation because on top of everything else, I'd been warned that my bar bill was too high, and that I had to have a quiet month running into Liverpool or I'd be in debt to the ship. This latest episode had put paid to any quiet bar bill for this month. The number of beers I'd have to buy for failing with Michelle, getting tricked by the lads and the gambling side of things all added up to something astronomical.

There was a knock on my door. I ignored it. Another knock. I ignored it again, but the door opened anyway. I waited for one of the mob to enter with some new joke they'd come up with, but it wasn't one of the boys. It was Michelle.

'Windy? Are you there? Sorry did I wake you?'

I sat up in bed. 'No, not at all. Er, how are you?'

'Bit of a hangover this morning, but I'm fine now. Listen, I just wanted to thank you for last night. You were so generous and kind, and then you put me to sleep when any other man might have taken advantage of me. And I wanted to apologise for my behaviour. I thought I could hold my drink, but it seemed to get to me in a big way last night! I was a dreadful embarrassment to you.'

I laughed. 'Not at all, Michelle. Being with you made it worth every moment.'

'You're too kind. And it must have cost you a few bob, too. How about I make it up to you. How about I take you out for dinner this evening, and I'll keep my intake down?'

I gave a hollow laugh. This sounded like a fantastic turnaround, leaving the episode ending happily in my favour if I could take her out and get another chance. That would have been nice, wouldn't it? But the cup was to be dashed from my lips once more.

'Oh, Michelle, I'd love to, but we're due to sail at ten this evening. I'll be working from around eight. There's no way.'

'What a shame. I am sorry.'

'How about in England? Can I see you in England?'

'Windy, I don't think my husband would like that too much. I'm sorry, looks like it just isn't meant to be.' She turned to go, then looked back at me and winked. 'And I would have slept with you tonight as well.'

I'm sure she meant that as a comfort to me, but it had just the opposite effect. She looked at her watch.

'Oh well, better get back. We only stopped for a quick break. We'll be finished in around an hour, so I'd best say goodbye now.'

She came over and kissed me on the cheek, then we grabbed each other and she kissed me long and hard on the mouth. She pulled away and that perfect behind left my room forever. So near and yet so far. I sighed deeply and went back to calculating my financial ruin.

A little while later I was contemplating how cruel life can be when the door opened again. This time it was NotNorman.

'Hi, Windy!' he said, cheerfully. 'Great gag, wasn't it? You should have seen your face! You are going to go down in history as the greatest tosser ever to sail the seven seas!'

I groaned. 'What a life, NotNorman. What a goddam life! Just when you think everything's going to work out your way, the pendulum swings back and you're shot away to nothing again! If only I'd given her one while she was unconscious, all this would have been unnecessary and I'd be solvent again.'

'Yeah, well, you're right. The boys would have admired you for that! And I suppose my news won't cheer you up, you must be desperate to get away from here. There's been a hold-up with the cargo. New departure time, noon tomorrow. Isn't that crap?'

I flopped back on my bed. Liverpool and home were but a few days away from the Azores, and now we had another night here. Especially the way I felt, I just wanted to get on with –

'WHAT? Wait a minute! Another night here? A WHOLE NIGHT?'

I leapt out of bed and barely touched the deck on my way out to the foredeck.

Twenty-four hours later, I stood in my boiler suit, staring down into the grey Atlantic waters as they scudded beneath the ship. I finished counting the money and tucked it away safely. Quite a windfall. I placed my chin on the rails and a smile on my lips. What a life. I'd found matters a little difficult to bear at one point, but now I looked at things squarely, I couldn't quite remember why. I'd be home within a week, I was a romantic and gambling success, and was not just financially solvent, I'd made a small fortune into the bargain. Perhaps life wasn't really so bad after all.

Chapter 25

The Return of the Native

NotNorman finds Liverpool overcrowded. A customs man makes an exciting find. Reunion.

We cornered the Porta Delgada lighthouse on two wheels, burned rubber across the Atlantic, and if anyone in County Cork blinked as we flew past they would have missed us. We gave an impressive handbrake turn into the Irish Sea and before we knew it, we were at anchor in the cold February air at the mouth of the Mersey, requesting a pilot over the radio. A calm, reassuring English voice came back to us, and I felt as safe and secure as I did in the womb. After six months, two weeks and three days of tough campaigning we were back in good old England. We were home at last!

Well nearly. They left us at anchor until four in the morning, then we had a two-hour passage to get up to the docks. The sun did its best to welcome us home, but the impression that England is protected from the sun by a huge Tupperware lid was as strong as ever. I didn't mind. English drizzle was exactly what I wanted to see. It was proof that we were home.

I smiled sweetly at the Liverpudlian wharfie who gave me a mouthful of Scouse abuse as I threw the line ashore without warning. I loved him. I felt like Sir Francis Drake returning from a pioneering voyage, and the King George IV docks in Liverpool felt like my true home. Yes, that's how bad my sentiment had got. I happily breathed in the crisp morning smog and took in the Englishness of the scene around me. The docks, the grey Liverpool skyline, the sun failing to break through. Even the girl waving her handkerchief had a certain familiar . . . girl? What girl? I looked more carefully and sure enough one of the dockside workmen was not a man. He was a girl. And the smiling face and hanky-waving antics told me exactly who he was. He was Cindy. I couldn't believe my eyes. NotNorman would not believe my eyes either. He was sleeping after his earlier bridge watch, so as soon as the gangway was in position, I nipped down to see what she was doing here.

'Hiya!' she said, throwing herself round my neck. She was brimful of happiness and expectation. 'Are you surprised?'

'Er, not half as surprised as NotNorman will be,' I ventured, not quite sure how much to say.

'I know, isn't it great? I didn't even go back to Oz. I flew straight here from Tonga. Aren't his folks great? They let me stay with them the last few weeks, and me and his mum, we've prepared EVERYTHING! There's a big surprise party for us tomorrow night, and the wedding will have to be in about three weeks because we want to get a honeymoon in before NotNorman and I have to go off on his next ship. Oooo, I'm so excited!'

'Er, did NotNorman agree to all this?'

'Oh, didn't he tell you? He proposed to me on our last night in Tonga together! It was sooooo romantic!'

'Er, I guess you didn't get any letters or flowers or anything from NotNorman?'

'Yes – well – no. That is, they got to my house in Sydney – my mum told me that loads of flowers and letters had arrived from NotNorman, but I didn't get to read them or anything because I came straight here. He's such a cutie-pie for sending them, though. I just love him to bits!'

I excused myself on the pretext of duty and promised to nip off and fetch cutie-pie from his bunk. Cindy was not allowed aboard as yet because Customs hadn't cleared us. I galloped up the gangway and along to NotNorman's cabin.

'NotNorman! NotNorman! Wake UP! You've got a visitor!'

'Wha . . .? Eh? Wassammarra? Are we alongside yet?'

'We are alongside – but *you* are sunk, Mush. You have a visitor.'

'Aw, shucks,' he said, 'I told mum not to come all this way to get me. I can catch a train straight to –'

'No, no, Notters. It's not NotMum. A rather less-expected visitor.'

'Well who is it then?' he began to sense the atmosphere. 'Must be one of my family.'

'Er, well. I suppose she *thinks* she is, yes.'

'Stop talking in riddles Windy, and get to the point or I shall, in the words of good old Rip, fillet your spine for you. Who is it? The police?'

'OK, calm down. It's not the police. It's worse than that. Stay lying down, 'cos you're not going to like this.'

Isn't it great when you're in command of some really powerful, dead juicy gossip? I could have messed him around for hours if I wasn't such a nice guy. Besides, I like my spine the way it is.

'Since we left Tonga,' I said slowly and quietly, 'England has increased its population of Cindys to the tune of one.'

NotNorman's eyes came out on stalks. His hair stood on end, his jaw flapped up and down like an epileptic bread bin, his tongue popped in and out and a siren sounded from the back of his head. It was like watching an episode of *Tom and Jerry*. While he animated thus, I filled him in on the state of things re: his mother's love for his fiancée, her failure to get the message in Sydney, the surprise party, oh – did I say fiancée? Yes, there was his wedding to prepare for and he only had three weeks. I expressed annoyance at not yet having received an invite, and suggested yellow as a good theme colour for an early spring wedding. I also suggested that, as a seventeen-year-old boy, he should maybe think twice about whether he was rushing into it a little, but shucks, what the hell, I gave him my blessing.

None of this man-to-man, old-friend stuff seemed to help. NotNorman was definitely NotHimself. He looked as Tom does when Jerry has just jammed his tail in the mains socket.

'I'll go and make sure she can't get on board for as long as I can. You think about what you're gonna do. I'll be back as soon as I can.'

We had a stroke of luck in that the Customs men had become suspicious and wouldn't be allowing outsiders aboard for some time yet. My family was in a hotel in town, and they were waiting for a call from the shipping agent before coming down to pick me up. They probably didn't know we were even alongside yet, so the magic moment when we would be reunited was once more delayed. Still, it was a reprieve for NotNorman.

Apparently a keen young Customs man – searching in a forward masthouse – had discovered a rather splendid, brand new and boxed stereo system hidden behind some ropes. He pulled the box out and turned to run proudly to his superiors with it, when much to his surprise, another one dropped down to replace it. With promotion glittering in his eyes, he pulled that box out too, only to have it replaced once more! Soon he had an impressive display of hi-fi equipment stacked up behind him, with further units appearing each time he removed one. The forward masthouse looked more like a Comet warehouse. It appeared some enterprising but foolhardy sailor had completely filled the hollow metal mast with cassette-radios, and was about to make a heavy loss on his investment. This meant that Cindy was not allowed on board, and that we all had the additional hassle of an interview with Her Majesty's Customs and Excise. It was 11.30 before we were given clearance.

The new crew arrived on a coach and began trundling their gear up the gangway. They looked depressed. Now I understood what it meant to receive a letter while on leave, telling you to join the *Global Wanderer*, and I saw it in their faces. They looked like a funeral procession. I saw a spotty nervous-looking lad who stood out like a skyscraper as a first-tripper. Had *I* been as obvious as that all those months ago? I guessed so. I looked at his colleagues and pondered what must be ahead for him. Could they possibly consist of another Jinx? Another Famous Dick Wrigley? Another Benny, Gonad, Crate, SmallParcel, MegaWatt, KiloWatt and the rest? Surely, not another Giewy? I felt a sudden affection for my gang, and a sudden warm realisation that I'd just had the adventure of a lifetime.

I helped the first-tripper carry his gear round to the cabin and listened to his tirade of jumbled, jumpy questions. There is a fine line between excited and scared, and this guy was springing from one to the other like a mountain goat with an itchy bottom. I gave him the 'don't-let-the-bastards-grind-you-down' routine, but for some reason I neglected to tell him anything about cranking competitions, mules, crossing the line, electric hammers and the rest of it. He'd find out soon enough about all this character-building stuff. He shook my hand and I shook my head. I knew what was ahead of him, and that he'd have the time of his life in the six months ahead of him just as I had done. No doubt about it, he was lucky – even privileged – to be here. I wasn't going to tell *him* that, though. I bit my lip, put on a nervous tick as I slugged hungrily at a whisky bottle (full of apple juice) and told him to run away while he had the chance.

Next came a long round of hand-shaking and number-swapping. The lads who had made my life such a living hell for the last six months were all very sincere in their goodbyes, and were generous in praise of how very enjoyable my gullibility had been for them.

I had to see the Captain in order to officially pay off and get my passbook stamped. He was pleasant and wished me well for the future. Everybody was just so offhand over a moment that to me, was momentous. I suppose in the Merchant Navy one just gets used to life becoming a series of goodbyes.

I went to say cheerio to the Mate. He was handing over to the new Mate who looked even more of an animal than our one. The two of them standing together looked like competitors in an illegal boxing match. I shook hands with Harry Tate, and he turned to the new Mate and, indicating my hand said, 'Do you know what? That's the first bit of shit I've had in my hand all day!' And they laughed long and hearty. Must be Chief Officer humour. Goes straight over my head every time.

I put my head round NotNorman's door and was met by two glaring faces and the message, 'Shove off, we're busy.'

I said, 'I'll call you next week,' and shoved off as bidden, although I was dying to know how he'd handle it. Knowing NotNorman, he'd probably marry her rather than upset her. We should soon see.

I made three trips up and down the gangway, saying fresh goodbyes on every pass. Soon there was a pile of luggage and souvenirs plus one me, waiting on the quay for my leave to begin with the arrival of my mum, dad and sisters.

I was going home.

Six months is a long time to be away from home, and for most sailors it becomes more and more difficult to reintegrate into 'normal' life as the years go by. The joys of another ship and the geographical jewels of the world pale behind the upset of family upheaval and instability. For me, however, the whole thing had been a long hard adventure. Too long really – I'd been wishing the days away since Samoa, and was more than ready to go home. Telling all my friends and family of my adventures would be a pleasure in itself (for me, if not for them) as well as spending all the money I'd won and saved. But seeing my family again after all this time was the big one. They were on their way – my three sisters, my mum and dad – and I could hardly contain myself. Absence truly makes the heart grow fonder, and I couldn't wait to see them.

Giewy came trotting down the gangway to say goodbye, and he gave me a nasty shock – and I don't just mean because he crept up unexpectedly from behind.

'Prob'ly see you next trip,' he smarmed, and it hit me. Next trip! I hadn't even thought about any next trip! All I could see were acres and acres of leave! As a cadet I'd earned six weeks' leave, and couldn't see beyond that. I was like a schoolboy, seeing the summer holidays as lasting forever with no concept of anything beyond that. I saw my leave as an everlasting orgy with no work to do and money to burn, but there would of course be another ship; this was my life now. And the chances were that because we cadets had all earned precisely the same amount of leave, we would share the joys and disappointments of the next trip, too.

As Giewy waddled back up the gangway, I was even able to look fondly on him. I called up the gangway to him, 'Oi! Giewy!' He stopped and turned back to me. 'Take care.'

He laughed stupidly, then there was a pause as he rubbed his chin and considered his answer. He lifted his eyes, pointed and winked at me. 'Giew!' he said nodding, then carried on up the gangway. My main concern was that I was beginning to understand what he meant.

I looked up at the great metal side of the *Global Wanderer*. My relationship with her had been hard graft for the most part, but now I was leaving, I felt a sentimental glow and realised I would miss her. I walked across and stroked my hand against her like a vet checking a beloved old horse. We'd come a long way together since I had stared up in trepidation at those great flanks in New Orleans six months earlier. Then I'd only seen fear. Now I saw a magnificent ship. A thing of great beauty and depth in which I had invested a lot of time and effort. There was hardly an inch of that ship I didn't know intimately, and not a square inch of wood, brass, rope or wire to which I had not given of myself.

Throughout all my scrapes, all around the world, she was always there waiting patiently for my return. We'd seen good times and bad, laughter and tears, pain and joy. She had been my home. I felt a great affinity for her, and a pang of sadness that she would be leaving Liverpool for her next adventure without me. I found myself picking at the plimsoll mark and criticising the workmanship. It needed repainting. I had half a mind to nip up and report it to the Mate. I knew how important it was for stability and cargo. I laughed at myself. When I'd first seen those marks in New Orleans I'd thought they were graffiti.

Suddenly, the sounds of skidding tyres and the heaving roar of a clutch slipping filled the air. Up at the gate my mum's car came bouncing on to the quayside, tooting the horn and flashing the lights. I saw five happy, smiling faces. Faces I loved. My crazy family. I felt tears of happiness welling up, and a lump in the back of my throat. There was a sister hanging out of each of the rear side windows, and another clinging on as she hung out of the sunroof. I saw them waving and heard their shouts as the car bumped over the crane-tracks towards me. I caught sight of my reflection in a van window nearby. I'd been through so much since they saw me last. They had said goodbye to a schoolboy six months earlier. Now they were welcoming home a hairy-arsed, confident man who knew his way around the world.

They all piled out of the car and ran screaming round me. They jumped on me all at once, and the whole family gelled as one, hugging and hugging longer and harder than any hug I've ever known. As we hugged, I made my first decision since coming home with my new-found worldliness.

I cried my damn eyes out.

Empire of the Soul
by Paul William Roberts

£7.99 • -paperback • 1 84024 188 8 • 129 x 198 mm/352 pp

'An outrageously funny, brilliantly penetrating and deeply affectionate portrait of India.' *Martin Amis*

'India is a harsh mistress: she seems to appreciate individual sacrifice so little. Yet she has never wanted for lovers . . .'

India demands a passionate response. In 1974 Paul William Roberts embarked on the first of many trips that began a lasting affair with the country. Spanning twenty years of travel, Roberts paints a picture of a place of constant change, of polarities and extremes, of holy men and millionaire drug dealers, of desperate poverty and riches beyond compare. With characters as diverse as the founder of India's first pornographic magazine to Mother Teresa, *Empire of the Soul* is a seductive, witty and truly unforgettable book.

Blue Cuban Nights
by Ted Ferguson

£7.99 • paperback • 1 84024 226 4 • 129 x 198 mm/320 pp

Poetry, politics and a pulsing Latin beat.

Ted Ferguson is in love with Cuba, a country that swings to rumba whilst embracing Communism: a country of contradictions. Breaking out of the tourist bubble and opening closed doors, Ferguson uncovers a cornucopia of colourful individuals and their idiosyncracies. He meets Roca, a collector of pig paraphernalia and Tony the jazz aficionado of bootleg Dizzy Gillespie tapes. He sees the mausoleums of the rich equipped with air-conditioning and telephones, and the poor who hunt the city's street cats for a decent meal. Ferguson's Cuba encompasses all that is sexy, vibrant and utterly alluring about the hotbed of the Caribbean.

La Bella Vita
by Vida Adamoli

£7.99 • paperback • 1 84024 220 5 • 129 x 198 mm/320 pp

An evocative, entertaining and poignant reminiscence of sixties and seventies Italy.

Southern Italy, 1960. Torre Saracena is an ancient Italian village, a huddle of shuttered houses and sun-baked streets perched on a rocky promontory above the sea. For centuries this insular community has closed its ranks against everyone outside its walls; even the inhabitants of the nearest town are classified as foreigners.

An 18-year-old Vida fell in love, married her Italian boyfriend and moved to Rome. Escaping from the bustle of the capital, she, her husband and two small sons immersed themselves in the apparent idyll of Torre Saracena. But from feuding and festivals through to murder and brushes with the Neapolitan Mafia, life is never dull. Vida's is a delightful story of twenty years living *la bella vita* with the villagers and bohemians who became her trusted friends.

Wild East
Travels in the New Mongolia
by Jill Lawless

£7.99 • paperback • 1 84024 210 8 • 129 x 198 mm/320 pp

'Engaging . . . a revealing and often amusing account of journeys through a beautiful country awakening from a tumultuous era.' *The Toronto Mail*

'I first glimpsed Mongolia from the air. The overwhelming impression was of space, beauty and a deceptive serenity; a gently undulating sea of rich grass, flecked with white felt tents, like aspirin scattered over a green bedspread.'

Mongolia conjures up exotic images of wild horsemen, of endless grasslands, of a ruthless Genghis Khan, and of weathered nomads – a mysterious land that time forgot. Jill Lawless arrived in Mongolia to find a country emerging from centuries of isolation beneath the shadow of its oppressive neighbours, at once discovering its Buddhist heritage and the trappings of the Western world. The result is a land of fascinating and bewildering contrasts.

The Nomad
The Diaries of Isabelle Eberhardt
Translated by Nina de Voogd
Edited by Elizabeth Kershaw and introduced by Annette Kobak

£6.99 • paperback • 1 84024 140 3 • 129 x 198 mm/208 pp

The fascinating story of a strange, passionate life.

In 1904 and at the age of only 27, Isabelle Eberhardt drowned in the deserts of North Africa. Buried beneath the rubble and mud that crushed her were found battered leather journals containing the extraordinary tale of her life. The illegitimate child of aristocracts, a 20-year-old Isabelle travelled to Algeria with her mother, who died 6 months after their arrival. Reinventing herself as a man, embracing Arab nomad tribes and their lifestyle, she wandered the Sahara on horseback.

A controversial figure and equally loved and hated, Isabelle's diaries recount her sexual adventures and drug-taking, her conversion to Islam and the mysterious attempt on her life. Experiencing moments of both desperate loneliness and euphoric joy, Isabelle struggles to find her place, her voice as a writer and the true purpose of human existence.

For a current catalogue and a full listing of
Summersdale travel books, visit our website:

www. summersdale.com

Spend...
rea...

Regency
NIGHTS

**Five of your favourite historical authors bring
you five seductive and sensual short stories
that invite you to indulge in the most
scandalous Regency pleasures**

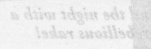

WICKED
Regency
NIGHTS

Nicola Cornick
Louise Allen
Bronwyn Scott
Diane Gaston
Annie Burrows

First published in Great Britain in 2010
Harlequin Mills & Boon Limited, Eton House,
18-24 Paradise Road,
Richmond, Surrey TW9 1SR

WICKED REGENCY NIGHTS © Harlequin Books S.A. 2010

The Unmasking of Lady Loveless © Nicola Cornick 2008
Disrobed and Dishonored © Melanie Hilton 2009
Libertine Lord, Pickpocket Miss © Nikki Poppen 2008
The Unlacing of Miss Leigh © Diane Perkins 2009
Notorious Lord, Compromised Miss © Annie Burrows 2008

ISBN: 978 0 263 87889 9

011-0510

Harlequin Mills & Boon policy is to use papers that are
natural, renewable and recyclable products and made from
wood grown in sustainable forests. The logging and
manufacturing processes conform to the legal environmental
regulations of the country of origin.

Printed in Great Britain by
Clays Ltd, St Ives plc

CONTENTS

THE UNMASKING OF
LADY LOVELESS

Nicola Cornick

Nicola Cornick became fascinated by history when she was a child and spent hours poring over historical novels and watching costume drama. She studied history at university and wrote her Master's thesis on heroes. When she isn't writing, she works as a guide for the National Trust in a seventeenth-century house. Nicola loves to hear from readers and can be contacted by e-mail at ncornick@madasafish.com and via her website at www. nicolacornick.co.uk

Don't miss *The Confessions of a Duchess*,
Nicola Cornick's fantastic new novel,
available in July 2010 from MIRA Books.

Chapter 1

London, December 1806—three weeks before Christmas

When Lord Alexander Beaumont entered Whites that night the entire room fell silent. No man would meet his eyes; their gazes slid away to study the pattern on the carpet or the brandy in their glasses. Throats were cleared, cuffs inspected with startling intensity.

"Gentlemen?" He raised one quizzical dark brow. "Would anyone care to enlighten me as to what is wrong?"

There was silence.

"Charles?" he prompted.

"Devil take it, Alex," his friend Charles Wheeler complained, "I knew you would ask me."

"That's what friends are for, Charles," Alex said smoothly. "Well?"

Charles stood up. He loosened his neck cloth, palpably ill at ease. "Don't know where to start, old fellow."

"Try the beginning," Alex advised.

"Good luck, Charlie," someone said sotto voce.

"It's Lady Melicent," Wheeler blurted out. "Your wife."

His wife.

No one *ever* spoke to Lord Alexander Robert Jon Beaumont about his wife.

"Thank you, Charles," Alex said. "We may have been apart for a couple of years now, but I am still aware who Melicent is."

Wheeler winced. Several men drew in their breath in sympathy.

"She's… She's written a book," Wheeler said. "Several books. This is the most recent." He grabbed a slim tome from the hands of a man at a nearby table and handed it to Alex.

"Steady on, Charlie," the man protested. "I was enjoying that!"

"Bentley…" Wheeler said in a warning tone.

The man's eyes flickered to Alex's hard face and he fell silent.

"'The Adventures of a Woman of Pleasure by Lady Loveless.'" Alex read the gold lettering aloud. He flicked open the book.

"'Being naked and laid open to him kindled so great a rapture in her that she lay in wanton pleasure waiting for him to plunge his huge—'"

A great harrumphing and clearing of throats followed. Alex closed the book softly and looked at his friend. "You are claiming that Melicent, *my wife*, is this Lady…Loveless?"

"Yes! Don't call me out," Wheeler added as Alex took a purposeful step toward him, murder in his eyes. "Bentley bribed the publisher and found out that the manuscripts are sent from someone called Mrs. Durham, from Peacock Oak in Yorkshire.…" He made a pleading gesture. "You know that was Lady Melicent's maiden name and that she resides there now." He shook his head. "She has to be stopped, Alex. She bases the characters in her books on members of the *Ton* and they are too accurately portrayed for comfort." He gestured to Bentley again. "Will's betrothal to Miss Flynn was ruined because there is a scene in the book where a character called Bill Gentley ravishes an actress in a box at the theater during a performance!"

"We all know that happened," Alex said dryly.

"That isn't the point!" Bentley piped up.

"Bentley lost an heiress worth sixty thousand," Wheeler said. "Lady Loveless's sources are impeccable. Which is why she has to be stopped."

Alex tapped the book thoughtfully against the palm of his hand. "She will be."

"What are you going to do?" Wheeler asked.

"I am going to Yorkshire," Alex said. He smiled at the look of horror on his friend's face. "No need to fear, Charles—it is the north of England, not the North Pole."

"Yorkshire in winter," Wheeler spluttered.

"Yes," Alex said, "and I will take this with me." He raised the book, and the candlelight gleamed on the gold-lettered name, Lady Loveless, on the cover. "It will prove useful…for research purposes."

"Devil take it, Alex," Bentley called, "I was reading that!" But he spoke to thin air.

Lady Loveless indeed.

How very apt for his estranged wife.

Out in the street it was snowing, tiny flakes on the edge of a cold east wind. Alex turned up the collar of his coat, refused the offer of either a hackney carriage or a sedan chair, and set off down the dark streets toward Cavendish Square. Almost he relished the idea of a run-in with a pickpocket or thief. It would at least relieve some of his anger and frustration.

The wind stung his face. He felt cold inside as well, his heart shriveled, encased in ice. *Melicent*. He thought of his bride on their wedding day. They had met for the first time a mere week before. Melicent had been a gangly debutante in her first season, with long conker-brown hair and huge brown eyes. She had been impossibly shy and seductively innocent. Even though Alex had been furious to be forced into marriage by his father, the Duke of Beaumont, he had tried not to blame Melicent.

He had been attentive to her throughout the wedding breakfast, trying to draw her out, thwarted by her reserve. Later that night he had consummated his marriage, treating his young wife with gentleness and patience, but the encounter had not been a success, for she had lain as still and cold as a statue and he felt unfulfilled and empty afterward. A few more unsatisfactory couplings had followed, but after a fortnight or so he had not sought her bed or her company any longer. Running the Beaumont estates had kept him fully occupied; they were both wife and mistress to him. He needed nothing more.

Occasionally he would appear at balls to squire Melicent in a dance or two. His mother insisted on it and it silenced the gossips and his own guilty conscience. He and his wife had never spoken of their unsatisfactory marriage. It could not be said that the two of them had drifted apart, he thought now, for they had never come together in the first place.

He was sure that no one, least of all Melicent, had guessed at the fury that had burned him up inside. She would have had no notion of the frustration and rage engendered by the threats the Duke of Beaumont had used to force his younger son into marriage. Alex's father had wanted to ensure the succession and he had known that his heir, Alex's elder brother, Henry, with his preference for men, would never marry. The duke had therefore blackmailed Alex, threatening to deny him the right to run the Beaumont estates if he did not wed. Alex had loved Beaumont with a passion from the moment he was born. The lands and the people were his life. He was the only one in the family who cared a rush for them. His father could not have chosen a more effective weapon.

The weight of the book in Alex's pocket brought his thoughts back to Melicent and reminded him that she might have been an untutored virgin when first they had married, but that she had certainly gained some experience from somewhere—*or someone*—in the meantime. The anger kindled in him once again. How could Melicent, with her sweet, honest eyes, her generous smile and her patent innocence, have become Lady Loveless, the shameless purveyor of erotic literature? It seemed impossible.

They had been married for two years and it was a month after the Duke of Beaumont's death when Melicent had told him that she was going to Yorkshire to care for her mother and that she would be staying indefinitely. Her own father had died the previous year, her mother was an invalid and Melicent's feckless young brother Aloysius was running wild.

They had quarreled for the first time in a married life previously marked by indifference. Alex had forbidden her to go. He could see now that he had been driven by pride; it was one thing for him to treat Melicent with careless unconcern, but quite another matter for her to defy him. And she *had* defied him.

"You don't want me!" she had said bitterly, her belongings scattered about her as she hastily packed a portmanteau. "You have never needed me. Mama does."

He had not heard another word from her in two years.

Now *she* would be hearing from *him*. He would go to Yorkshire and confront his errant wife. He paused. No. He would go to Yorkshire and *seduce* his errant wife according to the style laid down by Lady Loveless. He would expose her for the wanton she must surely be.

Chapter 2

Peacock Oak, Yorkshire—two weeks before Christmas

Lady Melicent Beaumont put down her pen and rested her chin on the palm of her hand. It was impossible to concentrate when she could hear her mother's querulous tones floating down from the room above:

"I want Melicent! Where is she? And where is the doctor? I told you to send for him hours ago! I feel as sick as a cushion, and if he does not come soon I am like to perish here and now in my bed! No, do not build the fire any higher, you foolish woman! It is far too hot in here and is positively smothering me—"

Melicent sighed. She could not have blamed Mrs. Lubbock very much if she was tempted to take the pillow and squash it firmly over her mother's face. Mrs. Durham, a hypochondriac whose imaginary illnesses were always so much worse than anyone else's, had taken to her bed when Melicent's father had died and she had made everyone dance attendance on her ever since. It had taken Melicent only a few short weeks to realize that her mother was a tyrant. Unfortunately by then it was too late to turn back. After her last, dreadful quarrel with her husband she would not, could not, creep back to London with her tail between her legs. And so she was trapped here in Peacock Oak, in the little grace-and-favor house provided by a distant cousin, the Duchess of Cole; trapped in this drab existence with her ghastly mother and her idle brother and a very long-suffering servant.

"Miss Melicent is working, ma'am," she heard Mrs. Lubbock say with stolid patience. The housekeeper was a treasure, unflappable and fortunately impervious to insult. "She has sent for the doctor—"

"I will not see him!" Mrs. Durham was becoming shrill. Melicent sighed.

She reread the lines she had just written.

"'Borwick Hall is built in late seventeenth-century style with decorative plasterwork in the drawing-room....'"

She sighed again. The style was very dry. Mr. Foster, the antiquarian for whom she worked, disliked flowery language in his architectural guides, and so her prose was dull enough to send even the most devoted country house visitor to sleep.

Mrs. Lubbock's heavy tread sounded on the stair and then the housekeeper knocked softly on the door of the study.

"Begging your pardon, Miss Melicent, but your mama is refusing to see the physician. I sent for Dr. Abbott, but he is out on a call and his wife said she would send his nephew, who is here to help him over Christmas, it being the time that many people fancy themselves ill, so Mrs. Abbott says…"

Mrs. Durham's bell rang sharply, simultaneous with the heavy knocker sounding on the front door. A wail came from upstairs:

"Lubbock, where are you?"

Melicent rubbed her eyes. They felt tired and gritty from writing in the afternoon's gray winter light. She really should have lit a candle, except that candles were expensive and she could not afford the luxury.

The knocker sounded again. Evidently the doctor's nephew was an impatient man.

Mrs. Durham's wailings intensified.

"Please go up to Mama, Mrs. Lubbock, and see if you may calm her," Melicent said wearily. "I shall explain to the new doctor that Mama cannot see him at present. I expect that Dr. Abbott warned him of Mama's caprices, but I do not doubt that he will still be annoyed, having come all this way for nothing."

Mrs. Lubbock lumbered back up the stairs and Melicent stood a little stiffly, wiping her ink-stained fingers on her brown worsted skirts. There was no time to check her appearance in the mirror. The hallway was cold. In winter they kept a fire only in the drawing room for visitors and in Mrs. Durham's bedroom, which was often unhealthily stuffy. The rest of the house felt like a cold larder in comparison. Mrs. Lubbock's fingers turned red and chilblained in the kitchen. Melicent kept a hot brick at her feet when she was working, but even so her hands sometimes became too cold for her to write.

She opened the front door. A blast of cold air

swirled into the hall, bringing with it a powdering of snow. The day was even more inclement than Melicent had imagined. Dark gray clouds lowered over the roofs of Peacock Oak.

She could barely see the gentleman standing in the shadow of the porch, other than to acknowledge that he was very tall and broad shouldered. The spiteful wind clipped her ankles and set her shivering, and she stood aside quickly to allow him entrance.

"Please come in, sir," she said. "You must be Dr. Abbott's nephew. Thank you for coming so promptly, although I fear you had a wasted journey. Mama will not see visitors today." She could not quite keep the exasperation from her tone, no matter how she tried. "Indeed, it is very bad of her to put everyone to so much trouble, particularly when she knows we cannot afford to pay—" He stepped into the light and she turned to look at him properly for the first time. For one long, agonizing moment her mind refused to accept the evidence of her eyes.

"But you are not the doctor!" she said foolishly. "You are…" Her voice dwindled to nothing.

The gentleman raised one dark brow in mockery, then bowed elegantly.

"Your husband," he said. "Indeed I am."

* * *

Melicent stared at him in wordless recognition. "Alex…"

Shock made her stomach turn over. It seemed impossible. She could not even begin to frame the questions that jostled in her mind.

"Why are you here?" she said. It seemed the best place to start.

Alex moved farther into the lamplit hall, and she could see what the shadows had previously hidden—the thick brown hair, the thoughtful dark eyes, the clean, hard lines of his face. He did not look a day older than when she had seen him last. He still showed the expensive tailoring, the air of unconscious authority and the town bronze that came from years of privilege. She had always felt like a country mouse beside his casual elegance. A hot wave of mortification swept over her as she looked down at her drab gown with its pulled threads.

"I came to find you." His voice was deep and it struck a chord inside her that made her shiver a little. "I thought that we had been apart too long." His gaze appraised her thoughtfully. "You look beautiful, Melicent."

It took her breath away even as her mind

protested that it could not be true. Heat swept through her as she stood beneath his disturbingly intimate and lazy gaze, heat that had nothing to do with the fire burning in the drawing room. He looked too masculine, too virile to be in the dull, dark atmosphere of the cottage. Melicent pressed her hands together nervously, and in doing so caught sight of her stained and frayed apron. A feeling of embarrassment replaced the sensation of sensual awareness. Whatever he said, she knew that she looked worn and old. Worse, she had inadvertently spilled to him various details such as her mother's hypochondria, her own exasperation and their straitened financial circumstances. And that was before he was barely in the door.

"You should have told us that you were coming." She resisted the urge to press her palms to her hot cheeks. "I hope you have not had too difficult a journey? The roads can be treacherous this time of year." She looked about them at the painfully bleak and unwelcoming hallway. She had not even had the time to decorate it with wintergreen to celebrate Christmas. Not that she had felt like celebrating anything this year.

"We are ill equipped to offer you hospitality

here, my lord," She said. "If you would prefer to stay at the inn in the village…"

She knew she was rambling. Alex took her hands in his, silencing her. Regret and pain sliced through her.

I came to find you, he had said. But he had left it so long. She had seen his absence as further proof that he did not care, had never cared. She had known from the very start that he had never wanted to marry her. She had buried her grief and regret and had tried to banish the foolish, childish infatuation she had felt for him. She had thought she had succeeded. But now, with one touch of his hand, he had shown that for the lie it was.

"Melicent," he said softly. His lips brushed her cheek, sending quivers of sensation tingling through her. Her breath hitched in her throat. She reminded herself that she was angry and hurt at his neglect and his callous indifference. She could not feel that and yet still respond to his touch. But when she looked up into his eyes she almost gasped at the expression of intense, dark desire she saw there. Her hands trembled in his. He drew her closer.

The front door opened and a young man of about twenty years burst in, shattering the moment. His fair hair was disordered by the wind. His clothes stank of stale ale. He skidded to a halt and blinked at them, swaying slightly.

"Melicent? *Beaumont*? What the hell—"

"Alex, you will remember my brother Aloysius?" Melicent said hastily.

Alex freed her gently. "Of course," he said. "How are you, Durham?"

Aloysius Durham squared up to him pugnaciously. "I said what the hell are you doing here, Beaumont? How dare you just walk in? I'd like to rearrange your face—" He stumbled, almost falling, and knocked over the hat stand.

"He's drunk," Melicent said. "I do apologize." It was not an uncommon occurrence with Aloysius, but she wished it had not happened now.

"No need for apologies," Alex said. He gave her a lopsided smile that set her pulse awry. "He does have a point. However—" he grabbed Aloysius by the scruff of the neck "—I think he should sober up before he is permitted to upbraid me."

Before Melicent's fascinated gaze he dragged her brother down the passage and out into the yard. She heard the sound of the water pump and then Aloysius howling. The noise was matched by a cantankerous wail from upstairs.

"Melicent!" Her mother was calling. "What is happening?"

Smothering a smile, Melicent ran upstairs. She was almost certain that her mother would have a miraculous recovery in order not to miss anything else. One way and another, Alex's arrival in their household had set the cat amongst the pigeons.

Alex built up the fire in the drawing room and settled back in a comfortable but faded Chippendale chair to the side of the hearth. This seemed to be the only warm room in the house. The rest of the place was colder and less welcoming than the grave. He disliked the thought of Melicent almost literally freezing to death in here, shivering in her plain, worn worsteds. It puzzled him, too. He had been meticulous in making sure that his agent paid her a monthly allowance. Where had the money gone?

He thought of Melicent in her stained apron, her hair awry, the lines of worry and tiredness etched deep on her face. A wave of tenderness took him by surprise. She deserved better than to have to manage a young drunkard of a brother and a bully of a mother.

He had sobered Aloysius up somewhat abruptly

and dispatched the youth upstairs to find a change of clothes. Aloysius had grumbled but had succumbed to Alex's authority. The lad was clearly running wild and, if the large bag of money in his pocket was anything to go by, was a gambler as well as a drunk.

Alex looked about the room. It was as bare and unappealing as the rest of the house, the furniture battered and old. From the drawer in a side table a few sheets of foolscap poked out. Alex took them out and held them up to the faint light, perusing them with mild curiosity.

"The Further Adventures of a Woman of Pleasure by Lady Loveless…"

Lady Loveless, he thought, should be more careful in concealing her inflammatory manuscripts. Not that Melicent looked anything like a writer of erotic fiction. One would never guess. The thick, heavy material of her winter gown concealed all the delicious lines and curves of her body. Alex was surprised to discover that he was very anxious to reacquaint himself with those curves. And then there was her rich dark hair, scraped back into an unbecoming knot but that would spread out over his bare chest like a swatch of silk. The image of Melicent, naked in his arms, soft, sweet and yielding as he remembered, hardened his body into arousal. He turned to the manuscript again:

"The soft sheen of the pearls glowed in the half light. He drew them over the swell of her breasts and down to pool about her navel...."

He had brought pearls as a Christmas gift for Melicent. The image of her wearing them and nothing else fixed itself in his mind; the slide of the jewels against the translucent pallor of her skin, the quickness of her breathing as her sensual pleasure mounted, the desperate little sounds she would make in the extremes of her ecstasy...

"She made a soft noise of surrender and spread herself for him, and he eased her thighs farther apart and slid—"

There was a scraping at the drawing-room door and Alex jumped visibly, shoving the sheets into his pocket. He tried to rearrange himself so that his physical state would not be too obvious.

Melicent stood in the doorway, dressed in an unfashionable evening gown. He found that he wanted to rip it off her and make love to her on the carpet. Clearly Lady Loveless's provocative prose was creating havoc within him. He struggled for some control.

Melicent looked at him, a slight frown on her brow. "It is very hot in here."

He knew.

"You look rather flushed, my lord. Are you developing a fever?"

He certainly was.

"I am well," Alex said. His voice sounded strangely husky. He cleared his throat.

"Dinner is ready," Melicent said, still looking concerned. "It is only mutton and vegetables. I am afraid that we do not keep a very elaborate table...."

She carried on talking about the food, but Alex could not concentrate. He was watching her lips move, plush and pink. He wanted to taste her. He could not help himself. He crossed the room in two strides, pulled her into his arms and kissed her.

It was heated, intimate and exactly like the fantasy he had imagined from the first moment he had read her writing. She made a very sweet sound of capitulation in the back of her throat and melted against him, eager and willing, her lips parting beneath the pressure of his, inviting him in. Her scent surrounded him, apples and honey; it was on her skin and in her hair, and suddenly his mind went blank of everything except desire and he was kissing her deeply, plundering her mouth, as his tongue moved against hers in demand and possession.

They broke apart as the dinner gong sounded. Melicent was panting, her hair ruffled, lips soft and damp, eyes wide and dark with desire. Alex felt another spear of lust go through him. He was not sure if he could wait until after dinner to have her. Never had the idea of forcing down a piece of overcooked mutton appeared so unappealing. But on the other hand, delay could be an aphrodisiac. Perhaps he could use the time to stoke their mutual desire. He rather liked that idea. For one thing was for sure, and that was that he would not be occupying the guest chamber that night.

Chapter 3

Melicent tried fiercely to concentrate on her dinner, but her efforts were to no avail. Alex was sitting opposite her and she was aware of nothing but him. The table was small and every so often his thigh would brush hers beneath the cloth. Each time it happened her nerves would jump with tension and barely suppressed longing. She was conscious of his hands, strong and tanned, as he held his knife and fork, and of his voice, low and intent as he maintained a scrupulously polite conversation with her mother. Most of all she was aware of his dark gaze resting on her face. It made her heat up from the inside out, so at least she did not notice the coldness of the dining room tonight. Her heart tripped in quick, flustered strokes. Her stomach squirmed with sensuous longing. She wondered what on earth was happening to her, for although she had conceived a schoolgirl tendre for her husband on sight, she had never felt this immodest, wanton and reckless lust for him.

He caught her eye. His firm lips curved into a smile that promised to fulfill every one of those wanton thoughts. Melicent almost whimpered aloud as her insides did another slow somersault.

On hearing of her son-in-law's arrival, Mrs. Durham had, predictably, risen from her bed like a phoenix, with no sign of illness at all, had donned her best evening gown and was now holding court. At the other end of the table Aloysius sulked and sighed his way through the meal, every so often shooting a look of extreme dislike in Alex's direction. Melicent smiled faintly to remember the summary way in which her husband had dealt with her brother's bad behavior. She imagined that Aloysius would be hoping for Alex's swift return to London so that he could make an equally swift return to a life of debauchery. She knew that she needed to talk to Alex about his plans. He had said nothing of whether he expected her to accompany him when he left. Many men, she was aware, were dictatorial enough to demand unquestioning obedience from their wives in such matters. Many wives would comply, thinking it their duty. She was no longer one of them.

The old hurt stirred in her. Alex could not simply walk in, *kiss* her and expect her to fall into his arms as though their estrangement had never occurred. She was no longer the starry-eyed innocent he had married four years before. She had worshipped him when first they were wed, and his cold preference for spending time on the Beaumont estates rather than on her had broken her heart. From the first she had sensed the slow-burning anger in him at being manipulated into marriage. It had terrified her, holding her silent, building a wall between them.

There was nothing remotely cold in the look that he was giving her now, though. She felt her skin prickle as his gaze slid over her like a physical touch.

"I am sure that a change in company would do you the world of good, ma'am," Alex was saying to Mrs. Durham. "It sounds as though you have suffered a terrible reversal in health in recent times, but with the right company you might find yourself miraculously restored. A small cottage in a seaside resort or in a fashionable spa would suit, perhaps? I am sure it can be arranged. And a congenial lady to act as companion…"

"That sounds delightful," Mrs. Durham simpered.

Melicent looked up sharply. She could see what Alex was doing. If the care of her mama were taken off her hands then her prime reason for staying in Yorkshire would be gone. She would have no excuses to hide behind.

"The society in Peacock Oak is very pleasant, Mama," she protested. "The Duchess of Cole has been kindness itself, and Major and Mrs. Falconer at Starbotton Manor are charming."

"The duchess has a young baby and I am sure she does not wish us to be forever hanging on her coattails," Mrs. Durham said. "As for the Falconers, I hear they are to visit his uncle, the marquis, in Scotland in the New Year. No, my dear, your husband is quite right. A remove to Bath or Cheltenham will be just the thing." She reached across the table and patted Melicent's hand. "Then I may return you to Lord Alexander's care. He has been most patient to spare you for so long, but it is selfish of me to keep you."

Melicent heard Aloysius mutter something that sounded like "It has never troubled you before, Mama." For once she felt completely in charity with her brother. She glared at Alex and met a look of limpid innocence in return.

Mrs. Lubbock entered to remove the plates and deliver a pudding of stewed rhubarb and cream.

"I have been reading some of your writings lately, my love," Alex said, passing Melicent the cream bowl. There was a spark of something disturbing deep in his dark eyes. "I wanted to tell you how much I enjoyed them."

Melicent was startled. "I did not realize that anyone knew I wrote them," she said. Mr. Foster generally took the credit for the architectural guides even though Melicent wrote at least half of the text.

"I believe your secret is out," Alex murmured. His gaze dwelled on her face, bringing the warm color up into her cheeks, making her tingle.

"Nor was I aware that anyone read them," Melicent added. She felt flustered. No doubt Alex would consider it eccentric at best and unacceptable at worst for the wife of a peer to write to supplement her income, but her mother's quack medicines were shockingly expensive and seemed to swallow the best part of her allowance—the part that Aloysius did not steal for his gambling, of course.

"I think you do yourself an injustice," Alex said, smiling at her in a manner that made her feel quite feverish. "I imagine that they must provide inspiration and entertainment for many."

"I suppose so," Melicent said doubtfully. Perhaps he was right—there were those who used the architectural guides to inform their country house visiting, but she would scarcely call them entertaining.

"I found them most stimulating," Alex continued.

Melicent's sense of astonishment increased. In no way could those dry tomes be considered stimulating, except... Alex had always been wrapped up in Beaumont, which was an architectural gem of an estate. Perhaps that was why he found her writings so interesting.

"I am glad that they please you, my lord," she murmured.

"Very much," Alex said smoothly. "I look forward to discussing them further with you. In private," he added.

"You must tell Mr. Foster that you have an avid reader, my dear," Mrs. Durham put in. "As the books were his idea..."

"Indeed?" Alex said. His eyes had narrowed. "Who, pray, is Mr. Foster?"

"Mr. Foster is an antiquarian who lives in the

village," Mrs. Durham said. "He is a very pleasant gentleman. He has always been most generous in involving Melicent in his projects."

"I see," Alex said. Melicent jumped at the undertone in his voice. He had turned slightly toward her. "You discuss your work with him?"

"Of course," Melicent said, perturbed by the look of fierce, primitive possession in his eyes and the tension she could see in his stance.

Alex paused, the bowl of steaming rhubarb before him. "And the practical aspects, the research, if you would care to call it that…"

"Oh, no," Melicent said. "That would not be proper." Mr. Foster had in fact invited her to accompany him on one of his trips to visit an historic house, but she had been obliged to decline because she had no chaperone.

Alex's expression relaxed slightly. "Well, I suppose that is a mercy."

"I might have known that you would disapprove." Melicent said with a flash of defiance. "Just because I am your wife—"

"That seems a good enough reason to me," Alex said. He turned to Mrs. Durham. "If you will excuse me, ma'am, there are matters that Melicent and I need to discuss."

"Of course," Mrs. Durham said, fluttering her hand, "but pray do not be too cruel to Melicent, my lord. We needed the money for my medicines, you see...."

"So you needed the money," Alex said between his teeth as he grabbed Melicent's wrist and practically hauled her from the dining room, "and you think that justifies you prostituting yourself like this?"

"Alex, no!" Melicent looked at him in horror. "It is not that bad! I know it is unorthodox of me—"

"Unorthodox? It is the most appalling thing imaginable."

"I had no idea you were so stuffy!" Melicent snapped. "How ridiculous you are—"

"We'll see about that."

He moved so quickly she had no time to evade him. One moment they had been standing in the dark, cold ground-floor passageway, where the air was thick with the smell of boiled vegetables, and the next he had grabbed her and his mouth covered hers and harsh reality simply melted away, leaving her feeling intensely alive and scandalously wild.

He kissed her fiercely, with primal possession, as though he wanted to imprint himself on her and claim her utterly. Melicent's knees weakened and she slid her arms around his neck to steady herself. One of his hands was resting in the small of her back and he drew her closer, fusing their bodies together so that she was achingly aware of his intense arousal. She gave a little moan and he deepened the kiss, ravishing her mouth, his tongue exploring her intimately. Her eagerness and hunger matched his. Her fingers burrowed into his hair and she offered herself with all the openness and generosity in her spirit, lost in the wonder and pleasure of the kiss. This desire that flared between them was so unexpected that it was in itself a seduction. She did not want to resist.

It was only when Alex loosened his grip a little that reality intruded once more and she could see the drab hall and hear her mother's shrill tones as she harangued Aloysius in the dining room, and then she wished to escape them all the more.

Alex was drawing her toward the stair. He was breathing hard and his eyes glittered with desire.

"Upstairs," he said. "Now."

Melicent's breath caught. A long shiver ran down to her toes. It seemed impossible that Alex was going to make love to her here in the dingy surroundings of Meadow Cottage and in doing so transport her from this dreary place to somewhere magical where she forgot all her regrets and her cares, and became as free and wild and wicked as she wanted to be. She trembled to think of it.

"We don't have a guest chamber," she began, and saw him smile.

"You don't need one, my love. I am your husband. I'll sleep with you."

Her pulse hammered. "Alex—" This seemed too swift. She could not understand it. She tried to hold on to her common sense, but she did not really want to. She wanted to run away, to find excitement in Alex's arms, even if it was only for a brief few hours.

"Yes, my sweet?" He was holding her lightly by the upper arms, bending to nip and kiss at the soft skin above her collarbone.

"Alex…" She forgot whatever it was she was going to say as his lips trailed kisses to the hollow of her throat and his fingers slipped to the buttons on her bodice. She felt one of them yield. Then another, a third, a fourth… Her gown hung open; she felt the heat of Alex's palm against one breast and shuddered with need. Alex buried his other hand in her hair so that he could pull her head back gently to allow his mouth to caress the sensitive, exposed skin of her neck. Melicent's whole body seemed to convulse with cool shivers at the brush of his lips, even as her nipples contracted to tiny, aching points that begged for his touch.

The door of the dining room opened and Mrs. Durham sailed out. "Melicent!" she called. "Where are you? I need you!"

Alex raised one dark brow. "So do I," he whispered. "And my claim is the more urgent."

He turned her smartly around before her mother could see her state of undress and grasped her wrists together behind her back. He held them in a light but firm clasp and gave her a little gentle push toward the stair, his body shielding her from view. He did not let her go as they mounted to the first floor, and with each step Melicent became more and more burningly aware of his grip on her tender flesh, the promise of it, the caress of his fingers against her pulse, the way the dark urgency grew between them until she opened the door of her bedchamber and he kicked it shut behind them. Only then did he let her go, spinning her around, ripping the buttons from her bodice and the neck of her chemise with it.

Melicent gave a gasp. "My clothes!"

"I'll buy you more." He sounded impatient. He was already kissing her again, deep, dark kisses that stole her soul, even as he slid the clothes down her body with impatient hands. She was shocked at his haste. When she had been his virgin bride he had treated her with gentle consideration. There was none of that now. His touch was greedy on her. He bent his head and sucked the tip of her nipple, and the pleasure lanced through her, spiraling down through her belly, molten and unspeakably delicious. She whimpered and her knees buckled. Alex picked her up and dropped her onto the bed, coming down over her so that his insatiable lips could once again take her breasts and draw them, hot and wet, into his mouth. Sensual bliss rippled through her at the unremitting assault. She arched to the demand of his lips, tongue and teeth, feeling her body swell with need and unfurl, lush and hot, for him.

Alex stripped off his own clothes, and she gasped at the sight of his magnificent and unabashed nudity. She had never seen him naked before. When first they were wed he had come to her room wearing a dressing gown and she had screwed her eyes up very tightly when he had divested himself of it. She had never dared look at him and even less had she reached out to touch him. Now, though, having thrown caution and modesty to the winds, she stared openly at his glorious masculine beauty, at the long legs, the hard, flat stomach, the muscular planes of his chest and shoulders, the honey-colored skin. He was hugely aroused and he looked enormous. Remembering the acute embarrassment and pain of her wedding night, Melicent felt a momentary pang of fear, but then he joined her on the bed and the delicious friction of bare skin against bare skin drove all anxiety from her.

He reached for something from the nightstand and Melicent saw that he had one of her quill pens in his hand.

"The tools of your trade," Alex said. "How appropriate." His eyes had narrowed to a dark glitter, heavy with lust. He took the quill and brushed it over her breasts, and Melicent was so shocked that she fell back, boneless with lust, on the bed. The touch of the plume was soft and sensuous, and the stealthy, subtle sweep of the feather over her nipples caused them to harden further. Melicent gave a gasp and arched helplessly, and Alex made a sound of satisfaction deep in his throat.

The feather danced its teasing way down the curve of her stomach, making Melicent's muscles tense and the goose bumps play across her skin. It was soft and tantalizing, making her squirm in sensuous torment. She felt Alex spread her thighs wide apart and push a pillow beneath her bottom, raising her, exposing her. Before she could form either question or protest, the naughty lick of the plume began again, stroking the impossibly vulnerable skin of her inner thighs, flicking upward against her cleft in a sly caress until she writhed, her fingers digging into the covers. The gentle brush of the feather became firmer and defter, back and forth across the very core of her, fierce, fast, wicked, working over her, until the tip of it found the center of all pleasure and the coiled desire within her burst and she tumbled over the edge in rapturous delight for the very first time in her life. She bucked, and immediately Alex held her hips down and his mouth replaced the feather, his tongue flicking relentlessly against her until the hot sweetness swamped her again, driving out all rational thought, and she lay limp and ravished, stunned and silent, on the bed.

"Turn over."

Melicent barely had the energy to move and Alex had to roll her over himself. She felt the pillow press into her stomach, and then Alex was lifting her onto her knees and his hands moved over the curve of her bottom, raising her, canting her body to exactly the right angle to take her. He slid inside her and they both cried out as he started to move within her in thick, hard strokes. She felt so tight and so full and so impossibly pleasured, but even as she was sure she could take no more, the ripples of ecstasy started deep in her belly.

"Not yet." He had felt it, too. He withdrew until there was little more than a tantalizing inch of him still inside her. "You owe me more than that."

Melicent did not know what he meant, nor did she care. His hands came around to toy with her breasts and she instinctively pushed back against him, wanting the penetration, wanting him deep within her. She could sense his control and his desperate desire to possess her, but he merely laughed and held back, taking her with quick, sharp, shallow movements that only left her wanting more. The ruthless invasion of her body went on and on, her breasts rubbing provocatively against the cover with each thrust until, tormented beyond bearing, she felt the rapture build inside her for a third time.

"Not yet," Alex said again, holding back.

"I can't help it!" Melicent wailed. Her entire body shook with spasm after spasm of helpless ecstasy and she fell forward onto the bed, her legs shaking too much to hold her up. Alex followed her down, still inside her, and they lay, she quiescent beneath him, whilst the tremors racked her and she sobbed her pleasure.

She could not understand what had happened to her. Starved of physical enjoyment for so long, she seemed utterly at Alex's mercy. To desire and be desired was so heady. The discovery of this wild, wanton passion within her was intoxicating, driving out all other thoughts and needs.

She was not sure how long they lay there, she twitching with the aftermath of passion, he still hot and huge and heavy inside her. Her mind reeled as he tumbled her over and took her still-shuddering body with his again. His strokes were hard, measured and deep, raising an echo of feeling in her that Melicent would have sworn was impossible after the bliss her body had already experienced.

"I cannot," she begged, even as the muscles in her belly trembled and jumped again in response to the demand of his body on hers.

"You can."

"Oh, yes…" Her word ended on a whimper of pleasure as Alex licked at her mouth and took her lower lip between his teeth, biting gently.

"I want to take you back to Beaumont with me," he whispered as his tongue took her mouth much as his body was taking hers, "and make love to you all the time, Melicent. Before breakfast when you are rosy and warm and soft from sleep, and when you have dressed, so that I can strip you naked again, and when you are getting ready for dinner wearing nothing but the jewels I will give you—"

His licentious words were too much for her, and Melicent climaxed tight and hard about him and he drove himself furiously into her, and finally the world shattered about them both and they fell together and shattered into bliss and eventually into peace.

Alex woke as the winter dawn light started to creep into the bedroom. Melicent was curled up against him, her head resting in the curve of his shoulder. Alex moved slightly and she burrowed closer to him. Her hair was spread across his chest just as he had imagined it in his dreams. She was deliciously warm and soft, and she smelled faintly of apples and honey. Her face was serene in sleep.

Alex had never woken like this before. When first they had been wed he had always left Melicent's room immediately after making love to her and had retired to his own chamber next door. He slept alone and woke alone. He had thought that he liked it; he had always been a man comfortable in his own company.

Now he looked at Melicent, so vulnerable and trusting, and he felt a sense of peace and protectiveness so profound that it shook him to the depths of his being. He had been driven by anger and lust and possessiveness the previous night, and it would have been easy to see Melicent's response to him as the brazen behavior of an experienced woman, the sort of woman he would expect the erotic writer Lady Loveless to be. Yet he could not believe Melicent had been unfaithful to him. Although she had met with equal passion every one of the sensual demands that he had made on her, there had been no artifice or calculation in her. The sweet honesty of her response to him had touched him profoundly. She had been as open and generous in her lovemaking as he suspected she was in every other aspect of her life. She was simply a very candid and giving person.

Alex felt a sudden pang that he had never taken the trouble to get to know his wife properly before. He had thought himself the injured party when his father had blackmailed him into marriage. But

Melicent, too, had deserved better. Now, though, he could make up for the neglect and the hurt of the past. He would court her, cherish her and show her how important she was to him. He felt supremely satisfied at the thought. He was even prepared— most magnanimously—to overlook her ventures into literature. Her work as Lady Loveless had been rather unorthodox, of course, but she had been doing it for the right reasons. Mrs. Durham was greedy and extravagant. It was easy to see from whom Aloysius had inherited his profligate ways.

Alex turned his head and saw that Melicent was awake. She had pulled the sheet up to her chin and was watching him with a mixture of shyness and wariness in her eyes. His heart turned over to see it. He pressed a kiss against the silken softness of her hair.

"Good morning, my love."

"Alex," Melicent said. Her eyes grew even bigger as she looked at the rangy length of him taking up most of the space in her chaste single bed. "Did I dream it," she began hesitantly, "or did we…"

"We did," Alex said, smiling, and saw the color deepen in her cheeks.

"Oh!" She scrambled away from him as though she had been scalded and climbed out of the far side of the bed, taking most of the bedclothes with her. The room was icy cold. Alex's erection, which had been swelling most enjoyably as a result of his memories of the previous night and the effect of having Melicent's yielding body pressed against him, dwindled rapidly in the chill.

"Melicent," he said, "please come back to bed." But she shook her head. She was backing away from him with something that looked like horror in her expression. Alex suddenly felt chilled by more than the cold room.

"I don't know how I could have done that," she said in a rapid undertone. "I must have been mad, when you care nothing for me and never have done! To have humiliated myself and behaved like such a wanton—"

Alex grabbed her wrist to stop her rushing from the room. The bedclothes fell to the floor, leaving her naked. She gave a little wail and tried to cover herself, but he was too quick for her, scooping her up and pulling her back to the bed.

"Melicent," he said. He was not sure if he was more concerned by her words or by the look of blank misery on her face. "I don't understand. You did not humiliate yourself last night. It was wonderful, perfect—" He tried to find the words but stopped in dismay as he saw a tear squeeze out of the corner of her eye and run down her cheek into her hair. She lay quite still, making no attempt to cover her nakedness now. She looked distractingly lovely, all lush curves and creamy skin—and tormented misery. Alex gathered her close in his arms, wanting only to comfort her.

"Tell me what is wrong," he said, his lips pressed against her hair.

He felt a sob shake her, but she repressed it. "I am so *angry* with myself for making love with you," she said. "I did not want to want you, but it had been so long and I… I am not sure quite what happened to me."

She sounded so lost and miserable that he hastened to reassure her. "Sweetheart," he said, "there is no shame in it. It was wonderful. And we are wed—"

She pulled herself abruptly from his arms and her eyes flashed with fury. "Yes, we are wed, Alex, but for all of our marriage you have paid no heed to me at all! You might as well have been a bachelor for all the difference it made!" She drew the blankets about her and sat looking at him with a sort of defiant, disheveled dignity. It made him want to kiss her, but he judged that this was not, perhaps, the moment.

"Oh, I always knew that it was your papa who desired the match, not you," Melicent said bitterly. "I knew you preferred Beaumont to me! Whenever you came to me you touched me as though you hated me! And when I left, you did not trouble to follow me, or even to write. I had more correspondence with your agent than I did with you, and I would have given everything for just one letter from you!" She swallowed hard. "I was so angry. But then last night I forgot all of that and was so shameless and so…so brazen!" She made a small, infuriated noise. "I cannot forgive myself," she finished, a little forlornly. "Not when I know you have never cared a rush for me and never will."

Alex was staring at her as though she had hit him over the head with a saucepan, Melicent thought. He ran one hand through his hair, disordering it thoroughly. He looked baffled and upset and so damned handsome that Melicent swore on the spot that she was not—she really, really was *not*—going to forgive him and fall straight back in love with him in the same foolish, immature and pointless fashion that she had done when she had been a nineteen-year-old bride.

Alex took her hands in his. She allowed them to stay there because it felt right, even though it should have felt wrong.

"Melicent." He sounded wretched. "Sweetheart, I had no idea. I thought that you did not realize…" He stopped.

Melicent's heart sank like a stone.

I thought that you did not realize…

Even though she had known he had not cared a ha'porth for her, it felt devastating to have the matter confirmed. She bent her head and stared at their linked hands.

"I realiszd from the start," she said. "Your father forced you to wed me, did he not? I do not know how or why, but I know he did."

"He threatened to take Beaumont away from me," Alex said simply. "He pointed out that I had no right to run the estates, and he was correct, of course, for he owned them and after him my elder brother, Harry, inherited. I had no claim at all."

"But you love Beaumont with all your heart," Melicent said. She felt cold with shock. So this was the threat the duke had used to coerce his son—taking away from him the one thing that gave his life meaning. "You are the only one who has ever cared for the land and the people," she said. "Without you the whole place would have gone to ruin long ago!"

Alex looked at her. His dark eyes were tired. "Papa wanted to ensure the succession of the title. He knew Henry would never wed. Put plainly, Henry's affections are not for the female sex. So he decided to coerce me even though I was young and was not ready for marriage." He looked rueful. "I was too wrapped up in my books and too in love with Beaumont to have space for anyone or anything else, Melicent. I am sorry."

"You were angry," Melicent whispered, "and now I understand why."

"I tried not to let it show with you," Alex said. "I knew it was not your fault." He shook his head. "But you are right—whenever I saw you, whenever I touched you, I felt such anger over my father's blackmail. It was inevitable that you should feel it, I suppose." His fingers tightened on hers. "I must have hurt you very badly. I am so very sorry, Melicent."

Melicent's throat tightened with tears. She was not going to say that did not matter, because it did. It mattered a lot. But with understanding came forgiveness of the fury and frustration of a young man who had been put in an impossible situation.

"Do you still feel angry with your father?" she asked.

Alex shook his head. "When he died, so did my anger. I realized I had been consumed with a fury that was futile and senseless." He raised her hand to his lips. "After he died I came to find you, Melicent—I was going to tell you everything and suggest that we should start again, but then you told me you were leaving and I thought it was too late for us. In my pride and my misery I let you go."

Melicent leaned forward and kissed him gently. "And *I* left because I could bear no more of our estrangement," she said. "I knew almost from the first that it was a mistake to come here to Peacock Oak, but in my pride I could not admit it." She sighed. "We have both been very foolish, but perhaps it is not too late for us after all. I would like very much to start again."

"I think," Alex said, wicked amusement in his eyes now, "that we already have."

"We started the wrong way around," Melicent said, trying to sound severe. "We should get to know one another properly first, before…"

Alex tumbled her into his arms. "Before we make love?" he said.

"Absolutely," Melicent whispered as her lips met his.

Chapter 4

The Night Before Christmas

Getting to know her own husband over the past fortnight, Melicent reflected, had been a delightful experience. Christmas this year was far exceeding her expectations. Together she and Alex had collected holly and mistletoe to decorate the house. They had visited the nearby village of Fortune's Folly to buy fuel and candles and a Christmas turkey (a great improvement on the pickled scrag end of mutton that Mrs. Lubbock had been planning to serve on Christmas Day), they had taken long walks through the snowy countryside and they had attended church together, where the gossip about the arrival of Lady Melicent's handsome husband, and his clear devotion to her, had barely died down sufficiently to allow the rector to deliver his sermon. They had taken dinner with the Duchess of Cole and with Major and Mrs. Falconer and had been very merry in company, for Mrs. Durham was so miraculously restored to health that she was even prepared to indulge in a game of Christmas charades. Alex, on seeing Melicent's raw and chilblained hands, had bought her some rose-scented hand cream and a pair of exquisitely soft kid gloves, and had offered to help her with her household chores, which Melicent considered a sign of true devotion.

Alex had already written to his agent to arrange for Mrs. Durham's removal to Bath and for the appointment of a lady companion for her. Which, Melicent thought as she knelt to light the fire in the drawing room on Christmas Eve, only left the problem of Aloysius. She wondered what they were going to do with him. He had no obvious talents, unless it was for the wasting of money, he had no aptitude for study and he was too lazy to join the army. She moved over to the desk to light the stand of candles, smiling a little as she remembered the unceremonious way in which Alex had woken Aloysius up on the first morning with a can of hot water and the words "I hear that you are too idle to help your sister with the household duties, Durham. Well, if you want a fire in your bedroom in future, you will have to lay it yourself."

Aloysius had sworn at Alex and thrown the can of water at him, but he was still up and dressed and shaved in time for breakfast, which was in itself something of a miracle, and he had helped clear the dishes afterward, albeit with an ill grace. Her little brother was thoroughly spoiled, Melicent thought, but he was also frustrated and angry in some way. Alex, with his own experience to draw upon, seemed to understand that, and his firm but fair approach was slowly yielding results.

The candles were good quality beeswax rather than the tallow they had used before Alex had arrived. By the golden light Melicent could see a couple of sheets of paper lying on the carpet beneath the desk. Alex had been writing letters earlier and she assumed he must have dropped the papers. She picked them up and glanced at the writing.

"He took the feather in his hand and trailed it tantalizingly over her plump cleft, plying it with little teasing darts and strokes until she was begging for surcease…"

Melicent gave a tiny shriek of shock and collapsed backward into a chair as she read the blueprint for her seduction.

Alex had been looking forward to this moment all day. In his pocket was the pearl necklace that he had brought with him as a Christmas gift for his wife. He knew it was customary to exchange presents on Twelfth Night, but he could not wait any longer. With each day that had passed he had watched Melicent blossom as they grew to know one another. They talked all day, and at night they lay in her little narrow bed and made the most perfect, passionate love. She was so beautiful in his eyes. He wanted to give her the pearls as a token of his regard for her. He paused with his hand on the doorknob. Hell, whom was he trying to fool? He had fallen head over heels in love with his wife and he wanted to give her the pearls as a sign of his love for her. And he was going to tell her so, too.

He opened the drawing-room door.... And was confronted by a termagant brandishing sheets of paper in his face.

Melicent was very pale, her eyes burning with fury. "Is this yours?" she demanded. "Did you bring this...this *smut* with you as some sort of guide to seduction?" The sheets shook in her hands as she started to read.

"'The feather skipped a wicked path across the soft skin of her inner thigh and tickled her most secret place....'"

Oh dear. Alex grimaced. He had almost forgotten about Lady Loveless in the pleasure of getting to know Melicent properly. Now, though, he rather thought that some difficult questions were heading his way and he was not at all sure he wanted to answer them. He could see his perfect, new domestic bliss disappearing faster than Aloysius's money in a gambling hell.

Melicent looked up, her eyes wild. "Alex, did you *write* this?"

"Of course not," Alex said. He had the feeling that things were going badly awry. "Of course I didn't write it," he said. "You did."

"What?" Melicent shook the papers again. The words danced before his eyes. *Caressing... breasts...pert and round...tight pink nipples...* Alex swallowed hard and tried to concentrate.

"You think that I wrote this filth?" Melicent demanded.

"It isn't filth." Alex felt moved to protest. "It is very well written and extremely erotic."

"I can see that!" Melicent snapped. She read a few more lines and a hint of color came into her cheeks. "Well, yes, perhaps I was wrong. I can see that it is rather sensuous and stimulating, but…" She frowned suddenly. "You said that you thought my writings were inspiring," she whispered. "You said they were exciting!"

"And so they are," Alex said. "They are nothing to be ashamed of, sweetheart. You write very vividly."

"But I write architectural guides to historic houses," Melicent said. "They are not in the least exciting."

She put the crumpled sheets down on the desk and took a step toward him, eyes narrowing. Alex's heart turned over. He knew what she was going to ask next.

"Did you come here because you thought I was Lady Loveless?" she asked. Then, when he did not answer immediately, her face crumpled.

"Damnation take it," she said. "You did!" Her voice was bitter. "There was I thinking that you had come because you wished us to be reunited, when all along you were here to unmask me as the author of erotic literature!" She glanced at the sheets of manuscript. "You used what you thought was my own writings as a manual to ravish me! That first night when I thought you really wanted me for myself alone, when I thought that everything was open and honest between us, you were simply following a calculated plan!" She stalked away from him across the room. "When were you intending to spring this on me?" she demanded. "Were we to have selected readings over Christmas dinner?"

"It wasn't like that," Alex said. He rubbed his forehead, trying to think straight. All he knew was that he could not risk losing Melicent for a second time. He would not countenance it. So there was nothing for it but the truth.

"Yes, I came here because I thought you were Lady Loveless," he said, "but as soon as we started to get to know each other I forgot all about it. I don't care about the books. You can have written a library full of erotic literature for all I care! All I want is you. I swear it, Melicent."

He stood waiting, his heart in his throat, as she looked at him. He could see she wanted to believe him, but she was not quite ready to capitulate yet.

"I cannot see," she said in a small, hurt voice, "why you thought I could possibly be Lady Loveless in the first place. The idea is absurd."

"I heard in London that Lady Loveless sent her manuscripts from Peacock Oak, under the name of Mrs. Durham," Alex said. "The publisher let the matter slip. And then when I arrived here I found some sheets of Lady Loveless's latest manuscript stuffed into the drawer over there. What was I to think?"

"Hmm. I suppose you would think it unlikely that Mama was your mysterious erotic author," Melicent conceded. She tapped the sheets thoughtfully. "But if it is not Mama and it is not me, then there is only one other possible candidate, and I do not mean Mrs. Lubbock."

They looked at one another.

"Aloysius," Alex said.

"I can scarce believe it," Melicent exclaimed. "He is only a boy!"

"A boy who spends a great deal of his time in the local gambling dens and brothels, unless I miss my mark," Alex said grimly.

"I didn't know there were any," Melicent said, perplexed.

"That," Alex said, taking her in his arms, "is because you are as innocent as I had always suspected, sweetheart."

The door opened as though on cue and Aloysius Durham walked in.

Alex loosed Melicent and they exchanged a look. Melicent saw her brother's gaze fall on the manuscript, saw him swallow hard and the color leave his face.

"What we were wondering, Aloysius," she said politely, "is where you get your ideas from?"

Aloysius gulped visibly.

"Best not to ask," Alex said, a wicked smile curving his lips.

Aloysius shot him a look of gratitude. "I did not realize that anyone knew," he muttered, suddenly sounding very young.

"I fear you are unmasked," Alex said pleasantly. "I must congratulate you, Durham. You have talents that no one would ever have guessed at. Your sister and I were wondering if you would care to move to London and set up in business properly?"

"Alex," Melicent gasped, "surely you are not suggesting that Aloysius should continue his career as an erotic author?"

"Unfortunately I think that Lady Loveless's career is over," Alex said. Some steel entered his voice. "We do not want your sister's name or your mother's bandied about London as the author of these tomes, do we, Durham?"

"No sir," Aloysius stammered.

"However, in return I am prepared to set you up in a small publishing business of your own," Alex said. "I mean *reputable* publishing, Durham, though what you do in your own time is, of course, entirely your business. What do you say?"

After Aloysius had shaken Alex fervently by the hand and gone out, no doubt to celebrate his good fortune in the gambling houses and brothels of north Yorkshire, Alex pulled Melicent back into his arms.

"Which only leaves you and I," he murmured against her lips. "Come along. We are going out."

They walked through the snow down the lane that led from Meadow Cottage toward Cole Court. The sky was clear and the moon was bright and white, shedding its cold light over the glistening landscape. Everything looked enchantingly pretty and on the night air soared the faint sound of carol singing.

Melicent's hand was warm in Alex's. She was muffled up in a thick coat, scarf, gloves and boots, but she was so happy that she felt as though she was floating along in a ball gown.

"I suppose I have forgiven you for suspecting

me of being Lady Loveless," she teased Alex. "And poor Mr. Foster! When Mama said that he was the guiding light behind my work I am surprised that you did not call him out!"

"I did feel like planting him a facer," Alex admitted, drawing her to him, "but thank goodness I did not. The man would have thought me mad when all he had done was ask you to work on his architectural guides."

He kissed her, his lips cold against hers. "We are here," he said drawing her down the path to Peacock Cottage. "Mrs. Falconer was understanding enough to allow me to borrow the house when I said that I required some time alone with my wife. It is not let at present. Meadow Cottage is very small and too full of people, and there are things that I need to say to you in private."

Inside, Peacock Cottage was blissfully warm. Melicent shed her boots and coat whilst Alex lit the candles. A sumptuous cold meal was laid out, and two beautiful crystal glasses stood waiting for the wine.

"Are you hungry?" Alex asked.

"No," Melicent said. Her throat felt dry with nervousness. To be alone with Alex, here, now... She did not intend to waste the opportunity, but even after all they had shared, when it came to initiating their lovemaking she still felt a little shy. She started to unfasten her gown, and saw Alex's eyes widen in surprise and darken with sudden lust. An answering spear of need sheared through her, making her fingers shake so much on her laces that after a moment she was forced to admit defeat. "You will need to help me," she appealed. "I must shamelessly beg you to undress me and make love to me."

Alex made an involuntary move toward her, but then held back for a moment, his hands urgent on her shoulders. "Melicent, I need to talk to you—"

"Later," Melicent said, reaching up, against his lips. She felt his body harden into powerful arousal as he returned the kiss, and desire swept through them both, hot and fast, deep and fierce.

"I expect there is a very big bed upstairs," Melicent whispered when they stopped kissing for a moment in order to draw breath.

"Later," Alex said, his fingers urgent against her breast, his lips tender on the soft skin of her throat.

As it turned out, the wide, cushioned sofa in front of the fire proved to be a very acceptable substitute for the bed, and when they rolled off that, the rug was soft enough. By that time Melicent had lost the last of her inhibitions and pushed Alex onto his back and straddled his thighs, glorying in his harsh gasp of torment as she eased her body over his, sliding down, taking the whole hard length of him tightly inside her. A wash of exquisite pleasure pierced her and she cried out, and then he thrust his hips upward and drove into her, turning her so that she was beneath him and he possessed her utterly, body and soul.

Later he carried her up the stairs to the enormous bed and they made love again, falling apart at last in blissful exhaustion.

"When we were first wed," Melicent said, dreamily, "we were so *bad* at this! What changed?"

"When we were first wed we did not desire each other," Alex said. A shadow touched his eyes. "I tried to be gentle with you, but I was still angry and confused and I think that you must have realized…"

"I did," Melicent said, snuggling close to him. "I knew that no matter how tender you were with me, deep down you hated to touch me because you had been forced to wed against your will, and so I withdrew and was cold and reserved with you even though I loved you desperately."

Alex tilted her face up to his. He looked shocked. "You *loved* me?"

"Oh, with a silly, girlish infatuation," Melicent said, sighing. She took a deep breath. She could feel her heart beating in light, quick strokes at the risk she was about to take. But she had to tell him. She had never been less than honest before and she could not change now.

"I love you differently now," she said hesitantly, playing with the edge of the sheet and avoiding his eyes. "I think I have grown up."

There was a moment of absolute stillness, then Alex pulled her so tightly against him that she could barely breathe. "I love you, too, Melicent, and I will never hurt you again." His voice shook a little. "I failed you so badly before, but if you can forgive me I will make sure that I never, ever do so in future." He sighed. "Perhaps I have grown up, too."

"I like our grown-up selves," Melicent said, kissing him.

Alex rolled over and reached for his jacket. He took a long, flat package from the pocket and handed it to her. "I hesitate to give this to you, sweetheart, as they form part of yet another erotic adventure charted by the pen of the inimitable Lady Loveless, but when I bought them for you I swear I did not know." He smiled at her. "The thing that should be important is that they are given with all my love."

Melicent's fingers trembled on the catch. "A Christmas gift given with love," she whispered.

"Always," Alex said, smiling.

Melicent opened the box. The pearls gleamed lush and pale on the bed of black velvet. She ran her fingers over them.

"Alex, they are so beautiful! Thank you." She bit her lip. "I have nothing to give you in return—"

"Except your love," Alex said, "which is more than I could ever deserve or ask for."

After a suitably blissful interval, Melicent lowered her gaze modestly and a faint blush came into her cheek. "Alex," she said, "what did Lady Loveless's courtesan do with her pearls?"

"I'll show you," her husband said, drawing her back into his arms, and demonstrating with ardor just how much he adored her, as the Christmas night wrapped them in peace and love.

* * * * *

DISROBED AND DISHONOURED

Louise Allen

Louise Allen has been immersing herself in history, real and fictional, for as long as she can remember and finds landscapes and places evoke powerful images of the past. Louise lives in Bedfordshire and works as a property manager, but spends as much time as possible with her husband at the cottage they are renovating on the north Norfolk coast or travelling abroad. Venice, Burgundy and the Greek islands are favourite atmospheric destinations. Please visit Louise's website – www.louise allenregency.co.uk – for the latest news!

Don't miss *Practical Widow to Passionate Mistress*,
Louise Allen's exciting new novel,
available in June 2010 from Mills & Boon® Historical

Chapter 1

⁓⁓⁓⁓

July 1816, Norfolk

The man in the mask ran one hand down the neck of the ugly gray hunter. 'Patience, Tolly. One more to go and then it's oats for you and two dozen of the finest old brandy for me.'

The horse snorted, his ear flicking back to listen to his rider's voice as Jonathan slouched into the familiar comfort of the saddle, eyes narrowed against the late-evening light. It was past eight now and no traffic had passed along the lane for half an hour. Up to then business had been brisk and last night's wager seemed easily won. He dug a hand in his pocket and drew out the tokens he had claimed, proofs of a kiss from each of the first five women who passed down the lane on their way back from market in St. Margaret's to the villages of Saint's Mead and Saint's Ford.

There was a downy feather from the empty egg bucket of the country lass who had giggled and returned his kiss with relish; a tiny corn dolly from the elderly dame driving her donkey cart back, her baskets of straw plait almost empty, a twinkle in her eyes as she pinched his chin; a paper of pins from the thin-faced spinster who had blushed like a peony when he had respectfully saluted her papery cheek; and a promissory note for one ginger kitten (guaranteed of good mousing stock) from the farmer's wife who had roared with laughter and tipped up her round red face with cheerful anticipation.

Jonathan pinned the corn dolly to his lapel, stuck the feather in his hat brim and wondered which of his housekeepers would most appreciate a kitten. His pleasure in the evening's sport began to wane. He had another hour before he was due to join his friends at The Golden Lion for supper to present evidence of his success and the chances of the required fifth female happening along seemed increasingly poor.

Tolly lifted his head and pricked his ears. 'Hoofbeats,' Jonathan concurred. 'One horse—

likely to be a man.' He nudged the gray through a gap in the thick hedgerow, drew the empty pistol, laid it along his thigh and waited.

'Despicable, hypocritical swine,' Sarah Tatton repeated, reining in her mare to a walk and dashing the tears out of her eyes with an impatient hand. Careering around the countryside sidesaddle in evening dress was far from comfortable now that her initial fury had simmered down, to be replaced by something approaching panic.

How could she have been so meek, so trustingly innocent? Eighteen months sitting in the country, perfecting her wifely skills in domestic management, needlework and entertaining, while Papa boasted to all and sundry of the excellent match he had made for his daughter—and what had she to show for it? Her linen cupboard was immaculate, her stillroom a marvel, she could play a sonata and hold her own in the most trying dinner-party conversation and, *finally*, her betrothed had deigned to turn up to discuss the wedding.

Sir Jeremy Peters might be only moderately good-looking and not possess a sparkling wit, but he was, as everyone had told her during the course of her second Season, *a catch* for the daughter of a country baronet with moderate looks and a moderate dowry to match. Wealthy, well-connected—she could not hope to do better to oblige her papa.

'Respectable?' Sarah swore under her breath. Half an hour in his company, during which he had congratulated her on her modest gown and presented her with a hideous string of lumpy freshwater pearls had made her heart sink; she had not remembered him as being so dull. But when she had gone upstairs to change for dinner Mary, her maid, had broken down in floods of tears as she fastened her gown.

'I've got to tell you, Miss Sarah. I cannot let you marry him, not even if it means my place,' she had wailed. What Sarah had heard took her breath away and left her sick and shaken. Sir Jeremy had assaulted Mary at the house party where he had proposed to Sarah and threatened that he would tell Sir Hugh Tatton that she had offered herself for money if she said one word of it.

So Sarah confronted her father with the fact that she had discovered her betrothed was the sort of man who would ravish defenseless young women—and Papa had dismissed the matter.

'Nonsense,' he blustered, slapping his newspaper down on his desk in irritation. 'Some young trollop looking to earn herself a few shillings, I've no doubt. Asking for it.'

'But no, Papa! This is a respectable girl.' She did not dare tell him who, not with the memory of the housemaid turned off without a character when Cousin William's visit had left her pregnant. Her father was of the old school when it came to domestic discipline. 'And even if it were the case that she was willing, you cannot expect me to marry a man of such loose morals.'

'A lady ignores such matters. It is her duty to remain faithful, above reproach, and to raise her children. Her husband may seek diversion elsewhere—'

'Diversion!'

He scowled. 'Diversion. It means nothing and no lady of refined mind should think of such things, let alone admit to knowing of them.'

'I cannot possibly marry Sir Jeremy,' she announced flatly.

'You most certainly will, my girl! I'm not letting a good match like that slip through my fingers because of some missish scruples. You marry him—or I will find out who has been filling your head with this scurrilous nonsense and see they suffer for it. Do you understand me?'

How could she find Mary a suitable new post, one where she would be safe from her father's wrath? If she had been in London she could have gone to a good agency, given her glowing references, but here, deep in the country, such a plan would have to be conducted by letter and Papa insisted on her chaperone reading all her correspondence.

And how she was going to be able to keep a civil tongue in her head over dinner she had no idea. She had stood outside the drawing room gathering her composure to enter when she heard the men talking inside.

'Modest virtue, that is the thing about Miss Tatton,' Sir Jeremy was saying. 'The assurance that one is marrying a virgin of impeccable upbringing and not one of those flighty girls who live for nothing but their beaux and their parties. How precious is a lady's purity! I searched long and hard before I was confident I had found such a prize.'

The hypocrite valued only her *virginity*? He debauched young women and yet he could say such things to her father who would smugly accept them?

Sarah turned on her heel. 'Tell Sir Hugh that I have a migraine and regret I will not be able to come down this evening,' she said to the footman.

The moment his back was turned she was away to the stables.

Leaving the house for an hour or so at least gave her a chance to cool her temper, but what to do now? Fear was beginning to overcome the fury as her imagination took hold, presenting her with a vivid image of what life with Sir Jeremy would be like. Her instinct was to run, but that was pointless; how would she live?

The question became academic as she rounded a corner and found herself staring down the barrel of a large horse pistol. 'Stand and deliver.'

A highwayman? They really said that? Sarah discovered her mouth was open and shut it. The figure confronting her was straight off any broadsheet telling the shocking stories of Dick Turpin or "Hell" Hawley. A big, ugly gray horse, a tricorne hat, a cloak thrown back over his shoulders despite the heat and a black mask covering the upper half his face.

She dragged Sir Jeremy's string of pearls over her head and held it out. He was welcome to them.

'No, I don't want those, sweetheart.' His voice was amused, educated and deep; it seemed to resonate at the base of her spine. A gentleman gone to the bad?

From somewhere she found her voice. 'What do you want then?'

'One kiss and a little token to show for it.' He urged the horse up alongside her mare and she realized it was not just the horse that was big. She made herself sit still and not flinch away.

And then she found she did not want to. 'A kiss?' He was clean-shaven, his teeth white as he smiled in the evening light. The breeze brought her not the rank smell of unwashed robber that she had been expecting, but the clean odors of leather and citrus. 'It is not gallant to jest! You may have the pearls and welcome.'

'No.' He took the pearls in an ungloved hand and dropped them back around her neck, holstered the pistol and leaned toward her, doffing his hat. 'I do not jest.'

His hair was dark brown, overlong, waving from the pressure of the hat. His eyes were green, shadowed by the mask, and yet when he smiled she could just see the laughter lines in the corners, the humor.

'Just one kiss?'

He nodded as she bit her lip in indecision, his mouth curving in a way that made her want to touch it. 'If you will grant it. I do not steal from women.'

What if she should kick her heels and send the mare plunging past him? He leaned down and took the reins as though he could read her mind. Sarah stared at him, wondering why she did not scream. He really was a very strange highwayman. And she was in a very strange mood. She was conscious of her heartbeat—that was trepidation, no doubt—but what to make of the warm feeling low in her belly or the fact that her lips were dry? Sarah licked them and saw his eyes follow the movement.

'Why have you a corn dolly in your button-hole?'

'A token from the donor of my second kiss. It is a fertility symbol, I believe, but don't worry, kisses are harmless.'

An interesting definition of harmless! 'Very well. I have nothing better to be doing this evening, after all.' She tipped up her face, turning her cheek toward him and closing her eyes. And then she felt his breath warm on her skin and realized he really was only going to take what she offered and some madness seized her.

She opened her eyes and moved her head and met the hooded green gaze and his mouth found hers. 'Oh!' As she gasped his tongue slid between her lips and his free arm went around her shoulders and he lifted her against him so she was standing in the stirrup while the kiss went on…and on…and the warm evening world spun around her and his heat and the questing invasion of his tongue filled her senses and she gripped his lapels and touched her tongue to his and thought she would faint from the intensity of it.

And then she was back in the saddle and they were looking at each other as though the earth had just shifted beneath them. He seemed to be breathing rather heavily. She rather thought that if she did not loosen her stay laces that breathing would no longer be possible.

'Madam,' he said at last. 'I must thank you for giving me the most precious thing in your possession. May I ask for a token, also?'

Sarah took hold of three or four hairs that had come down from her topknot of curls, tugged them free and held them out to him. He bowed slightly and curled them with care around the corn dolly. He thought her kiss precious? A highwayman's opinion of her kiss was certainly more acceptable than Sir Jeremy's hypocritical valuation of her virginity.

'Sir, that is not the most precious thing I possess.' The words left her lips without conscious thought.

'It is not?' The green eyes rested on her face.

'No. I am a virgin.'

The gray tossed its head as though its rider had clenched his hand on the reins. 'Ma'am?' She saw him swallow.

'And that is something of a burden to me, just now,' she confessed.

'Indeed?' He looked, not shocked, but interested.

Somehow the story tumbled out. How she came to be recounting such intimate details to a complete stranger, a man—a rogue—Sarah could not fathom. Why she was not sliding from Daisy's back in a pool of embarrassment, she had no idea, but she did not even seem to be blushing. It could only be her desperation and the utter seriousness with which he was listening to her.

'In short,' she concluded, 'my father plans to marry me to a lecherous, hypocritical excuse for a gentleman for whom my only virtue appears to be my—well, my *virtue*.'

'If you were not a virgin, he would not be interested,' the highwayman remarked.

'Well, I am, so there's nothing to be done about it.'

'You could have a frank discussion with a married lady, discover some, er…details and inform your chaperone that you have lost your virtue, describing the experience so she had no doubts,' he suggested in a matter-of-fact manner, as though they were puzzling over some trivial problem.

'There is no one I could talk to.' If only her good friend Jessica was home from her honeymoon by now! She would enter into this scheme with complete frankness, but it would be another two weeks and that was too late. 'I do not think that anything less than firsthand experience would do. I can hardly make it up. But thank you, it was a very good idea.' She sighed, feeling the tears beginning to well up in her eyes again. She bit down hard on her lip to stop them; weeping and moaning was not going to get her out of this fix.

The gray backed away and she glanced up at its rider's face. Below the mask his mouth was set. He looked somewhat grim. 'I could help you.'

'Describe...*it*?' she faltered, finding she could blush, after all.

'No. I doubt I could, from a woman's point of view. No, more practically, we—'

'You want to take my virginity?' Her voice emerged as a squeak. Daisy tossed her head, catching her mistress's sudden panic.

'No, but I could *almost* take your virginity.'

'Almost.' The light was beginning to fade and she was not able to make out the nuances of his expression beneath the mask. His tone was pitched somewhere between appalled and amused.

'Almost. Just so you get the idea. Have you any knowledge of the theory, Miss, er…?'

'Sarah,' she said shortly. 'No, not much. I know it hurts and I know there is the danger of becoming pregnant and I have no desire for the former experience and certainly none for the latter.'

'I promise that neither would be the case.'

'Are you mad?' she inquired, more of herself than of him. He did not appear to be deranged and if he was an evil seducer, he was certainly going about it in a most original way. And she was beginning to find the preposterous, shocking suggestion positively…possible.

'I know you did not rob me just now, or ravish me,' she said, frowning at him in the twilight. 'And you could have done either, quite easily. I liked the way you kissed me, although I should not. You appear to be a man of principle, even if you do earn your living in an illegal manner.'

He shook his head, seeming to withdraw from the idea even as she became convinced. 'You are right, I was mad to suggest it. There must be some other way out of your predicament.'

Sarah contemplated her situation. She was not lacking, she felt, in either determination or imagination, but she could see no other way out of this. 'No, you are quite right: it is the perfect solution. And if you will not then I must find someone who will help me.' There wasn't anyone, of course, but she put every ounce of conviction she could muster into the statement.

Jonathan could feel his will being sapped by the intensity in the gray eyes fixed on his face. He believed she was in trouble, else why would she be riding alone in evening dress? She appeared to be in her right mind—which was more than he had been a moment ago as he had articulated, without thinking, the idea that had come to him.

There was an edge of desperation in her tone that convinced him that what she said of her betrothed was true and it was not simply a matter of a lovers' quarrel. And now that he had put the idea into her mind he feared she really would seek out another man if he refused her. And then there was that kiss. The taste of her like honey and roses and a hint of spice and the heat and the response that he would swear was instinctive, innocent—and deadly.

She had no idea, of course, of what he would be letting himself in for. No concept of the willpower it would take to go so far and then stop, to pleasure her just so far and no further. 'Very well.' Her expression made him smile. Her eyes widened with surprise, relief and apprehension in almost equal measure. 'I know an inn not far from here.'

'The Golden Lion.' She nodded. Of course, she must live hereabouts and know it. And be known, if only by sight. This would take some care.

He led her back along the woodland path he had come by, stopping at the shepherd's hut he had noticed earlier. 'We'll leave your mare here. There is shelter and water.' She let him lift her down, silk and light boning and warm, slender waist under his hands making his imagination run riot while he saw to the mare, conscious of Sarah's eyes on his back as he worked.

'What is your name?'

'Jonathan. Here, take this.' He swung off his cloak and tied it around her neck, flipping up the hood to cover hair and face, then boosted her up onto Tolly's broad back and swung into the saddle behind her. Ah, more torture, the soft weight of her on his thighs, the little wriggle she gave to get her balance, the scent of her body pressed warm to his chest.

'You are a successful highwayman then, Jonathan, to be able to afford The Golden Lion and yet resist my pearls?'

'Shall we say it is more of a recreation than a business?' he suggested, guiding Tolly toward the stable yard, puzzling about the woman in his arms. Not just out, certainly. Twenty-two or -three, he would guess, with some authority about her. Well-bred, respectable and, presumably, an obedient daughter up to the point her father introduced this undesirable suitor. He had never seen her before, which meant she did not move in his circles, but even so, to avoid embarrassment he rather thought he would keep his mask on.

He helped her down in the shadows and led her up the side stairs and to his room without being seen. 'Wait here. I'll not be long.'

His six friends were in the private parlor, cards on the table, bottles open, food spread out on the sideboard. They got to their feet, grinning, as he came in, still masked. 'Well,' Griffin demanded, 'have I won back the money I lost on yesterday's prizefight or am I out a dozen of my best cognac?'

'You're out.' Jonathan tossed his hat on the

table. 'Here—a feather from a maid who'd taken her eggs to market and came back with a kiss to spare for me, black hairs from a fancy young thing with her nose in the air, a corn dolly from an old duck in a donkey cart and a paper of pins from a severe dame who is doubtless still blushing. Oh yes, and the promise of a ginger kitten should I care to collect it.'

'Damn me, I never thought you'd do it.' Lord Gray splashed port into his glass and downed it in one gulp. 'I wagered against you. Get some food and come and help me win it back.' He gestured at the litter of vowels on the table.

'No, I'll leave you to it.' Jonathan walked over to the sideboard, rubbing his back. 'Pulled a muscle somehow. Damn sore. I'll take some food up and see if bed will put it to rights.'

He retreated, with a laden plate and a wine bottle in his pocket, amid gibes about what had caused the strain and ribald suggestions for curing it.

Sarah perched on the edge of the bed and wondered if she had gone mad. If she had misjudged her man, she was in serious trouble. Even if she had not, she was deliberately setting out to ruin herself. And then there was the undeniable fact that she was about to commit acts of shocking intimacy with a man. A stranger.

What was almost more disturbing, she found her heart was beating with wild anticipation at the thought of it. She wanted him in almost equal measure to the fear. Her highwayman. Jonathan. She had never wanted a man before; at least she had never wanted more than a mild flirtation, a daring kiss to set her a-flutter for an evening, to be forgotten in the morning along with the champagne and the foolish flirting.

Now… She jumped as the door opened and he came in, locking it behind him. He handed her the key before putting a plate on the table and taking knife, fork and bottle from his pocket.

'Food first?'

That voice seemed to curl round inside her, making her hot and flustered and strangely jumpy. 'No.' *Eat? Is he mad?*

'Wine, then?'

'Yes.' That would help. She studied him as he eased out the cork. Long legs, broad shoulders, enough muscle to be a fighter and a smile on him that turned the hot, flustered feeling into a deep, disturbing, low ache. He still wore the mask and she was glad of it; somehow it made him less real.

'Thank you.' She gulped the wine and handed him back the glass. 'I am a little nervous, I confess.'

'Understandably. Do you still want to go through with this?' Sarah thought of Sir Jeremy, thought of Mary's tears, and nodded. 'We will proceed to the matter at hand then? Would you like to undress first, or shall I?'

Chapter 2

'You will have to help me.' Sarah got to her feet and turned her back. That was easier, she did not have to look at him. She tried not to flinch as his fingers, busy on the buttons, brushed the bare skin of her neck, then her shoulders, then were kept from her naked skin by her chemise. The gown sagged and she caught it, stepping out and standing there, his warmth at her back as he began to untie her stay laces.

'You are very adept at this,' she said, attempting to sound cool and sophisticated and aware she was achieving neither. The release of pressure on her ribs was not, oddly, helping her breathing at all. *I can still stop, I can still say no…*

'I have had a little practice,' Jonathan conceded.

She could hear he was smiling. 'You can turn round now.'

He was standing there shrugging out of coat and waistcoat. Despite the mask she could see his eyes on her, a dark heat smoldering there. 'Will you untie my neck cloth?'

That brought her close, as he no doubt intended, her fingers clumsy on the simple folds. His clothes were respectable, but plain; she tried to concentrate on that while she unwound the warm muslin from his throat and pulled it free. He was waiting, it seemed, for her to unbutton his shirt, so she did that too, feeling a little light-headed as so much chest became visible right in front of her face. It was a very impressive chest, with flat, sculpted muscle and lightly tanned skin as though, perhaps, he had swum that summer or worked with his shirt off. He must undertake other, more honest, labor from time to time.

And then there was the hair, crisp and startling as it brushed her knuckles, growing thicker and more focused as she worked down, until it vanished into his breeches. Sarah undid the last button and tugged so the shirt came free. And then there he was, clad in nothing but buckskins and boots and there she was, feeling as though she was wearing nothing but a blush.

'It isn't compulsory to proceed, you know,' Jonathan said, watching her face. 'We can just have some supper and I'll escort you home.'

'Oh yes it is,' she retorted, suddenly sure, despite feeling more nervous than she could ever remember. 'It is this or marriage to the swine who raped my maid and then threatened her. Papa considers him such a good match in material terms that I cannot think of any other way than this to get free from him.' He still seemed to hesitate. Sarah swallowed down the lump in her throat . 'Are you going to take your boots off?'

That provoked a snort of laughter. 'But of course. It is *de rigeur* to remove one's boots before making love to a lady.' He sat and began to pull them off.

'You are a very strange highwayman.' She supposed she should remove her petticoats. Was there an etiquette to this lovemaking? Sarah stood there in chemise and stockings watching the play of muscle on Jonathan's back as he tugged. It was important to be able to describe the intimate appearance of her lover if she was to convince Mrs. Catchpole, her chaperone, of her ruin, she thought, finding strength in the reminder of why she was doing this.

'I have had a sad life,' Jonathan explained, glancing up and catching her staring.

'No doubt.' He was, thank goodness, retaining his breeches. The amount of bare man on display was already rather more overpowering than she had bargained on. For some reason she had thought this would all take place in the dark.

'Now, I have been wanting, for the past hour, to kiss you again.'

It was interesting, Sarah thought, striving for rational thought, how different a kiss was when there were so few clothes in the way. His arms around her seemed to caress her skin, she could smell his warmth and the intriguing male scent of sweat and plain soap and something citrusy and horse and leather, and he tasted of wine and man. And his mouth on hers was not smiling any longer.

Rationality slid away to be replaced by a need Sarah did not know she had. She was shocked by the intimacy of his tongue in her mouth, inciting hers to touch and invade in its turn and surprised to discover that without having any idea what she should be doing, she was twining into his embrace and pressing herself against the outrageously hard ridge that lay against her stomach.

She gave a gasp, startled and embarrassed and

not a little fearful until Jonathan's hands came down to cup her buttocks, lifting her against himself, rocking her into the hardness until she moaned, the fear subtly becoming another kind of trembling altogether. 'Oh yes, sweetheart,' he murmured against her neck. 'Oh yes.'

She was on the bed, Sarah realized, as her chemise was lifted over her head, and then there they were, her against the pillows wearing nothing but her stockings and Jonathan leaning against the bedpost breathing hard and looking as though he was counting.

'Oh!' One arm across her breasts and one hand flat at the junction of her thighs were not a great deal of covering, not when he was still in his breeches. He was watching her and she should be dying of shame—and part of her was and part of her was trembling with the need for him to hold her again. 'Aren't you going to take those off?' she blurted, suddenly anxious to have this over and done with.

He did, dropping them to the floor and making no attempt to cover himself. 'Oh,' Sarah said again. Her gaze skidded away, up his body, and met the masked green eyes. Now, his body naked, the mask seemed sinister and she swallowed, hard.

Something must have shown on her face, for he raised one hand to the black silk, hesitated, and pulled it off. 'Better?' She nodded, studying his face intently, fearful of finding something there that the mask had hidden, but the green eyes were clear and frank and his expression serious. Removing the mask made him look younger.

'Good,' he said, his mouth curving up into a slow smile. 'Are you all right?'

She managed another nod as he came and lay down next to her, pulling her against him. 'Stockings?'

'I like the stockings.' His voice, coming as it did from the valley between her breasts, was somewhat muffled.

'Oh.' She stroked his hair, then found the curl of his ear and played with that with one hand while the other pressed him to her breast and she became aware that she was whimpering softly and his lips and teeth had found a nipple and were tormenting it until she thought she would scream.

Then he released her and propped himself up on one elbow, smiling down. 'Is this what you had in mind?'

'Mind?' Sarah blinked at him. 'I don't think I have one.'

'Oh well, I'll just have to carry on then.' He moved down the bed and began to untie her garters while Sarah lay back, panting. She knew what happened with animals: the male pounced and it was all very hurried and rather violent. Not like this at all.

This seemed a little safer; he showed no intention of pouncing… 'Oh!' Jonathan was licking up her leg from her ankle, up to the back of her knee. Her legs, with no conscious thought from her, fell apart shamelessly, and with a chuckle he lowered his head between them as she tried to close them, feeling that she would die of shame. What had come over her? 'No!'

'Yes.' And his mouth was *there*, flicking and teasing a tiny point of intense sensation that seemed to dominate every other feeling. It was outrageous, inflammatory, something was going to break, shatter—she had to resist, to hold on, to… She shattered.

'Jonathan?'

'Welcome back.' He sounded pleased with her. 'More wine?'

'What was that?' Sarah blinked in the candle-light. Jonathan was off the bed, pouring wine, still shamelessly naked. Still very aroused.

'An orgasm.' He handed her the glass.

'But we didn't…'

'No. We don't have to,' he explained, comfortably matter-of-fact as he sat beside her and took his turn with the wine.

'But if we had been doing…doing everything?'

'Same result, some extra preliminaries.' He dipped a finger in the wine and dripped the red drops onto her left nipple, then bent his head and began to lick.

Sarah surrendered to the sensation, her hands clutching his shoulders as his hand slid down, touched where his mouth had been, his thumb circling the sensitised nub. Jonathan lifted his head. 'Relax.'

'I am!'

'More.' And he slid a finger into the wet heat, into the aching tightness and she arched, panting. Then another, and still his thumb wove its wicked pattern of arousal and her body clenched around the intrusion and her groping fingers found him and closed on mobile satin skin and bone hardness and heat and he moaned and thrust into her grasp as she lifted against his hand and there was darkness and stars and his mouth hard over hers as she screamed and he surged against her. And then a slow slide into oblivion.

Jonathan was asleep when she awoke. She lay there for perhaps ten minutes, just looking at him while her mind and her body returned to something like normality and the impact of what she had done came to her.

She was naked, in bed with a naked man with whom she had been utterly shameless, with whom she had experienced pleasure she had no idea existed. And now she was ruined. Sarah had no idea whether she wanted to laugh or cry, but she knew she had to go before he awoke, slip away, get to the hut and saddle up Daisy, ride home—all without him following her, discovering who she was.

She sat up and Jonathan stirred. No, she had to delay him. He would be alert in a second if she tried to creep out. One silk stocking curled across the rumpled bedspread. She eyed the man beside her, sprawled in utter relaxation on his back, arms thrown above his head.

So, she wanted to play games? Amused and aroused, Jonathan kept his eyes closed as silk trailed up his arm, caressed his wrists. How very sophisticated for such an innocent! He let her imprison his wrists, felt her fumble at the bed head. Then the knots tightened, something rattled and he was wide awake, straining to be free against bonds that did not yield one inch.

'What the hell!' Sarah was dressing, her hair scraped back into a tail and tied with one stocking. The other, presumably was what was imprisoning him.

'I'm sorry, but I cannot risk you finding out who I am,' she explained, her face rather pale in the candlelight. 'I am very grateful.'

'Grateful!' he exploded, bucking futilely against the knots.

'It was wonderful and so…helpful. And I really appreciate that you did not take advantage of me.' She picked up his cloak and edged toward the door. 'I will leave the cloak in the hut.'

'Helpful?' Jonathan demanded of the door as it closed softly behind her. '*Helpful?*'

The storm that shook Saint's Ford Manor had subsided to merely hurricane velocity by ten the next night. Mrs. Catchpole eventually recovered from the hysterics brought on by her charge's careful description of exactly how a man's member felt when held in the hand and had braced herself sufficiently to assure Sir Hugh that, indeed, it would appear his virginal daughter had been deflowered. And what was worse, that the young woman was so far abandoned to propriety that she was threatening to tell Sir Jeremy about it, in detail, if she was compelled to persist with the betrothal.

Sir Hugh had subsided from puce to mottled crimson and stopped shouting long enough to agree that, to prevent scandal, he would inform Sir Jeremy that Sarah had changed her mind and there was nothing to be done about it. The spurned suitor had driven off in high dudgeon.

That had all taken until midafternoon. The rest of the day had been filled with recriminations, more hysterics, demands to know who the man was—and firm refusals by Sarah to say—and dire warnings of what would become of her should she prove to be with child.

She nearly blurted out that there was no danger of that and bit her tongue, concentrating on looking determined—which she was—and ashamed of herself, which she most assuredly was not. What she was also feeling was an alarmingly awareness of her own body and an utterly immodest desire to do it all over again. And again.

Finally Sir Hugh had retired, muttering, to his study with a full set of decanters, Mrs. Catchpole had succumbed to a migraine and Sarah deemed it tactful to retire to her bedchamber for the night.

Mary, beaming with delight that somehow her mistress had routed the feared Sir Jeremy, was agog to know how she had done it, but all Sarah would say was that she had stood up to her papa and that finally he had accepted, with very bad grace, that she could not be forced into the match.

The maid left Sarah in nightgown and robe, a book of poetry in her hand, and went off to raid the cooking sherry in celebration.

Quite how Sarah realized she was not alone, she was uncertain. There was no sound, no stirring of the air—just a tingling down her spine. She put down the unopened book with care and turned, her fingers closing around the candlestick. A tall, masked figure materialized from the shadows in the corner by the window.

'Jonathan! How long have you been there?'

'An hour.' His voice sounded cold as he put up his hands to untie the mask, tossing it aside, his eyes not leaving hers.

'While I was undressing?' she demanded, then realized how foolish it was, after yesterday, to be indignant about that. 'How did you find me?'

'I followed the hoofprints of your horse, made some inquiries in the village. It was not hard.'

'No.' Her heartbeat was all over the place. 'You must have heard me taking to Mary; you know my plan succeeded, thanks to you.' He must have done more than listen; he had been there in her most private, feminine space, a space she had expected only a husband to enter. 'Why have you come?'

'To return these.' He tossed the long rope of pearls on to the bed and this time she could hear the anger in his voice.

'I'm sorry I tied you up.' Sarah found she was stammering more than she had when she confronted her father. 'I did not want you to find out who I was.'

'It certainly gave my friends considerable entertainment to find me tied naked to the bed by one silk stocking and a string of pearls,' he said, his lips thin.

'Oh no!' Sarah stared back, aghast. 'I thought it would be easy to get free.'

'Silk tightens under stress and those pearls are an expensive string, the thread is strong. No, Sarah, I was trussed like a gamecock in a basket and had to wait to be rescued.'

'I am so sorry. I can understand why you are angry,' she murmured.

'I am hardly angry about that. My friends dismissed it as a drunken, amorous romp—they just want to meet the lady involved, whom they think must be a most inventive playmate. No, what angers me is the fact that you saw fit to pay me for my *services* last night.' He gestured abruptly toward the pearls.

'I didn't! At least, they seemed like something useful to help tie you and then I thought, you have a living to make...' Her voice trailed away.

'Not as a male whore,' he said harshly.

'Oh no, never that,' she whispered. 'You did me a favor. I had no thought of payment, just a gift.' He was right, it had been insensitive, insulting. She straightened her spine. 'I apologize. I have no idea how I can make amends. I just wish I could.'

She saw his eyes close and the harsh line of his mouth relax into a rueful smile. 'I am a stiff-rumped idiot to take offense. It was a miracle you were thinking straight at all, and as you say, you thought I had a living to earn.'

'You haven't?'

Jonathan smiled, silent.

'Who are you?' He shook his head.

'That is unfair,' Sarah protested. 'You know my name now.'

He grinned. 'All part of your punishment for the offense to my pride.' The smile was positively wicked now. Something inside her tightened in fearful excitement.

'Part?'

He withdrew his hand from his pocket and there was the silk stocking, dangling from one long finger.

She edged toward the bed. 'You...you want to tie *me* up?' Her voice rose to a squeak as the excitement turned hot and lodged low, sending shocks of anticipation into the secret places that were becoming damp even as he watched her so intently. 'And make love to me? Here?'

'Mmm. If you would like me to.' Jonathan seemed so cool, but she could see the pulse hammering in his throat where his shirt lay open and his lips were parted, so very temptingly.

It was madness. They would have to be so quiet—*could* she be quiet if he touched her as he had before? Could she trust him to untie her again? But the excitement was building, coiling, making her feel different—dangerous, reckless. Jonathan had awakened something inside her that she could hardly recognize.

'Only if you promise to untie me before you leave,' she said, trying to match his teasing tone.

'I promise.' And the look in his eyes was no longer teasing, no longer hot. For a moment she saw tenderness and melted. He locked the door, then moved suddenly, like a cat, to spin her into his arms. The robe was off her shoulders, the nightgown sliding toward the floor, even as his mouth crushed down on hers and his arms lifted her, tossing her onto the bed, gasping with laughter and a delicious, fearful anticipation. 'I need another stocking.'

'Top drawer of the dresser.' She watched him tear his own clothes off as he walked across the room, his very urgency arousing her. He was so beautiful, she thought, feasting her eyes on taut buttocks and the elegant dip of his spine at the waist, the length of his legs and the definition of the muscles. Last night she had been too apprehensive to really look at him. Even his feet, with their long tendons and the flexible toes curling into the Chinese rug, were beautiful.

He came back, stocking in hand, and stood contemplating the bed head. He was already aroused, she saw with gathering excitement, as he tied one stocking to each of the top corner posts, then looped the free ends around her wrists so that she was lying back against the pillows, her arms outstretched. 'Comfortable?'

'Yes,' she admitted, wary.

'I will not take any notice of demands to stop or cries of *No!* If you want me to free you, say *Release me,* and I will, at once.'

'Promise?'

'Promise.' Jonathan strolled round to the foot of the bed and took her right foot in his hand, lifting it to his mouth. 'Are you ticklish?'

'No,' Sarah said, lying, as he began to suck her toes. *Toes? Toes were not sexual, toes were... Oh!* By the time both feet had been nibbled, sucked and licked she was in a state of bemused desperation. Was he punishing her? Was he never going to kiss her, touch her breasts, do any of those things he had done last night, or would he drive her insane just by sucking her toes and never move above her ankles?

Chapter 3

'Jonathan!'

'Yes?' He looked up, face serious, an unholy twinkle in his eyes.

'Please?' Sarah was not sure what she wanted, she just knew she needed it *now*. He grinned and began to lick upward. *Oh yes.* At last he was going to stop tormenting her and tip her over into that blissful state… He just kept going, up her thigh, lingering on her hipbone, across her belly to her naval. 'Oh.' It was nice, it was more than nice, but it wasn't *that*. The skin across her belly tightened as though to control the heat that was swirling inside her and she tilted her hips up, hoping he would take the hint. If she only had her hands free!

Then he reached her breasts and settled down,

comfortably propped on one elbow, to continue tormenting her, nibbling and licking like a man with a bowl of strawberries who wanted to savor the scent and the taste for as long as possible. He reached out for something with his free hand, drew it toward her and she felt the snaking slither of the pearls, cool against her skin as they trailed over her hipbone and slid between her thighs.

Jonathan began to tweak the string and they grazed over the sensitized soft skin, touching, just, the aching nub that she so wanted him to caress, a teasing, frustrating counterpoint to the shocks of sensation his lips and teeth were sending direct from her nipples to her groin.

She was moaning, her head restless on the pillows as she felt him sit back on his heels, one hand still trailing the pearls through the moist, swollen ache between her thighs. He was watching her, she knew it, but fear and shame had dissolved in the cauldron of sensation he was stirring up within her.

Sarah opened her eyes and looked at him, his erection straining up against his flat stomach, and realized, through her own haze of desire, just how rigidly he was controlling himself to pleasure her and how much she wanted to touch him. As he bent to flick his tongue across the track of the pearls, she felt, with an intensity that shocked her, that she wanted to caress him like that.

'Release me,' she said, wriggling back so she was half sitting against the pillows. 'Please, release me.'

As she hoped, he straddled her body, moving up the bed so he was astride her rib cage as he reached for her right wrist. His erection was right in front of her face, so close she could see a pearl of liquid at the tip. As he stretched across she raised her head and took him into her mouth and they both froze, he with a gasp of shock, she with the rush of sensation.

'Sarah!' He tried to pull away, but she closed her teeth in delicate warning and he was still again while she moved her lips, her tongue, fascinated by the taste and the texture and the effect she was having. Jonathan began to work at the knots and suddenly her hand was free and she could flatten it against the taut buttocks, holding him to her while he freed the other wrist, and then his weight shifted and she realized he was gripping the rail above her head.

He was so still, his breath rasping as she sucked, drawing her tongue up and down, loving the intimacy and the power. She could sense, as her hands held him, the effort it was taking him not to thrust into her mouth, realized the strain she was putting him under and somehow summoned up the will to release him. He moved with the speed of a lunging swordsman, sliding down her body, crushing her under his weight, his pelvis pressing against hers, and she reacted instinctively, opening to him even as her fingers bit into his shoulders.

Jonathan found himself stretched over Sarah's body, her legs cradling him, his hips tensed to thrust. He caught himself, the effort wrenching a groan from deep in his chest. 'God!' He rolled off her, forearm flung across his eyes, fighting for control. She had trusted him and he had damn nearly...then her hand took him, sure and generous, and he turned back to caress her, shaking in her embrace as they fell into ecstasy and darkness together.

Sarah was curled against him, sleeping, he realized, as he came to himself. That had never happened to him before. His mistresses had never shown any inclination to snuggle confidingly against him, and that avoidance of feigned sentiment suited him perfectly. Caroline, his current *maîtresse,* most certainly never clung. The thought

of appearing anything less than perfect sent her
from the bed the moment he left it to retreat behind a screen and emerge ten or so minutes later,
cool and immaculate. And by then he would be in
his robe pouring champagne ready for an unin-
volved exchange of civilized pleasantries. All so
very sophisticated, all so very…cold.

This was not cold. Sarah's body hugged his
with the trusting, innocently sensual abandon of a
sleeping kitten, her breath tickling the hairs around
his left nipple, her right arm flung over his rib
cage, her right leg across his thighs. They were
both hot and damp, sticky and tousled, and he
found that strangely pleasurable.

Jonathan wondered how long he had slept, then
stopped caring and rubbed his cheek against the
tangle of brown curls that was all he could reach.
After a moment he dropped a kiss on the crown of
Sarah's head and smiled as she stirred, muttering,
and caught his nipple between her lips, playing
with it in her sleep. It hardened and other parts of
his body began to react. Jonathan shifted a little,
so she let go with a soft sound of protest and lay
still again.

He had not reckoned on feeling like this when
he had let his temper and his pride ride him that

morning. He had spent the day tracking her down and the evening finding his way into the house. An unlocked storeroom window had given him access, then he had slipped upstairs to check each bedroom until he had found hers.

The alcove with its swathe of drapery had been perfect—perfect to wait unobserved as the maid closed the curtains across the windows, and perfect, as he had rapidly discovered, to torment him with first the scent and then the sight of Sarah.

He had closed his eyes as the maid undressed her: he had not lost all control. But his eyes might just as well have been wide open as he followed every whisper of silk, every rustle of petticoats, the sound of her sigh of relief as her stays were unlaced, the maid's comments on the pretty clocking at the ankle of her stockings.

Then there had been the soft sound of a loose nightgown falling over her head to toes that, his imagination was telling him, were bare, and the murmur of their conversation. All so intimate, so feminine, as the two young women shared their joy that the unwelcome suitor had been routed.

Sarah had not confided how she had achieved that to her maid, he noticed, realizing he would have been well served for his intrusion if he had

had to spend long minutes listening to a dissection of his performance.

But that realization did nothing to dampen the heat of the anger that the discovery of the pearls had ignited. His friends' teasing had been bearable, rooted more in admiration of his prowess at finding a bedmate so inventive rather than scorn at the predicament he had found himself in. No, it was the fact that she had carelessly left him jewelry worth a considerable sum laced mockingly into his bonds.

It was not until he had seen the remorse in her wide, gray eyes and understood that she genuinely had not counted their value, had thought only of delaying him long enough to escape, that the hurt pride vanished like smoke in the wind.

Idiot, he thought now, stroking the warm, soft skin of her shoulder with his palm. Sarah was not some pouting Society beauty buying what she wanted, careless of the feelings of those she used. She was different, and he was beginning to find that very difference disturbingly appealing.

The clock struck one as he pulled the light coverlet up over their bodies and let himself drift off to sleep, his mind full of new and disconcerting possibilities, his arms full of curves and fragrance.

* * *

'Sarah.' She came up out of a dream of Jonathan to find him there, bending over her, fully dressed.

'You are real,' she observed, half-fuddled with sleep and pleasure, then smiled as his eyes crinkled with amusement at her folly. 'Of course you are. What time is it?'

'Four. I must go before the household stirs.'

She sat up, careless of the way the sheet fell to her waist, and surprised at how quickly she had become so shameless in his presence. 'You are leaving Saint's Ford, aren't you? You will not be coming back.' Of course he would not; this was merely an unusual incident for him. For her, she realized, watching his face in the candlelight, it was everything. She had solved the problem of Sir Jeremy and paid with her heart for it.

Jonathan stroked the back of his hand down her cheek. 'Your highwayman will never come back, Sarah. Would you be glad to think that perhaps you have reformed me?'

'I do not think you were ever a very dangerous highwayman,' she observed, fighting to keep her tone light. 'So I doubt I can claim much merit for any reformation that has occurred. But yes, it is not a safe occupation for a man such as yourself: I would not like to think you might have ended on a gallows.'

'A man such as myself?' he asked, his mouth twisting into a smile that seemed to mock himself, not her.

'Honorable, kind, brave and clever,' Sarah said, wondering at Jonathan's sudden stillness.

'Thank you,' he said softly, lifting her hand and pressing his lips to her knuckles. 'You give me something to live up to, my sweet.' He was on his feet, and unlocking the door before she could say anything else. Then he paused in the open doorway before slipping like a ghost into the dark corridor and away.

'I suppose you expect me to allow you to go to that house party your school friend invited you to, despite your behavior,' Sir Hugh Tatton snapped as Sarah sat nibbling listlessly at her bread and butter ten days later.

'Jessica Gifford?' She had forgotten all about that invitation. Jessica, a firm friend despite a two-year difference in their ages, had left school to earn her own living as a governess, and then, by some miracle, had met and married Lord Standon.

'She is the Countess of Standon now, Papa. And

it is Lady Dereham whose invitation it was. She is a cousin of Lord Standon's.'

'Lords, ladies—hah! Aye, and there was something smoky about that match, from what one hears,' Sir High grumbled. 'Henrietta wrote to me from London to say Standon was kicking up no end of a to-do, flaunting his new mistress all over Town, and the next thing we know he's off on the Continent marrying some governess he finds there, if you please.'

'She has obviously reformed him, Sir Hugh,' Mrs. Catchpole ventured nervously, still obviously expecting retribution for not exercising sufficient control over Sarah. 'And she must be a superior young woman if she went to Miss Fletching's Academy, as Sarah did.'

'Hah!'

'And it might be as well if dear Sarah does attend the party. There will be numerous eligible gentlemen present. Gentlemen who would be interested in making a speedy match if the dowry is right…' She let her voice trail away as Sarah felt her blushes mounting. Somehow she kept her mouth closed on the vehement rejection of any suggestion that she might try to palm off her love child on an unsuspecting husband.

'Indeed,' Sir Hugh said slowly. 'A point well made, ma'am. One trusts that there is no need for haste, but still, one cannot be too careful.'

As if I would, Sarah thought, laying her hand protectively over her belly, then realizing the hollowness of the gesture. There was no chance she was pregnant, thanks to Jonathan's care of her, but if she were, under no circumstances would she let his child grow up as any other man's. Not the child of the man she loved.

'Sarah?' Mrs. Catchpole was on her feet.

'I…I'm sorry, a crumb…' Sarah said, wildly catching at any excuse for leaping to her feet, her hands pressed to her mouth. 'Water, I'll just go and get…' She fled. *Love? I am in love? Of course I am. I am in love with an utterly unsuitable man whose full name I do not know, who is never coming back and who, obviously, does not love me.*

'Mary,' she said firmly, startling the maid, who was standing in the middle of her bedroom frowning at the black silk mask in her hands, 'we have to think about what to pack for Lady Standon's party. It seems I must catch myself a husband.'

'Yes, Miss Sarah. What is this? I found it at the bottom of your stocking drawer.' The maid held out the band of silk.

'A souvenir of an adventure,' Sarah said, blinking back a tear. 'One that is about to become just the memory of a dream.'

Chapter 4

'Jessica!' Careless of waiting servants or other houseguests, Sarah threw herself into her friend's arms. 'Oh, Jessica, I am so happy to see you!'

Reeling slightly from the impact, Lady Standon hugged her tight, then held her at arm's length, the better to look at her. Jessica looked radiant, Sarah thought.

'What's wrong?' She tucked Sarah's hand under her arm and drew her into the house. 'Come and meet Bel—Lady Dereham—and the others and then I'll show you your room and you can tell me all about it. Whatever it is.'

Coppergate, the Derehams' country house, was deep in the Hertfordshire countryside and had the warm feel of a home. Lady Dereham greeted her with a smile, introducing her to the other guests, who were all relaxing, comfortably informal, in the big salon. Sarah did her best to commit the names of the host of assorted Ravenhurst relatives to memory before letting Jessica whisk her away.

'So, tell me what is wrong. There are dark circles under your eyes and I would swear you have lost weight. Is it Sir Jeremy?'

Jessica curled up in the window seat and listened as Sarah paced the room recounting the tale of Sir Jeremy's infamy, her impetuous ride and her meeting with Jonathan. When Sarah got to the part where he made his outrageous suggestion to rescue her from her fiancé, Jessica clapped her hands over her mouth and stared in horrified amazement.

'Sarah! You let him deflower you?'

'No! I told you—he *almost* did.' Jessica closed her eyes for a moment. 'Jessica, I am in love with him.'

'My dear! It is impossibly romantic. Does he have a nickname for the broadsheets and ride a black stallion?'

'He has a very ugly horse and no nickname I am aware of.' Sarah sighed. 'It is mad of me even to dream. He's a gentleman gone to the bad, I think.'

'It won't do,' Jessica said with a shake of her

head. 'You know that. This isn't a Minerva Press novel and he won't appear in the nick of time transformed into a duke.'

'I know.' She was resigned to it, after so many days of sighing for him.

'Well, the last thing you'll want is to be flirting with the young men at the party, that's for sure. You can always take refuge with Elinor Ravenhurst, who is very rational and regards all men as unnecessary frivolity, and Lady Maude Templeton, who declares she knows who she wants to marry but hasn't organized it yet. The poor man has no idea he is about to be organized, of course, and he is quite hopelessly ineligible.

'Falling in love is painful, but will get better in time,' Jessica murmured. 'I just hope you do not truly *love* him, because if you do, that will take a long time to heal.'

There was a difference, Sarah thought, as she went down to dinner attempting to ignore Mrs. Catchpole's prattling. Being in love or loving. Which was it? Loving implied knowing a person deeply and truly. What did she know about Jonathan?

He was intelligent and honorable, he had a

sense of humor, he was forgiving, he made love like…'a devil or an angel?' she murmured, causing her chaperone to glance sharply at her.

'Sarah, this is no time for wool gathering. This is a significant opportunity for you to meet not just eligible young men, but influential hostesses. Now smile!'

'Yes, Priscilla,' Sarah said meekly to Mrs. Catchpole, pulling herself together. She owed it to her hostess to be an amiable guest, and that would not be aided by her thinking about the caress of Jonathan's mouth at her breast or paying attention to the low, demanding pulse that made her fidget and ache.

Informal Lady Dereham might be, but she arranged her dining table in accordance with precedence, and Sarah was partnered by the vicar and had, on her left side, Lieutenant Harris, a cheerful military man with a bluff sense of humor.

Her mood, when the ladies rose to leave the men to their port and politics, was therefore rather more tranquil. It would be interesting to seek out the two young ladies Jessica had mentioned. Miss Elinor Ravenhurst was easy enough to locate, a tall redhead sitting in a corner with her nose in a book and dressed in a gown of a depressing beige.

'Miss Ravenhurst? I am Sarah Tatton. I hope I do not interrupt, but Lady Standon mentioned you as someone with a very rational turn of mind and I thought I would like to speak with you.'

'Rational?' Miss Ravenhurst smiled and closed her book. 'She means that she despairs of interesting me in a young man or finding any young man prepared to take an interest in me. Are you a scholar, too, Miss Tatton?'

'No, I am not in the mood for masculine company,' Sarah confessed, sitting down.

Intelligent hazel eyes studied her. 'Either you are in retreat from an unwelcome suitor or you are in love with someone unsuitable.'

'Both,' Sarah confessed, startled.

'Then you must meet Maude.' Elinor waved her fan, a battered affair that seemed to have been sat upon, and received an answering wave from a handsome young woman chatting with three army officers.

'She will not wish to be interrupted,' Sarah began, but Lady Maude abandoned her swains with a flirtatious smile and came across.

'Maude, this is Sarah Tatton, who is unsuitably in love,' Miss Ravenhurst announced with the air of a scholar identifying an interesting specimen.

'Really?' Lady Maude sat down in a flurry of expensive silk skirts and held out her hand. 'Is it mutual?'

'No, Lady Maude. He has no idea of my feelings and I have no idea of his name, his whereabouts or anything, other than that he is entirely ineligible.'

'Call me Maude, please.' Her ladyship, dark, vivacious and enviably pretty, perched on the sofa next to Miss Ravenhurst, a contrast in styles. 'And I see you've already met Elinor, who is a lost cause as far as men are concerned, but who will talk common sense and try to persuade us from rash action. Mind you, I cannot help but believe that somewhere is exactly the right man for her, just as there is for you and for me.'

'Not rash, merely irrational, Maude,' Elinor corrected. 'A female should not be dependent upon a mere male for her every happiness.'

'I quite agree, insofar as most things are concerned. But there are areas of happiness for which one must depend upon mere males, are there not, Sarah?' Maude's wicked twinkle left no doubt which areas she was referring to and Sarah felt herself color. 'Oh, my! You blush. Is he such a great lover, this unsuitable man of yours?'

'Wonderful,' Sarah admitted, amazed that she

could confide so easily. But she sensed that these two young women, so very different, would be both kind and discreet. 'I will tell you what occurred, if you promise not to say anything to anyone else.'

'We are both,' Elinor announced, leaning forward, 'agog.'

Sarah awoke the next morning feeling somewhat better. True, Jonathan was still lost to her, but she had made two new friends and had found that her old friendship with Jessica was as strong as ever. Confiding in all three of them had stilled her uncomfortably active conscience. They had reassured her that of course she should not have obliged her father and married Sir Jeremy, having discovered his unpleasant character.

When she went down to breakfast she found it an exclusively female company, for the men, Bel informed her, had all gone out to inspect the stables.

'We are having a dance this evening,' Bel announced. 'A nice, formal, *refined* dance. Everyone will have arrived by then and the men may wash off the smell of the stables and behave like civilized human beings. Discussion of politics, horses and hunting will be forbidden and no one under the age of sixty-five may play cards.'

The last thing that Sarah felt like doing was participating in a ball, but she knew what was expected of a good guest. 'Lovely! I am so glad I brought a new ball gown,' she declared brightly.

It had not occurred to Sarah, until she was standing in the doorway and watching the house-guests and the neighboring gentry mingling and laughing in the long room, that being hopelessly in love did not just entail the pain of losing the man of her dreams. It also meant that either she must remain a spinster, and childless, all her days or marry a man she did not love.

'Sarah?'

'Elinor, I am sorry, I am blocking the door. What a delightful scene, is it not?'

'Very animated,' Elinor agreed, as they entered side by side. She was dressed in gray silk with a cream lace trim, both of which colors effectively killed any glow in her cheeks. 'And noisy. However, I have a book hidden behind the sofa cushions in the retiring room, so once I have been observed treading on at least one pair of male toes, I can probably escape.'

Maude, who was, of course, surrounded by young men, waved and Sarah heard her companion sigh as they crossed to her. Feeling she had to compensate for Elinor's lack of enthusiasm, she assumed her best social smile and soon found her dance card much in demand.

When she had first come out such popularity would have thrilled her; now she felt like someone who had an antipathy to cats but who was proving irresistible to the creatures.

'No,' she said firmly to one of Lord Dereham's friends, 'Thank you, Major Piper, but I do not waltz.' Never having achieved the exalted status of holding a voucher for Almack's, Sarah had not been approved by a Patroness and knew that to waltz without such blessing would label her as fast.

So she danced the first set of country dances, then the quadrille, and wondered that she could still keep smiling and pretending to flirt when what she wanted was to be alone with a big man with smiling green eyes and a deep voice and a mouth made for sin.

The third set was a waltz so she could make her excuses and go to where Elinor was sitting out in an alcove sipping lemonade and reading a small book behind her fan.

She had almost reached her when Bel spoke behind her. 'Miss Tatton! I believe you have no partner for the next set.'

'No, ma'am,' Sarah said, turning. 'I have not been approved to—'

The man beside Lady Dereham was tall, powerfully built, and in formal evening attire. His dark brown hair was cropped fashionably, his expression one of polite expectation. But the look in his green eyes was one of shock that matched her own and the lips of his sensual mouth were slightly parted as though on a sharp intake of breath.

'Oh, that is of no matter in a family party.' Bel dismissed the rules with a flick of her exquisite French fan. 'May I introduce the Earl of Redcliffe? He is hoping you will stand up for him for this set. Lord Redcliffe, Miss Tatton is a dear friend of Lady Standon's.'

'Miss Tatton.' His bow was immaculate, his voice deep and achingly familiar. It could not be. It was impossible that her highwayman—*her love*—was standing there in front of her, a respectable member of the aristocracy.

'Redcliffe!' It was Gareth, Lord Standon. He slapped the big man on the shoulder, then took his hand. 'You are so late I thought you weren't coming.'

'I apologize.' Jonathan shook hands with his friend. 'I had to go into Town unexpectedly. Things to arrange. But nothing would make me miss your party' He glanced at Sarah. 'Almost nothing.'

And then the paralysis that had come over her when she had seen him began to ebb away and she realized the hot sensation that coursed through her was anger.

Chapter 5

'Thank you, *my* lord.' A fine line appeared between Bel's brows at the emphasis. 'I do not waltz.' Her voice rose, heads turned.

'Sarah—'

'I do not want to dance.' She could hear her tone becoming shrill and modulated it, forcing something close to a smile. 'Thank you.'

'Miss Tatton,' Jonathan said. 'I would not *constrain* you to anything against your will.' She felt the color rise in her cheeks. It was as though the scene in the ballroom was shifting in and out of focus and the man in front of her was alternately formally attired and standing against a background of chattering couples, and stark naked in her bedchamber, a wicked smile on his lips and her stocking dangling from his fingers.

'Let us try, shall we?' he suggested. 'You can always tell me to *release* you, should you find the experience disturbing.'

Disturbing? The heat was gathering low in her belly, she felt light-headed and breathless and *wanting,* and the anger pulsed through the arousal and the ache and she just needed to hit him and kiss him and…

Her hand was in his and she could not, without making a scene, escape. Jonathan drew her onto the floor and took her in a firm hold. 'You are doubtless as surprised as I am, to meet like this.'

'I am most certainly surprised, my lord,' she said. *Oh God, he smells the same. Leather and citrus and man.*

'My lord?' He quirked an eyebrow at her as the music began. 'What has happened to *Jonathan*?'

'I do not know. Tell me, what *has* happened to Jonathan?'

The fact that she was angry and upset and not merely shocked seemed finally to penetrate his consciousness. 'What is the matter?'

'Matter?' Somehow she managed to keep her voice down as he swept her the length of the room and round into a complicated turn at the end. She had never danced the waltz except with a dancing master; now, she realized, she was so preoccupied that she simply followed Jonathan's lead through the most difficult steps.

'You lied to me, you deceived me, you took advantage of me and you wonder why I am angry?'

'Yes,' he said bluntly, the arched dark brows lowering in answering anger. 'I never took advantage of you, I never deceived you, I never lied to you—'

'You lied by omission.' He forced her into a tight, swooping turn, her skirts swinging out, the room shifting dizzyingly about her. Sarah glimpsed Maude's face, staring. 'I thought you were a highwayman, or if not that, at least an ordinary man, a gentleman who had fallen on hard times. How could you not tell me who you were?'

Then the reason he had not, and the real reason she was so upset, hit her like a blow and she stopped dead in the middle of the floor as couples swerved to avoid them.

'But of course you could not tell me,' she whispered. 'Because if you had, you thought I would say that you had compromised me, that as a gentleman you must marry me and you would have been trapped. That is it, is it not?'

* * *

'No!' Jonathan somehow managed to keep his voice down from a bellow.

'And I suppose you laughed about it with your friends,' Sarah added. 'It was all for a bet, I presume? The highwayman act.'

'Of course it was a damn bet!' A couple gliding past stared at him. Sarah was glaring at him as if he was some kind of libertine bent on ravishment. 'And of course I said nothing about you to them. For God's sake, let's get out of this confounded dance.'

'Certainly, if only to take myself out of range of your blaspheming and bad language.' She turned on her heel and stalked off the floor, leaving him standing there, the focus of all eyes.

'I trod on her feet,' he explained to those couples within hearing and followed her, attempting to look ruefully amused when all he wanted to do was snarl.

By the time he reached the edge Sarah had vanished. Jonathan, despite his height, could see no topknot of glossy brown curls, no slender figure in almond silk. A dark-haired beauty with a heart-shaped face and an expression of exasperation appeared in front of him. He dredged into his memories of last Season. Lady Maude Templeton. 'She's gone out onto the terrace. That way.' She pointed, then walked off. Jonathan thought he heard her add, 'Men!' as she went.

Jaw set, Jonathan stalked off in the direction indicated. Idiot woman, of course he hadn't told her who he was! Couldn't she see why? And why wasn't she pleased to see him? He was pleased to see her. More than pleased. It upset his plans, but to hell with that; Sarah was here and he wanted her. After he'd boxed her ears.

The torch-lit terrace held a scattering of couples strolling and flirting. There was no sign of Sarah, but he had not expected her to stop here, in full view. He took the sweeping steps down onto the lawns and glimpsed the flutter of pale skirts in the darkness.

When he reached the same spot, treading quietly, his dancing pumps making no sound on the close-scythed turf, he could not see her. Then he realized that the shrubs that had been planted along this wing of the house had a narrow gap in them. Slipping through, he found a graveled walk between them and the house walls. Sarah had her back to one of the sloping buttresses of the old wall, her gaze fixed on a group of tumbling cherubs set amongst the greenery.

Her head came round as he stepped onto the gravel and he felt his body tighten at the sight of her wide eyes, the rise and fall of her breasts in the low-cut silk.

'Go away.' She stood her ground, chin up.

Jonathan kept walking. 'No. Why are you so angry with me?'

'I told you!'

'Did you really expect me, when we first met and we made our extraordinary decision, to whip off my mask and introduce myself as the Earl of Redcliffe? My concern was for your protection.'

'Poppycock!' Sarah snapped. 'Have you any idea how humiliated I feel? Had you no thought that this might happen if we met again? Or was it impossible to believe that humble Miss Tatton might move in the same circles as yourself?'

'Well, you hadn't up to then,' he retorted.

'No, and I imagine you are none too pleased to find I am now!' The color was flying in her cheeks, he could see angry tears sparkling, and the effort not to seize hold of her and shake her and kiss her and take her was almost overwhelming.

'It was certainly not what I planned. I intended—' He never got the words out. Sarah thumped him on the chest with her clenched fist. 'Damn it, that hurt!'

'*Good.*' She did it again. 'That's how I feel, as if someone has punched me in the chest. I *trusted* you and all the time you were just amusing yourself with some silly little gentry virgin who had got herself into a pickle.'

'Amusing myself? If I had been amusing myself, Miss Tatton, you wouldn't still be a virgin, believe me.' Jonathan grabbed her wrists before she could land another blow and yanked her hard against himself. 'If I had been *amusing myself* things might have gone rather differently.'

She glared up at him, lips parted, face flushed, the scent of hot, angry woman filling his senses and bringing with it the prickle of awareness that she was not afraid of him, not just angry with him, but that she desired him and that he wanted her. Here and now.

Sarah gasped as he pushed her back against the buttress, its slight slope bringing his weight down on her, crushing his loins against her pelvis as he spread his legs to trap her. Her wriggling thrust her against him, and he thrust back, gasping as the heat of her met the aching length of his erection, their naked flesh separated only by thin, silk breeches and the flimsy defenses of her gown.

He trapped her hands above her head, his big

hand enveloping both wrists easily, and smiled down into her face, lit by the spill of light from the window above. 'Now *this* is amusing myself. Be honest, sweeting: do you want me to let you go?'

Sarah went still beneath him, her eyes searching his face, her heart beating against his shirtfront. Then her eyelids closed as though they were too heavy and she whispered, 'No.'

Shaken by her reaction, he schooled himself to be gentle, lowering his mouth over hers, determined to coax her, but she nipped at his lower lip with sharp teeth, took his mouth with a raw need that was fueled still by anger, and his own frustration rose to meet hers and the kiss became fierce and rough and she matched him, grazing teeth, thrusting, tongues dueling, pressure and demand, with no yielding, no softness.

Beneath his weight her body bucked, not to throw him off but seeking the friction of his hardness against her soft core. His hand left her breast to pull at her skirts until his fingers touched her thigh and he could push between their straining bodies, find the hot, wet folds and part them.

Sarah went still, hanging, waiting for the touch he had taught her to expect, but he slipped one finger past the tight, desperate knot of flesh and slid it into her, gasping against her mouth at the sensation, muffling her own cry of shock and arousal as he added another finger, feeling her tighten around him instinctively.

Her reaction was so arousing he thought he would come just from that alone, and forced himself to stillness, only his mouth ravishing hers, as though to release her would be to cease to breathe. Then she whimpered against his lips and he began to thrust and she arched under him, clenching, matching his strokes until he felt the quivering desperation building, building, and took pity on her, brushing his thumb against her, one touch sending her over into shuddering collapse.

Sarah sagged, her head thrown back against the warm stone, only the weight of Jonathan's body and his grip on her wrists keeping her upright. The anger had burned away. All she knew was that the man she loved had driven her into a mindless inferno of sensation and need and the impossibly wonderful satisfaction of that need.

'Sarah,' he murmured against her neck. 'Sweetheart. Are you all right?' He released her wrists and her hands fell to his shoulders and he stood upright, bringing her with him.

'Mmm,' she managed to murmur, every inch of her aware of him, his strength and the scent of aroused man and the hardness pressed against her.

'I didn't hurt you?' She shook her head, the world gradually stopping spinning. 'You were angry. I was, too, because you were. I didn't know you would be here, any more than you knew I would. Listen, sweet—' he cradled her against himself, rocking her gently '—this can't go on, we have to talk…to resolve this.'

'No, I don't want…' she began, trying to explain, terrified what his sense of honor might compel him to say. One moment she thought herself in love with a man who knew he could never offer for her, even should he wish to, the next she found he was a man who would feel obliged to do so. Which, her spinning brain tried to fathom, was better? Or were they both too bad to bear?

'You don't want me?' he asked softly, holding her tenderly now as though that turmoil of exciting, angry passion had never been. 'I might have something to say to that.'

'You cannot force me,' Sarah began and felt him stiffen as though she had hit him again. 'I—'

'Was that a bat?' an alarmed feminine voice demanded just the other side of the bushes. 'Because if it is, I am going right back inside, Elinor Raven-hurst. I don't care how interesting the stars are.'

Maude? Elinor?

'Don't be foolish.' That was Elinor. 'It is an old wives' tale that they get into your hair.'

'Lady Maude, Miss Ravenhurst! Have you seen Miss Tatton?' Mrs. Catchpole sounded breathless. 'I do not know where she can have got to. I am most alarmed. Lady Dereham must organize a search party.'

Jonathan appeared to be shaking, then she realized he was laughing. Sarah elbowed him sharply in the ribs.

'Oh, she's here, Mrs. Catchpole,' Elinor said blithely. 'In those bushes. It was the bats, you see. We came out to look at the stars, the three of us, and then the bats swooped down and Sarah screamed and dived into the bush.'

Jonathan reacted faster than she did, brushing down her skirts, pushing a loose curl behind her ear. 'We will speak tomorrow,' he whispered, giving her a little push.

Sarah stumbled out onto the lawn looking, she was certain, as though she had been pulled through the hedge backward, rather than having merely taken refuge in it.

'Sarah! Look at you,' Mrs. Catchpole fussed.

'We'll go to my room and tidy up.' Maude tucked her hand into Sarah's arm and whisked her away down the path toward the house, leaving the chaperone trapped by Elinor's careful explanation of how one could identify the constellation Leo.

'What is going on?' Sarah demanded as Maude shut the door and stood there beaming at her.

'It's him, isn't it? Your highwayman, only he's really Jonathan Kirkland, Lord Redcliffe. I've known him for years, so I could see he'd had a shock, and then I saw your face and the two of you were having that really splendid tiff, so we thought, Elinor and I, that we had better leave you to it, but keep an eye on you. And then Mrs. Catchpole started flapping about so we came to rescue you.' She sat down on the bed. 'But what was he doing pretending to be a highwayman?'

'It was a bet,' Sarah said as Elinor came in.

'Well, you've found each other now,' she said prosaically. 'I wonder why lovers so often have such huge rows? It seems most strange.'

'I know why *I'm* angry,' Sarah said, sitting down before her knees gave way. 'But I don't know what he has to be cross about. He didn't tell me who he was because he thinks I'd have expected him to offer for me.'

'Did he say so?' Maude began to brush the back of Sarah's dress. 'Tsk! Lichen everywhere.'

'No, but what other reason could there be for not saying, once he knew my name?'

'Have you asked him?' Elinor inquired, looking up from her notebook.

'Not exactly.' Sarah bit her lip. 'I hit him. On the chest with my fists and I shouted at him. He was quite angry.'

Maude began to giggle. 'I'm not surprised. Wait until the morning. I am sure you will both be in a better frame of mind by then.'

The morning, after a night of restless sleep disturbed by quite shocking dreams, hardly seemed more promising. The breakfast parlor was populated by heavy-eyed guests sipping coffee, while many seemed to have decided to stay in their rooms.

Jonathan was seated at the far end of the table when Sarah entered with Mrs. Catchpole. He rose with the other men, then resumed his seat with a fleeting glance in her direction.

She was still pushing her omelette listlessly around her plate half an hour later when Lady

Dereham appeared at her side. 'Lord Redcliffe has asked if he might speak with you in my sitting room at your convenience.'

Sarah stared. Her chaperone sat bolt upright, looking for all the world like a pointer that has sighted game. 'Sarah, dear! We must—'

'Do not disturb yourself, ma'am. I will escort Sarah.' Bel had her out of the room before Mrs. Catchpole could react. 'You look very well, my dear. There is no need to go and primp. Here we are.' Bel opened the door, gave her a little push and closed it, leaving her alone with the Earl of Redcliffe.

'Oh.' It was not the most intelligent thing she could have found to say. Sarah bit her lip and regarded his unsmiling face.

'Sarah. I have, this morning, written to your father. I thought I should show it to you before I send it.' He held out a sheet of paper.

'Written?' She took it. The words were out of focus.

'Yes. I realize that to call would be more conventional. It was my intention to return to Saint's Ford Manor and do the thing in style, but now… Sarah, there is no way I can wait.'

'You intended to come back to me?' She stared at the firm black letters, willing them to make sense.

'Of course. I had to lose the highwayman, speak to my bankers about the settlement, have a haircut—all the things a hopeful suitor needs to do.'

'Suitor? Why?' She thrust the letter back at him. 'I cannot seem to focus.'

'Sit down then, and I will read to you.' He guided her to the sofa, then stood before the hearth and cleared his throat.

'"Sir Hugh, I write to inform you of my intention to pay my addresses to your daughter, Miss Sarah Tatton. I cannot pretend that my attachment to her was not sudden. In fact I believe it was, if not love at first sight, then most certainly love from the first moment she allowed me to press a respectful salutation upon her lips."'

'You spoke?'

Sarah shook her head, dumb with delight. *Respectful salutation?* That must be the first kiss that he took when they met. He was making it sound as if he had met her for the first time here, when in fact…

'"My standing and circumstances you may ascertain from an inspection of the *Peerage*. In regard to my intentions as to settlements, I trust the enclosed papers from my lawyer will prove satisfactory…"' etc., etc.' Jonathan folded the paper.

'Well, Miss Tatton? You are, I believe, of age, which means that I need not await a response from your father but may do this now.' He went down on one knee beside her. 'Sarah.' His voice was husky and she found she could not breathe, just stare into his eyes, trapped by the intensity in them. 'I love you. I think I loved you from that first kiss. I *knew* I loved you when I felt the pain of thinking you had offered me payment for lying with you. My fault, I confess, was to go and leave you without explanation, but I did it intending to return as an entirely respectable suitor. Like an idiot I wanted to surprise you, to have everything in place, perfect. Do you forgive me?'

'Oh yes. I love you, too, you see. I don't need everything to be perfect, I just need you.' She had found her tongue, and her eyes focused clearly on his face and she reached out and cupped his cheek with a hand that was steady.

'And you will marry me?'

And instead of answering, she simply leaned forward and kissed him and never noticed until afterward that her cheeks were wet.

'Lady Redcliffe, you are blushing.' Her new husband set Sarah on her feet beside the wide bed and bent to kiss her. 'Now what, after all the things we have enjoyed together, can be making you shy now?'

'This is different,' she confessed, reaching up to undo his neckcloth.

'Yes,' Jonathan agreed, leaving her fully clothed while she undressed him and then slowly, gently, unveiling her body until they stood facing each other in the twilit room, naked. 'I love you and now you are mine.'

'I know. And you are my husband and we no longer have to be careful. Will you show me how to love you?'

And without answering with words he lifted her onto the bed and began to woo her with lips and tongue and gentle, wicked fingers until the familiar, insistent throb took over and her head began to turn, restless on the pillow, and her own hands stopped caressing and could only hold him and he shifted his weight and lay between her thighs.

'Don't be frightened.' He moved slowly, nudging, and she smiled, heady with pleasure, tingling with anticipation.

'I'm not frightened. I just want you so much. Want you inside me, to be around you, to hold you in every way I can.' It felt strange and powerful, the inexorable, heavy pressure, but her body seemed to know what to do and was accepting him. She shifted, searching for the best position, and then he smiled and surged against her and she gasped, pain flickering past to be replaced by an overwhelming sense of completion.

Jonathan stilled above her, his eyes intense on her face. They were so closely joined that she could feel the pressure of his hipbones, the tantalizing brush and weight of his testicles, the friction of his body hair. And then, as she dared to breathe again, to relax, she could feel him inside her and realized that she could tighten around him and that when she did he groaned and closed his eyes and thrust.

She could match the surging, deep rhythm, tightening, caressing, and his eyes opened again and the look in them took her breath and she held on and let herself fly until he thrust deeper than ever with a hoarse cry and she felt him convulse inside her, spilling life and heat into her, and she let go and joined him in the velvet darkness.

Sarah came to herself to find they were wrapped together, her head on his breast, their legs twined. 'In August,' Jonathan said, his hand stroking possessively down her body, 'I asked you for the most precious thing you possessed. Thank you for giving it to me.'

'My virginity?' Sarah queried, raising herself on her elbow to smile at him.

'No.' The deep green eyes smiled back. 'Your heart, my darling.'

'How could I help it?' She bent and kissed him. 'A highwayman stole it quite away.'

* * * * *

LIBERTINE LORD, PICKPOCKET MISS

Bronwyn Scott

Bronwyn Scott is a pen name for Nikki Poppen. Nikki lives in the Pacific Northwestern United States, where she is a communications instructor at a small college. She enjoys playing the piano and hanging out with her three children. She definitely does not enjoy cooking or laundry – she leaves that to her husband, who teaches early morning and late evening classes at the college so he can spend the day being a stay-at-home daddy.

Nikki remembers writing all her life. She started attending young-author conferences held by the school district when she was in fourth grade and is still proud of her first completed novel in sixth grade, a medieval adventure that her mum typed for her on a Smith-Corona electric typewriter! She has since moved on to RWA conferences and a computer. She loves history and research and is always looking forward to the next story. She also enjoys talking with other writers and readers about books they like and the writing process. She'd love to hear from you! Check out her Harlequin Mills & Boon links and her personal web page.

**Don't miss *A Throughly Compromised Lady*,
Bronwyn Scott's breathtaking new novel,
available in August 2010 from Mills & Boon® Historical.**

Chapter 1

Vienna, 1823

Julian Burke surveyed the glittering ballroom with a predator's eye. "Who shall it be tonight?" the Viscount St. Just murmured quietly beside him. The other two gentlemen with him laughed knowingly.

In the months Julian had been in Vienna, the routine of seeking out a lively partner had become a weekly, sometimes nightly ritual. His reputation as a libertine was firmly established and the women didn't seem to mind. Vienna was a city bursting with energy, drawing people from all over Europe to its ballrooms and palaces. Exciting places drew exciting people. Wallflowers and virtuous debutantes did not populate this crowd with any great regularity.

Julian rather liked these continental women. They were mature. They understood the rules of the game. They accepted the fact that affairs ran their course, and expected nothing more.

Julian's gaze passed over the ballroom again, lighting on the figure he'd been visually pursuing all evening. Time and again, he'd come back to her; his eyes were drawn to her movements on the dance floor, the saucy tilt of her head and her easy smile. "That one, St. Just." He nodded in the woman's direction.

"Ah," Valerian Inglemoore, Viscount St. Just offered approvingly. "She's very beautiful, very vivacious it seems. I have noticed her too. She is also younger than your usual sort, Burke."

The other two gentlemen, Truesdale and Mathison, eyed her appreciatively. "Good choice, Burke," Truesdale said, lifting his preposterous quizzing glass. "She's quite lovely. I don't see how I missed her."

Mathison elbowed him. "You were too busy looking at the brunette on the other side of the room."

Julian clapped St. Just on the back. "I am off to conquer the fair maid's heart. I'd ask you to wish me luck but I won't need it. I will be on the dance floor with her in ten minutes."

St. Just raised an eyebrow at his friend's cocky farewell. "You don't have a place on her dance card."

"A minor technicality." Julian shrugged. "I will give you gentlemen good-night. I doubt I'll be seeing you again this evening."

"Be careful, Burke," St. Just replied as Julian melted into the crowd.

Julian squared his shoulders and began to work his way to the woman's side. He would be careful tonight. He'd been right when he'd said he wouldn't need any luck. Tonight was all about acting on the planning he'd done during the last several weeks. St. Just knew, as the others didn't, that his true purpose in Vienna was to reclaim for England a diamond jewel set currently in the hands of the evening's host, a French comte. The jewels were upstairs in a safe. But he couldn't go haring upstairs without making his presence known downstairs first. That's why he'd picked the lively young woman.

Everyone, except Truesdale obviously, had noticed her. Her smile alone would have drawn people to her. Her entire being radiated a certain magnetic joie de vivre. The fact that she was positively beautiful was simply an added benefit. There was no question in Julian's mind that this lovely creature broke hearts on a nightly basis wherever she went. Of course, his heart was in no danger. She was welcome to work her wiles if she liked, but in the end, all he wanted from her was one dance, enough to get him noticed so that when and if the hue and cry went up about the missing jewels, people would only remember he'd spent the evening dancing if they connected him to the incident at all.

Julian approached the little group she was with as the orchestra struck up a waltz. "Mademoiselle, I believe this dance is mine." Up close, her beauty was breathtaking, Julian noted objectively. Her hair, the color of pale gold, and the smooth ivory sheen of her skin gave her the look of a fairy princess straight from a child's book of tales.

A look of confusion flitted briefly across her heart-shaped face. She scanned her dance card. "I believe you're mistaken, monsieur. I have elected to sit this one out." Her tone was gracious, but something in her eyes did not match the politeness of her rejection. Those sharp green eyes were not the eyes of a delicate princess. They were a hoyden's eyes, and right now they were dancing with mischief, challenging him. He would answer that challenge with one of his own.

"Perhaps you were just waiting for the right partner. Please, the music awaits." How fortuitous. This dance was empty, the only dance not spoken for, although it struck him as odd that she would sit out the waltz. Julian offered her his arm, reissuing his challenge. This time, she took it.

Julian swung them on the floor, marveling at the way she felt in his arms. His hand fit smoothly at the small of her back and she let him draw her to him as if they weren't strangers. He liked the Viennese style of waltzing better than the version danced in England. Holding a woman so close, feeling her reactions as they moved from contrachecks to fleckerls, he could tell if she was worth bedding. This one definitely would be, Julian reflected, guiding them through a passing change at high speeds.

She laughed up at him, enjoying the moment. "You dance very well, Julian Burke."

Ah, so she knew him. "My reputation precedes me. I fear you have me at a grave disadvantage, miss."

She laughed again; if sunlight had a sound, it would be this. "Of course I have you at a disadvantage. A woman's reputation should never precede her."

Julian smiled at her sharp rejoinder. She was beautiful *and* witty. It was definitely too bad he didn't have time to seduce her. His body wanted to argue that point. His eyes kept straying to the sweep of her décolletage and the high, firm breasts it put on display to their best advantage. In the dance, those breasts were just two tempting inches from his chest. In his mind, he could imagine the weight of them in his palms with alarming accuracy. His hand at her waist could feel the feminine indentation and the soft flare of her hip beneath her layers of clothing. The beginnings of an arousal were starting to stir, and he knew from long years of experience they would be magnificent together.

"You can put aside whatever lascivious thoughts you may be entertaining behind that smile, Mr. Burke," his light-footed angel said bluntly. "You cannot seduce me. I will not be another of your conquests."

"Are you certain?" Julian saw no reason to apologize or to lie, although he was stunned she'd found him to be so transparent in his thoughts. His partner was clearly up to the task of managing him, which in itself was a novelty. He pulled her even closer, until her body was flush with his, and whispered in her ear, "Why don't you let me try and we'll see if you're right?"

An English debutante would have slapped him across the face and stalked off the dance floor, but the woman in his arms merely laughed as if he'd said something humorous.

"How, precisely, would you go about it then, Mr. Burke?"

The cheeky vixen! It was all Julian could do not to throw back his head and laugh in the most conspicuous way. Julian could not remember when he'd been so utterly enchanted with a woman. He wanted to flirt with her simply to see what she'd do next. And she wanted him to. In spite of her claims to the contrary, she was intrigued by him.

Julian still held her close. He took advantage of that proximity now. "I would start with strawberries and champagne beneath a spring moon on a clear night," he whispered huskily. "I would slide this gown of yours off your arms and down to your waist. I would lay you on a blanket of softest wool and let you revel in the sensation of the wool at your back and the light spring breeze playing across your naked breasts before taking them in my warm palms, in my mouth."

When he paused, waiting to gauge her reaction

to his boldness, part of him expected her to be scandalized at such talk. No part of him had expected her to simply look up at him and say, "And? Surely there is more than that to your seduction, Mr. Burke."

Julian gave her a dark look. "My dear, this is but a sample. Anticipation, not expectation, is the essence of any sensual encounter. To tell you everything would give you nothing to look forward to."

She was about to respond when the dance came to an end and with it, the end to the magic they'd woven between them. It was time to go to work, but Julian pushed aside thoughts of the task. The diamonds were in a safe. They could wait a few more minutes. Perhaps he could at least steal a kiss for pleasure and for purpose. His minx needed a quick lesson in playing with fire. "Would you like a glass of champagne?" Julian solicited, moving them toward the veranda and the privacy of the night.

She looked up at him with her green eyes, her whole face shining with enjoyment. "Champagne would be perfect. Shall I wait for you outside?"

Julian grinned. He couldn't have planned it better himself. He found a footman with a tray and grabbed two glasses, congratulating himself on a quick mission. He'd feared the time it would take to wend his way to the refreshment room. Those congratulations were short-lived, however. When he returned to the veranda, it was empty. There was no sign of his lovely partner. She'd given him the slip. It was then that Julian realized she hadn't given him her name.

Omens didn't get any clearer than that. Julian swallowed his champagne in a single draft. His mysterious dance partner had played the role he needed. He'd been noticed on the floor. Apparently that was all he was going to get from her. Now it was time to get to work.

Chapter 2

Sophie DuPlessy watched Julian disappear into the crowd on his quest for champagne. She had to act quickly. Dancing with Vienna's premier lover had been an unlooked-for complication but not necessarily an unenjoyable one. He was as handsome in person as he was reputed to be, and just as rakish.

In spite of her intentions to remain aloof, she'd found it impossible to ignore the seductive maleness of Julian Burke. His hot, dark eyes, his grace on the dance floor and the intimate feel of his hand at her back had been a powerful elixir. But he had not left well enough alone.

His hand had not stayed strictly at her back. Rather, it had strayed from her back to her waist, his thumb lying discreetly at her hip bone, conveying a secret message of its own; that the owner of that hand knew a woman's body, and could with a simple touch bring that body pleasure. Then he'd started with that sinful litany of feats he'd perform, and she'd thought she would melt right there on the dance floor. Surely if a girl was going to be seduced, Julian Burke was the man to do it. And he had the arrogance to know it. He'd known exactly what he was doing with her. He probably knew what he was doing *to* her as well, and she would have indulged in his temptations to a certain degree if she hadn't had other plans tonight.

Sophie looked around her once more and slid back into the crowded ballroom. Julian Burke would have to wait. Tonight, she was nearly at the end of her quest. By midnight, she'd have the jewels in her possession. In the morning, she'd present them to the Italian count who'd hired her and claim her reward. Then her life could begin, her real life, the life she'd dreamed of for the past seven years.

Sophie navigated the ballroom and made her way upstairs, ostensibly in search of the ladies' retiring room. At the last moment, she changed direction, making her way cautiously down the hall toward the west wing of the house and the family's private chambers. Her luck held. She encountered no one. The hall was darker toward this end of the house, no doubt to discourage anyone from wandering far from the party.

The dimly lit hall posed no barriers to Sophie. She'd memorized the upstairs floor plan days ago in preparation for this evening; down the hall, a left turn at the first corridor and then three doors on the right. The third room was the private office where the safe was located behind a portrait of a relative; a great-uncle from whom the house was inherited, to be precise, and Sophie DuPlessy was always precise. It was the trait that had made her so very successful in her line of work.

Sophie turned the handle of the door and stepped inside. As expected, the room was dark, lit only by a small lamp on the desk. Sophie shut the door softly behind her, expecting to savor the moment of peace before taking the final steps in her mission. She inhaled deeply and stopped. Something was wrong.

Her eyes went immediately to the portrait of the great-uncle across the room. She couldn't see it well as her eyes adjusted to the gloom, but it didn't appear to be disturbed. No, it wasn't the portrait. The room was alive with energy, with a presence.

With great deliberation, Sophie reached into the

hidden pocket of her gown for the small gun she carried there. She withdrew it, reassured by the smooth feel of steel in her palm. She kept the weapon concealed in the folds of her skirts, thankful for the fuller fashions.

She debated the wisdom of simply backing out of the room and trying again later. But her mental debate was purely academic. There was no "later." How would she gain legal entry into this home again? It was unlikely this family would host another party soon enough for her needs. No, backing out of the room was not an option. She would have to brave it out.

"Excuse me, is anyone there?" Sophie called out in guileless tones. No one hearing her would guess she concealed a weapon in her gauzy pink skirts or that she'd entered the room intent on committing an act of a dubious nature. Truly, it wasn't stealing. She was merely returning the items in the safe to their rightful owner.

Should he make himself known? Julian Burke cursed his bad luck. There were twenty-five rooms upstairs for a lost young lady to wander into, and yet the young lady had picked his, as unlikely as it was, since the room was so far from the main corridor. Well, maybe not so unlikely if she was meeting someone, a young beau perhaps, for a private assignation. The thought of being a party to such an untutored interlude galvanized Julian into action. His decision was made. He *would* make his presence known and gently guide the intruder back to the main venue. Then he could return to his rendezvous with the portrait and what lay behind it.

Julian raised his dark head over the back of the sofa where he'd taken refuge. "A thousand pardons, mademoiselle. It seems this room is indeed occupied."

Recognition hit him as soon as the glib words were out of his mouth. What was *she* doing here? She couldn't possibly have followed him. She'd been gone when he'd returned to the veranda. In fact, if this was her destination, he was lucky to have gotten here beforehand. She must have gone through the ballroom, which would have slowed her down quite a bit. Still, such conjecture didn't explain what she was doing here to start with. This wasn't exactly a room one deliberately sought out.

Her eyes followed the sound of his voice until they found him rising from the sofa. She masked her own surprise quite well. "Is this where they're keeping the champagne these days?"

"I brought the champagne. You were gone," Julian replied tersely. He stepped around the sofa and moved closer. "Have you gotten lost? I'd be glad to escort you back to the ball."

"Oh no, I'm not ready to go back to the ball," she demurred politely, moving to take a chair near the sofa he'd just vacated. "In truth, Mr. Burke, I am hiding from someone. It's why I had to slip off and leave you, much to my regret." She shook her head most convincingly. "When I saw this dreadful person, I couldn't bear the thought of being discovered by him. He's quite odious in his attentions. I think I shall rest here a bit. You don't need to wait for me if you wish to return downstairs. I doubt anyone will find me here."

Julian crossed his arms. "True enough. It's amazing *you* found your way here, so far from the ballroom." Her answer was not conducive to his plans. He needed her out of this room. He'd spent months planning this. He would not be subdued at the end by a pretty, nameless chit. But she showed no signs of moving from the chair.

"It could be compromising for the two of us to be found in this room alone together," Julian pressed, finding his patience quickly waning. She had deserted him on the veranda and now she had suddenly appeared again with no intentions of leaving in the near future.

"As you said, this room is not on the common path. It's doubtful anyone will come across us," she said confidently, then added coyly, "If you're worried for your reputation or mine, you could always leave."

The pretty minx was getting on his nerves. Julian decided to be blunt. "On principle, you should leave. I was here first."

"On principle, you, as the gentleman in this scenario, should leave and accede to a lady's wishes," she said sweetly before adding, "But principles and reputations are moot issues really after our earlier discussion. Unless I misunderstood you in the ballroom? Was all that talk of strawberries and wool blankets just a gentleman's daydream?" She dropped her eyes to a place a lady was *never* supposed to look on a man while managing to give the impression of demureness. "I thought you were going to try to seduce me and I was going to try to resist."

Julian's jaw clenched. It was time to test this dichotomous angel's mettle. Was she as innocent as she looked, or was she the adventuress her dancing eyes and wicked challenges suggested? He stepped toward the chair she occupied and bent forward, a hand resting on each arm of the chair, effectively trapping her. She caught her breath.

"You are a master flirt, my pretty vixen. I would be happy to seduce you if you think you're up to it." He expected her to push at him. It was what he wanted. He'd let her succeed and race toward the door. No self-respecting society miss would countenance such a naked invitation. It might be one thing to tease a man so avidly on a dance floor surrounded by hundreds of others. It was a far riskier proposition to flaunt those wiles in private with no one to interfere. Here in the dark, the proverbial safety net was gone.

Instead, she propelled herself into his arms with three little words he'd have loved to hear if circumstances had been different: "The sofa, quickly."

Chapter 3

The force of her motion drove them both backward onto said piece of furniture. Julian hit the sofa hard with her on top of him in an inelegant sprawl. Then he heard what she'd heard moments before: people. Someone else had found the dratted room, two of them with libidinous intentions from the sounds they were making. Good lord, the entire party would soon be ensconced in this most remote chamber.

"Don't just lie there, kiss me, or we'll be stuck here for the duration of their affair." She jerked her head toward the sounds of the interlopers, whispering in stern, dictatorial tones that didn't sound in the least like the dulcet voice of an innocent young lady. Come to think of it, she didn't *feel* like an innocent young lady either. The breasts crushed against him, spilling out of her ball gown, were definitely a woman's breasts, full and lush. Julian's erection stirred to life. How could it not? She was stunning in the flush of excitement—her breath coming fast, her green eyes flashing, her hair falling out of its coiffure around her face.

Intuition told him she wasn't what her appearance led him to believe. For the first time, it occurred to him that she was possibly a liar, a very beautiful liar. The thought completed his arousal, the proof of which was pressing against her stomach in obvious force. She really mustn't wiggle like that.

Suddenly Julian jerked. The minx had her hand on him in a most indecent way. He was no prude, but he at least liked to exchange names before such proceedings. Before he could protest, she silenced him with an openmouthed kiss. She moaned audibly, her hand running the length of him, taking his measure through his trousers. "Oh my lord, you're magnificent, so big, so powerful." She gasped and giggled, making every effort to be heard. She lifted her face far enough from his for him to read her arch expression.

Julian smiled. He understood her game, a clever ploy to expel the new invaders from the room. "It is you who makes me such a stallion, my sweet-

ling," he parried, nipping at her bottom lip and co-
ercing a surprised squeal from her. It served the
wench right for taking his trousers at unawares.
She sucked at the delicate lobe of his ear in retal-
iation. He groaned his appreciation and the game
within the game was fully underway.

This venture was quickly becoming less about
driving the intruders from the room and more
about something else altogether. His stranger was
an able partner; nibbling at his ear, stroking him
expertly with her hand until he thought he might
lose control without even taking his trousers off.
That would be a first.

His minx drew back as suddenly as she had engaged. "I think they're gone." Gingerly, she lifted
her head to peer over the sofa. Julian decided to
tickle her one last time for good measure. He told
himself such precautions were to keep up the be-
lievable pretense. But in reality, he knew better. He
wasn't ready for the game to be over. She gave a little scream and he pulled her back down onto him.

"What was that for?" she scolded, pushing at his
chest to lever herself upright.

"Just in case they were still here. Are they?"
Julian asked, admiring his view of her breasts,
which were rising and falling in her indignation.

He ached to cup them, to feel their purported firmness fill his hands. And why shouldn't he? Such an action would only be returning the favor.

"No, they've gone." She moved, trying to disengage. Julian held her firmly by the hips.

"Good, then we can get back to our unfinished business, as it were." Julian boldly glanced down at his aroused member.

"I think not, sir. You have misconstrued my motives. Such actions were merely a distraction, a decoy. Now, if you'd please release me?"

Julian chuckled. The innocent-young-lady facade was back. "Hasn't anyone told you it's bad manners to leave a gentleman aroused?"

"A gentleman wouldn't be ill-mannered enough to mention his, ah, 'condition' to a lady," she said in shocked tones.

Julian snorted. "You would have me believe that the woman who expertly—and I do mean to emphasize expertly here—*expertly* stroked me into full arousal is now appalled by the nature of our association?"

She looked meaningfully at the bulge in his trousers. "You were excited long before my hand came along."

"You, miss, are a tease of the highest order."

Julian sat up in a fluid movement, purposefully spilling his golden-haired vixen onto the floor.

"How dare you!" She stood up rapidly, shaking out her skirts, her eyes scanning the floor. For a moment Julian thought she'd lost something. Then the sensation passed.

She looked entirely enchanting in her dishabille; hair tumbled, dress rumpled, one sleeve askew. Julian could not resist the temptation that rose in him. "I think you'll find that I will dare quite a lot, my dear."

He reached for her, an arm sliding about her waist to pull her to him, his other hand at her nape, guiding, angling her mouth to his for the perfect kiss, the right amount of penetration. He wanted her to know she wasn't the only expert in the room. When a woman had been kissed by Julian Burke, she long remembered it.

She sighed her pleasure into his mouth as he deepened the kiss. He moved a hand to the breast he'd coveted, caressing, teasing her nipple beneath the thin fabric as she had teased his arousal. Her body responded, her nipple hardening with rising desire. She cried out, pressing her body against his. He could feel her hands on his body, on his chest, inside his shirt, everywhere, in an attempt to slake her need. He pushed her dress down to her waist, desperate for those breasts of hers. Her hand had found the core of his manhood again and was stroking vigorously. He groaned without restraint, without a care.

He was reaching for the hem of her skirts to drag them up and complete their passion when the gentleman in him prodded his conscience. How far was he going to let this go? The experience was as extraordinary as it was unorthodox. A gentleman did not simply engage in sex with a nameless stranger in a dark room. This was not a bacchanal; this was a society ball, for heaven's sake, and he'd best remember that.

Julian drew back and gently disengaged her. "I think we'd best stop before we do anything regrettable."

She turned away from him, suddenly modest while she pulled up her bodice. "Is that how you'd describe sex with you? Regrettable?" She tossed him a saucy look over one shoulder.

Julian laughed. He stepped toward her, intending to take her in his arms again and dispel any doubts about his capabilities with the force of his lingering erection against her buttocks. But she was ready for him and neatly sidestepped his efforts.

She had the chair between them with a swish of her skirts. "Uh, uh, uh." She wagged a finger in playful scolding. "Now who's the tease? You said it was finished for tonight. You must stick to your rule, monsieur. I will bid you adieu."

She was almost at the door when Julian remembered what had brought them to this unsatisfactory conclusion—something about sex with a nameless stranger. "What's your name? How will I find you again?"

She gave him another of her smiles, but no answers. "That is part of the charm, *n'est-ce pas? Bon soir, monsieur.*"

His desire remained nameless. Julian watched her sail out of the room. He was already contemplating the next time. Nothing would stop him then. Next time, they would consummate their mutual need. There would be a next time, name or not. He'd find her.

He sank into a chair, letting his legs sprawl. Alone at last. Whew, what a way to get what he wanted. Julian stared at the portrait. Finally he could complete his business. He strode to the door and locked it this time. He should have locked it the first time, but locked doors were hard to explain, and he'd had no reason to fear discovery.

Now he was on alert. He could take no chances in case the whispering strangers returned. The quicker this was accomplished, the sooner he could be en route to England to restore the missing jewels to the monarchy.

Julian crossed the room to the portrait, his mind on the task at hand, when a glimmer under the sofa caught his eye. Julian bent down to investigate. His hand closed around steel. He held the object to the dim light, a frisson running through him. It was a gun, a small gun, a weapon to be used discreetly. And it was still warm, as if it had recently been pressed against someone's body. There was no chance the weapon had been misplaced and left for days under the sofa.

Julian swallowed. There had been only two people in this room and the gun wasn't his. The only conclusion seemed illogical. Why would his stranger need a weapon? This was followed by the realization she'd been on top of him with a loaded firearm. Good God, she could have gelded him. Julian fiercely pushed those morbid thoughts aside and tried to focus on the mystery at hand.

He'd already established that she was not what she seemed. Why had she been in this room? It made little sense to think she'd abandoned him on the veranda only to follow him here. There was only one reason he could think of as to why anyone would purposefully come here. His eyes flew to the portrait. His hand flew to the pocket of his evening coat.

Julian Burke swore out loud. The pocket of his coat, in which he'd carried an excellent paste replica of the diamonds, was empty. He could see the scene in his head now. Her hands on him, slipping and sliding all over his body, and he too far gone in his passion to conceive of ulterior reasons for those caresses. There was no doubt a hidden pocket in her gown, probably where she'd originally carried the gun, and she'd slid the diamonds into it with ease. He knew now that it was the gun she'd been looking for during that uncertain moment after he'd dumped her on the floor. Damn, had she had the gun all that time?

There was nothing for it. He'd have to take the diamonds and hope he got out of the country before anyone noticed they were missing and connected him to the situation.

He'd planned to replace the diamonds with the faux gems in order to avoid immediate detection of the theft. With luck, it might take years before anyone realized the gems were fake. By then, the trail to him would be ice-cold.

Julian lifted the portrait down off the wall and went to work on the safe. It was a matter of a few minutes before he had the safe open. There were other jewels inside but he took only the ones required by England and the crown. He tucked them into his pocket and rehung the picture. Now he'd casually return to the ballroom, say good-night to his hostess, politely inquire about the identity of his stranger and walk out the front door and to bed with his treasure intact. Tomorrow would be a busy day—starting with a visit to his lady of mystery. Whoever she was, she would be in for a very unpleasant surprise.

Chapter 4

The diamond necklace threw sparks of colored light against the wall of Sophie's rented rooms on the *Schonlanterngasse*. Sophie turned the necklace a fraction and watched the prisms dance in the morning sun appreciatively.

This morning she was filled with satisfaction. She'd sent a note immediately to the Italian count. She only had to await his direction regarding how he wanted the diamonds delivered. She stretched on the faded sofa, enjoying the elation of a job completed. In this case, a career completed.

Never again would she have to take the risk of running afoul of the law. She understood that not everyone viewed her job the same way she did. What she saw as the task of returning misplaced property to its rightful owners, others could easily see as thievery of a sort. After all, if people were willing to simply give back their misbegotten items she wouldn't have had a job; a job she'd desperately needed, but hadn't planned on.

No decently brought up girl planned on a career like hers. She certainly never had. But then she'd never planned on being evicted from her girlhood home by a distant male cousin, or having to make her own way in the world.

Sophie put down the necklace and picked up a bracelet, letting it slide over her slim wrist. She felt no qualms about trying on the merchandise. Once she returned to England, there would be no more luxuries in the earthy life she planned for herself.

She did feel a twinge of regret over that aspect. She'd become accustomed to a life of pretty dresses and glittering ballrooms, although she was never more than a visitor in that milieu. When she had her horse farm, there would be no more silks, champagne parties and no more well-heeled men like Julian Burke, who were as dangerous as they were handsome.

While Sophie didn't give a second thought to taking the jewels, her behavior with Julian Burke had been quite scandalous—appalling, really. She'd fondled him! And he'd fondled her, she reminded herself in all fairness. It was quite equitable. Yes indeed, a most equitable amount of kissing and caressing had occurred. But it was also as shameful as it was equitable. She hardly knew the man except by reputation alone. Lord knew that reputation wasn't sterling. After last night, that reputation would need some polishing if anyone found out. Julian Burke, a jewel thief! She shouldn't be surprised.

Sophie had learned quickly in Vienna that few people were what they appeared to be. Julian Burke was obviously no exception. To the public eye he was an Englishman here on diplomatic business and pleasure. From what she'd experienced, that was absolutely true, pleasure being the larger part of his obligations. But he had them all fooled. No one knew he was also a jewel thief.

Sophie sighed and lay back against the arm of the sofa. Last night had been an incredible stroke of luck. If she'd backed out of that room and quietly gone on her way, she would not have discovered the diamonds had already been retrieved. The discovery had been sheer accident. She couldn't take intentional credit for it. She could only take credit for having been in the man's arms, for giving in to the temptations he roused in her. Those temptations had led to the intimate explorations she'd been undertaking when her hands had run across the diamonds in his pocket. She'd studied the drawings of the jewels long enough to recognize the contours when she felt them.

It had been simple enough to encourage him to explore the fever rising between them, and to slip the jewels from his pocket, although it would have been easier if the man hadn't been struck with a guilty conscience and ended the interlude so soon. Oh yes, encouraging him had been the easy part. Forgetting the reciprocal feelings he'd raised in her was proving to be far more difficult.

What she'd done with him was outrageous. She could pretend with herself that it had all just been part of the job, but she could not forget what he'd roused in her. She needed to set those feelings aside. She would never see him again and it was for the best. She had a respectable life waiting for her.

Sophie raised her arm, turning her wrist this way and that to show off the bracelet, focusing her attentions on the dancing facets.

"They look lovely on you," an all-too-recognizable voice said from the doorway. *So much for never seeing him again.* Sophie shot up, reminding herself to stay calm. There was honor among thieves to some extent and there was certainly something more than honor that had sparked between the two of them last night. She was not without defenses, although the first line of defense—the remarkably inquisitive landlady—had certainly failed this morning. In her kinder moments, Sophie liked to think of the landlady as a version of Cerberus, the three-headed dog guarding the underworld in Greek mythology. Between the woman's sharp eyes, curiosity and her unnerving penchant for poking her nose into everyone's business, no one got in or out of the front door. And certainly no one set foot on the stairs without her knowing about it. But Julian Burke had made it all the way to her rooms. Most unnerving indeed.

Sophie fixed him with a coy stare. "You found me. You're faster than I thought you'd be. I wasn't expecting you until tonight."

"The truth is, my dear, you weren't expecting me at all." He pushed off from the door frame and crossed the little room toward her.

No, she hadn't been expecting him. She'd been so lost in her daydreams she hadn't heard the door open. She'd been so confident in her landlady's ability to scent out a stranger the door was un-locked. Both errors were proof enough that she'd underestimated him in many ways. In the daylight he was taller than she'd realized last night; taller, broader, more handsome, more commanding, more everything.

His gaze dominated her with its slow perusal, his sharp eyes a dark shade of gray reminiscent of a topaz necklace she'd reclaimed once for a Russian prince.

"I was unaware you had an appointment to call," Sophie said with a bravado she didn't feel. They both knew why he was here.

A smile flirted on his lips and Sophie remembered the feel of that mouth on her; on her mouth, on her breasts. Her body warmed at the indecent thought. "I'm here for my diamonds, Sophie DuPlessy."

Ah, he had her name. Perhaps he was more than a thief. A thief would not have stopped to ask the hostess for a name, and that was likely where he'd gotten it. An invited guest, then, in the house of an French Comte? If so, that made him a man of means and influence. He was recognized in Vienna's prominent social circles.

"If they're yours, why did you have to steal them?" Sophie challenged.

"Why did you?" He took a step closer, making Sophie intensely aware of the breadth of his shoulders.

"They belong to my client. I am returning them to their rightful owner."

"The Count di Brazzo?" He gave a disdainful chuckle. "They're not his diamonds, my dear."

Sophie hid her surprise. "How do you know about him?" Someone, somewhere had been willing to talk, and Julian Burke had cared enough to find him. The thought made her distinctly uncomfortable.

"Does it matter?" He scooped the necklace up from the table where it lay, arching a sardonic eyebrow that foreshadowed ill tidings. "Anyway, he won't want these, Sophie."

"Why not?" Sophie said hotly, watching the gems dangle from his hand, trying to ignore the delightful tremor that shot through her at the sound of her name on his lips.

He smiled wickedly and leaned close to her ear, as he had on the dance floor, his breath feathering her neck. Her pulse raced at his closeness. She could smell soap on his skin, all spice and manliness.

"Because, my dear, they're nothing but paste. Very good paste, naturally. They've been fooling the public at the Tower of London for centuries now, but they're paste nonetheless."

Sophie recoiled visibly. She'd stolen fakes! She'd nearly passed them off as real to di Brazzo. She couldn't get the bracelet off her arm quickly enough. She dropped it as if it were too hot to hold.

The dratted man laughed at her. "Are you upset because you've been caught or because they're fakes?" He stepped around her and took a seat on her sofa, propping his long legs up on the low coffee table, making himself comfortable.

"Get out!" Sophie gestured toward the door. "Take your paste jewels and get out."

"I wouldn't be so hasty to see me go, Sophie." He was still laughing, his gray eyes sparkling with impishness at her discomfort. "I have something you want, and you, my dear, have something I want." His hot look left no room for misunderstanding.

Sophie drew a deep breath. She did not care for the insinuation that she had no morals. "Last night was merely a distraction to gain the room."

His raised eyebrows suggested his doubt. "A very effective distraction, I'd say. I was 'distracted' all night. How about you?"

"I won't sleep with you, if that's what you're after."

His grin broadened. He settled his hands behind his head. "I'm not in the habit of negotiating for sex. No need to, really."

Sophie stamped her foot in frustration. In one sentence he'd made *her* protest sound like a coy come-on. "You're the most irritating man I've ever had the misfortune to meet, Mr. Burke."

"I liked it better when you called me Julian. Now, do you want to hear what I have to say or do you want to continue your tirade?"

He was scolding her as if she were an errant child. Sophie reined in her temper. "What do you propose?"

"As I said before you interrupted me, we are both in possession of something the other wants, agreed?" Sophie nodded and he continued. "I say we play for them. You win, you get your item. I win, I get you. Do you play piquet?"

Sophie nodded again.

Julian removed an untouched deck of cards from his inner jacket pocket. "You may inspect the cards if you wish." He passed the deck to her. "Perhaps we could sweeten the pot with a side wager. For every point one of us wins in our march toward victory, we can ask the other to pay a forfeit."

Sophie smiled, in no way concerned over what

she stood to lose. He'd had a deck of cards at the ready, giving every impression that he had planned such a gambit, but Julian Burke was about to get his comeuppance. He could have no idea how good she was at piquet. She would gladly wager her 'favors' against the diamonds. By the time a messenger came with a reply from di Brazzo, she'd have won the real diamonds *and* the shirt off Julian Burke's back, quite literally. Sophie shivered with delight at the image of Julian's torso naked and revealed.

"Planning your forfeits already? It's bad luck," Julian said with a wink, dragging a table over for them to play at.

"Luck is just luck. Skill is something else altogether," Sophie said smugly, taking her place at the impromptu card table. She removed all the cards numbered two through six and shuffled deftly. She dealt twelve cards to each of them, picked up her hand and scanned it with a broad grin. But she was all seriousness as she eyed Julian across the table. "Let's play."

Chapter 5

Sophie won the first hand easily. "Take off your coat, Julian." He would think twice about giving her permission to use his first name when she was done.

No need to hurry the experience. She would win plenty of points today. She planned to savor this disrobing. Julian Burke's arrogance needed to be taken down a notch and she was glad to be the one to do it. In turn, she'd be able to quench her growing curiosity about what was under those clothes. For the second hand, she said, "Roll up your sleeves, Julian." She was going to play the dilettante and enjoy each moment of this. She had plenty of clothes to lose and from the looks of it, he had far fewer.

He did so without flinching, his gray eyes ever fixed on her while he flicked back the cuffs of his shirt and rolled the sleeves to the elbow, revealing tanned forearms sprinkled with dark hair, a strikingly masculine contrast against the pristine backdrop of his immaculate white shirt.

Sophie bit her lip, fighting the rush of desire that coursed through her at the sight. She'd always found a man in rolled shirtsleeves so very appealing. But this man was more than simply appealing. Even after this first win, she was tempted to skip the whole game and… No. she couldn't do that.

"I trust you're not disappointed?" Julian said coolly, dealing another hand.

"Not at all." Sophie dimpled.

She wasn't disappointed but she was, unfortunately, distracted. When she triumphantly played a ten thinking to take the trick, she was surprised to see him overplay her with a jack; she'd made an error in her counting.

"My turn at last." Julian heaved a sigh and relaxed back in his chair, studying her with his gray eyes. Just the feel of his eyes on her, roaming at their leisure, sparked something wanton in her. The length of his perusal unnerved her. She fought the urge to fidget.

After an interminable amount of consideration, which left her feeling naked already, Julian drawled in low, firm tones, "Take down your hair,

Sophie." A splendid shiver shot through her as he added, "Slowly."

Two could play this game of allure. If she was going to risk distraction at the sight of his arms, perhaps he would find her hair just as distracting. Sophie held his gaze and reached for the comb holding her hair in a loose twist, knowing that as she did so the fabric of her gown drew tightly across the breasts he'd adored the previous night. She shook her hair free, letting it fall about her shoulders and down her back in an unrestrained cascade of gold waves. Julian drew a gratifying sharp breath. "Be careful what you play at, Sophie," he cautioned in a predator's growl.

Sophie tossed him a sly look through the curtain of her hair, undeterred by his warning. "I'll take your shirt next and your trousers will follow."

"Probably should take my boots first," he quipped. "For convenience sake, you know—easier to get the trousers off."

"As you wish," Sophie said smoothly, picking up her cards and sorting her hand with expert deftness. She felt his eyes on her, and looked up. "What?"

"Don't you want to know what I'll take next?"

Sophie feigned indifference and furled her

hand. "You can tell me if you like. Seems you have your heart set on sharing."

"I'll have that pretty yellow dress of yours, Miss I'll-have-your-shirt-first-and-your-trousers-next."

"It's always good to have dreams, I think. It gives us something to work for." There was so much on the line; the diamonds, her freedom. But as serious as the stakes were, she hadn't had this much fun in ages. Sparring with Julian Burke was good sport. He was funny, witty and positively charming while he lost. It was hard to remember why she had to keep her guard up. It was hard to remember the game was about more than divesting the handsome man across from her of his clothing.

Julian chuckled at her sassy retort. "Just in case, you might want to build up the fire in here." He shot a pointed look at her breasts. Sophie fought the ridiculous urge to cross her arms and shield herself. She wouldn't let him see that he discomfited her. Damn him, could he tell her nipples were already pebbling at his merest suggestion? She had the elder hand so she unfurled her cards into a neat fan and named her points. Julian responded with 'equal,' indicating he had a suit of similar length and strength. Sophie glared at him.

Julian arched his dark brows. "I mean to have that dress, Sophie."

It was war then.

He lost his shirt and took his own sweet time peeling it off his back while Sophie watched in unabashed delight. Julian really did have the most delectable chest; one of those sculpted, smooth and hairless chests with a bronze tan. The only item that marred his torso's perfection was the small half-moon scar under his right breast.

"How did you get that?" Sophie asked in an awed whisper. She nearly had to sit on her hands to avoid going over and tracing the mark with her finger.

"I got too close to someone else's knife once," was all Julian offered.

It was clear that Julian was going to say no more on the matter, and that was fine. Her mind was swiftly moving its attention to other considerations. There was something about the smoothness of Julian's chest that made her want to touch it, to run her hands over the hard shape of his muscles even though this game was strictly look-but-don't-touch. That rule had been quickly established by their pattern of forfeits. To touch might result in a repeat of last night's madness. Might? Who was she kidding? Julian Burke was a man to be desired, and she definitely desired him.

Still, looking wasn't without its risks. It wasn't every day a woman had the good fortune of having an exquisite representation of manhood sitting un-shirted across from her. Perhaps, given the circum-stances, it wasn't surprising that Sophie lost the next hand and her dress. She had the good sense of a sportsman not to protest his choice, but she did shoot him a scolding look for good measure, just to ensure that he knew she wouldn't give up without a fight.

"What?" Julian responded to her stare. "I told you the dress was next and I am a man of my word."

In the end, the thought of sitting there in her un-dergarments was far more risqué than the actual event itself. Her petticoat and camisole left not much more bare than a low-cut ball gown, and there was still her corset and stockings beneath that. Not to mention that her latest ensemble was working in her favor. Julian's eyes had turned the color of hot liquid mercury. He lost the next hand and consequently his first boot.

He lost the second boot quite quickly after that.

Sophie picked up the next hand, hardly able to contain her glee over the excellent cards. Julian threw his hand down. "I surrender. You win."

The announcement was strangely deflating. "Are you sure? You have your trousers to lose yet," Sophie cajoled.

"That would be the end of our game, and I'll definitely lose with this hand," Julian said casually.

"Oh." Sophie colored slightly at his implication. He must not be wearing any small clothes beneath. She cleared her throat. "I see."

"You have me at a disadvantage with your numerous undergarments." Julian gestured to her petticoat and blue-ribboned camisole. "I am assuming there's another layer beneath it? It was hardly a fair game. I had no chance to win against the dictates of female fashion.

"Is that disappointment I sense? I thought you'd be more than pleased to win our little competition."

Ohhhh, the man was insufferable. Even in defeat he was high-handed and arrogant. She'd never admit her disappointment now. Instead, Sophie smiled grandly. "I accept your surrender, sir." She could be magnanimous in her victory. She held out her hand. "I'll take what is mine, please."

"Of course." Julian reached for his long-ago discarded jacket. Sophie stared in confusion as he withdrew a small silver object from his outer pocket. "It's a nice lady's piece." Julian placed her gun in her open palm. "I can see why you'd want it back."

Sophie's good humor vanished. "I want the diamonds. We played for the diamonds."

Julian frowned. "I must respectfully disagree, but we said we'd play for something I wanted and for something you wanted." He shrugged negligently. "I thought you'd want the gun back. My mistake." He reached to take it from her, but Sophie snatched it away.

He managed an ingenuous grin. "Oh, then you do want it."

"Of course I want it—it's mine," Sophie snapped. "You tricked me." The smug look on his face was confirmation that he'd known all along what she'd inferred about their wager.

"My apologies if you see it that way." Julian managed a proper bow with elegance in spite of his missing shirt.

"You're intolerable. Get out!" Sophie grabbed the boot nearest to her and threw it at him. She didn't know what he was playing at but it was no game to her. She had to get those diamonds. Di Brazzo would be furious if he thought she'd lied about acquiring them, and she couldn't risk passing off the fakes. He would see her dead for such a betrayal.

Chapter 6

She'd thrown his boot at him! Hours later, Julian was still musing over Sophie DuPlessy's eviction. He couldn't remember a woman ever throwing him out of her house before. His morning interlude with Sophie certainly hadn't gone in the direction he had been expecting. Usually an episode of strip piquet ended with some excellent lovemaking. Instead, this one had ended with him fleeing the house in haphazard fashion, stocking-footed and his boots in his hands like a sneaky lover in a Drury Lane farce.

Absently, Julian moved a pawn into position on the chessboard. Across from him, his partner—St. Just—tsked lightly. "Your mind is not on the game," he noted, taking Julian's pawn easily with a rook.

Julian leaned back in his chair, massaging his

forehead. "I know. You'll have me checkmated in three moves and there's nothing I can do about it."

Valerian nodded his agreement. "Would you care to talk about it?"

"The game?"

"No, whatever is ailing you," he said seriously.

Julian looked around the *koffeehaus*. The place was quieter than usual. A few groups of people were scattered throughout the establishment, busy reading newspapers or with conversations of their own. He'd been glad to find the place nearly empty. He wanted to be alone with his thoughts. It had been surprising to find St. Just there without the usual entourage of mutual acquaintances. Julian rather liked the serious young man sitting across from him. The viscount was the nephew of one of the British diplomats posted to Vienna, and very good at his work. Julian knew that even as young as he was, St. Just had been a trusted member of the British team that had gone into Turkey last year to negotiate water rights to the Dardanelle Straits.

"Does it have to do with your mission?" St. Just said politely, prompting him to speak. There were only a handful of people who understood Julian's true reason for being in Vienna. To Julian's mind, the fewer who knew, the better. There was little glory or respect in being a spy. There was absolutely none for a man who stole jewels, even at the behest of his monarch. Technically, he was lower than a spy. Socially, he was passing himself off as a diplomatic assistant to Valerian's uncle—a completely respectable occupation for a second son.

"Somewhat," Julian offered vaguely, reaching for his cup of rich Viennese coffee. He'd been pondering his situation with Sophie DuPlessy all afternoon, but now that there was a chance to talk it through he was reluctant to do so. He tried a new direction. "By the way, what are you doing here? It's not your usual time of day. I didn't expect to see you."

Valerian shot him an arch look over the rim of his own coffee cup. "If you must know, I'm soaking in the last of Vienna for a while."

"Are you going home to England at last?" Julian queried. He'd thought it more than passing strange that Valerian, with his title and estates, would elect to stay in Vienna as long as he had. But Valerian had always been rather closed on the subject of his life in England.

A dark look clouded the younger man's face at the mention of England. "I leave for Italy in the morning. I'm to check up on the situation in

Naples. But you'll have to do better than that, old man, if you want to distract me. I'm not like all those effortlessly diverted women you charm in the drawing rooms."

Julian sighed and said in a low voice, "It's complicated. There's a woman involved."

"Isn't there always?" Valerian said in a tone that caused Julian to wonder just how many secrets Valerian kept hidden beneath his cool exterior. If he had to guess, Julian suspected there were far more than the usual number young men kept.

"She's stolen my paste version of the jewels. She lifted them right out of my jacket pocket last night."

"And you didn't notice?" St. Just queried.

"No, not until after she was gone. We were engaged in some, ah, distracting activities, shall we say," Julian confessed. Normally he had no trouble discussing such things with his circle of friends. Today, talking about what had transpired with Sophie seemed demeaning. What they'd done had only been a game but he still didn't feel right making it public knowledge. If their regular companions, Truesdale and Mathison, were here, they'd be laughing their heads off—and he hadn't even gotten to the part about finding her gun under the sofa. Julian didn't want anyone to laugh.

St. Just seemed to understand even if he didn't. The viscount stroked the length of a bishop piece with his long fingers, thinking. "You have to get them back. The king can't have an excellent forgery loose in Europe. There's all kinds of mischief that could come of it. Have you approached her about the incident?"

"Yes, I went to her place this morning."

"Obviously with an unsatisfactory outcome," his friend surmised. "What did she say when you asked for your paste diamonds back?"

"I didn't precisely ask for them back. I told her I'd play her for them."

"So?"

"We played strip piquet."

Coffee spewed inelegantly out of St. Just's mouth. He dabbed at his mouth and trousers with a white napkin. "Good lord, what were you thinking?"

"That's just it. I was thinking that I rather liked her. I've yet to meet a woman who strikes me so powerfully. She's beautiful, passionate, witty, daring. I find myself wanting to know what she'll do next. I only suggested we play piquet for clothing because I didn't think she'd accept. Before I knew it, we were sitting there in our underwear."

"You don't wear underwear," Val corrected.

"That's why I lost. She'd already won the shirt off my back. I had to stop the game before she took my trousers."

St. Just stifled a laugh.

"Shh. It's not particularly funny." Julian looked around to make sure they weren't drawing undue stares.

"It is when it's you, my friend. You've had your way with every woman you've laid eyes on. These continental women have made it far too easy for you. You toss them aside after a week when someone new captures your meager attention span. Finally you've met a woman who challenges you, pushes you and apparently has the ability to best you. I like her already."

"She's mine. You'll have to get your own, maybe a pretty *signorina* in Italy," Julian jested. But St. Just didn't laugh. He looked away, glancing at a spot over Julian's shoulder, pretending that his attention was caught by some activity at another table. Julian wasn't fooled. In a fleeting moment of insight, he knew why St. Just avoided England. "Tell me about her," Julian said quietly.

"Who?" It was St. Just's turn to be obtuse.

"The woman who keeps you from England. The woman who holds your heart."

"It hardly matters anymore. She's married to another. Her family needed more money than I had to offer." Valerian shrugged and contemplated the dregs in his coffee cup. "A cautionary tale, my friend, about how little love matters and how little love can do in this world."

"I only said I liked her. I didn't use the word love," Julian protested. "I'm merely worried for her."

St. Just furrowed his brow. "Don't be naive, Julian. She stole what amounts to diamonds from you. She's not as pure as the driven snow. Don't be taken in by her beauty alone."

"Whatever her usual game is, I think she's in too deep this time. She's working for Count di Brazzo. He's the one who hired her to get the diamonds."

St. Just let out a low whistle. "That is deep. If she's with di Brazzo then it means she's done this before. He wouldn't hire a novice. The count is known for his collection of rare gems. This new Europe has proven to be quite useful in expanding his collection, I hear."

Julian nodded. He knew precisely what St. Just was referring to. Many valuable items had gone missing in the political shake-ups since Europe was released from Napoleon's grip. Small kingdoms had been eaten up by new borders, old kingdoms had been absorbed into larger nations. Other principalities had suffered internal revolts and monarchs had fled their thrones, fearing a similar outcome to the one in France. It was a perfect time for looting unprotected treasuries.

Anyone with knowledge of those treasuries and skill in discreet removals would thrive. Julian's own presence in Vienna was for that very reason. The Count di Brazzo was also such an individual. All reports indicated di Brazzo was without scruples and selfish to the core; a mean man all around. It did not sit well with Julian to know that Sophie DuPlessy, with her sunlight laughter and zest for life, did business with that sort of man. For that matter, he didn't like the idea that she was in that sort of business at all.

"I'm sorry if I've tarnished the image of your golden angel," St. Just remarked on Julian's prolonged silence.

Julian shook his head. "I knew before this that she was not all she seemed. But that doesn't help me make any more sense out of why she'd be involved in such a scheme. I have to figure out where she'll be tonight. I'll go back for the fakes when she goes out." Julian rose.

St. Just rose with him. "That shouldn't be too

hard to do. Just ask yourself where you would be if you were her."

Valerian's parting comment caused Julian to maintain a quick pace home to his rooms in the Belvedere Quarter. If he was after those diamonds and he knew where they were, he'd simply go get them. When someone took what was yours, you were obliged to take it back, and Sophie DuPlessy had every right to feel the need for vindication.

It wasn't only that he wanted to protect the diamonds. If she took them, he'd steal them from her again. He was more concerned about protecting her from herself. She was in more danger in possession of the diamonds than she realized. Julian wouldn't put it past the count to exterminate her after she produced the diamonds. A man like di Brazzo was careful. The count wouldn't let Sophie live and risk her spreading the story of her heist.

Julian picked up his pace. If he didn't get to Sophie first, she was as good as dead. That prospect sat quite poorly with him for reasons he'd rather not examine for fear of the answer: after years of playful bedroom pursuits with no meaning, he'd finally fallen irrevocably and completely in love in the most unorthodox way with a most unsuitable woman for a man of his station—the brother of an earl.

Chapter 7

Sophie surveyed the large, airy rooms belonging to Julian Burke with a growing amount of frustration. The man had very little furniture in these rooms and that meant he'd been creative in where he'd hidden the diamonds. She didn't have time for 'creative.' She'd sweetly cajoled the landlady, who was much nicer and blinder than her own, into letting her in, and she wanted to be long gone before the landlady told Julian she'd been here.

She needed the diamonds desperately. Count di Brazzo's messenger had returned late in the afternoon with a response. Di Brazzo would be glad to meet with her in the morning and collect the diamonds. He would bring the reward money with him.

Sophie's eyes ran over the painted blue walls

decorated with gilt-trimmed panels in the Baroque style. These were expensive rooms. But then the Belvedere Quarter was an expensive part of town to live in. The quarter was built around the borders of Belvedere Palace, and several nobles wanting the status of living close to the royal family had made homes here in the previous century. The current archduke didn't live at Belvedere but the coterie of ambassadors sent to Vienna by their nations found the old homes of nobles excellent residences for conducting their business and entertaining on a grand scale.

Julian struck her as a man who desired the best. Finding that he lived in such exalted quarters did not surprise her. Discovering that he possessed little else beyond the elegant address did. The walls were empty of pictures that might hide a safe. The drawers of his Biedermeier-styled desk had turned up nothing. There'd been no sign of false bottoms in the drawers. She only had the bedroom left to check and she didn't hold out much hope. She'd seen the bedroom on her initial walk through his lodgings. It held only a bed and a bureau. The little dressing room off the bedroom held strictly clothing.

Sophie started with the bureau. She opened the

top drawer and was immediately assailed by the smell of him. The spicy scent she'd come to associate with Julian rose from the lengths of cravat cloth neatly folded in the drawer. There was a carved wooden box in the drawer as well. Sophie opened it, acutely aware that she was invading someone's privacy. There were no diamonds inside, only folded papers. Sophie quickly put the lid back on. Whatever was in those papers had nothing to do with her, and the less she knew about Julian personally the better off she was. Sophie ran her hands expertly across the back and bottom of the drawer, looking for a secret compartment.

"They're not in the bureau."

Sophie jumped and stifled a scream. Julian lounged against the door frame, acting as if he'd been expecting to find her going through his personal things all along. Did nothing ruffle this dratted man? "You startled me," she scolded.

Julian gave his low chuckle. "*I* startled *you?* Have you forgotten these are *my* rooms? You're not supposed to be here."

Julian entered the room and started pacing. He emanated restless energy, and for the first time Sophie noticed the little details about him; his hair was mussed, his boots were dusty and caked with dirt in places, as if he'd run in them. A slight film of sweat glistened on his brow.

Julian stopped at the long window and looked out into the courtyard garden below. "Sophie, we have to talk."

Those words confirmed her suspicions. Julian had run here, had hoped to find her here. It was unnerving to think the man knew her so well.

"Please, sit down." Julian gestured toward the bed, the only piece of furniture in the room that would accommodate the action of sitting. "Sophie, you can't have the diamonds," he began once she was settled on the big four-poster.

Some of the tension went out of her. He'd seemed so serious. She'd thought for a moment something important had happened, but it was still the same conversation they'd been having since this morning. "You disappoint me, Julian. I thought you'd have something original to say." Sophie moved to slide off the bed.

"Wait! This is not about you or me having the diamonds." The force of his voice caused her to halt. "You're in danger, Sophie. The moment you hand over those diamonds to di Brazzo is the moment you are dead."

That got her attention. "I think you'd better explain," Sophie said quietly, resuming her place on the bed. Frankly, Julian's words scared her. In many ways, retrieving the diamonds was the riskiest job she'd done. She hadn't liked the count on first sight but the money he offered would be the making of her new life.

Julian strode to the bed and reached for her hands. The warmth of his grip was reassuring. "Di Brazzo can't risk you telling anyone about the jewels," he explained softly.

Julian was trying to be gentle. But she didn't want gentle, not right now. She yanked her hands from his and moved off the bed. She knew Julian meant well and she was truly scared. But she was something else too. She was *angry.*

In fact, she was angrier than she'd ever been in her life. She was angry at fate for letting her come so close to succeeding. She was angry at di Brazzo for not playing fairly—there was honor among thieves, and he should have honored the code of their dealings. Most of all, she was angry at herself. She should have gone with her initial instincts about di Brazzo. She should have seen di Brazzo's secret plan from the start and stayed away.

Sophie paced the room in long, determined strides, stopping occasionally to look about the chamber while she vented her anger. She'd come so close to succeeding. Now she wasn't simply going to fail and fall short, she was going to die. Maybe not tomorrow if she could work a miracle. But she couldn't outrun di Brazzo forever. She thought of the paste jewels back in her rooms. They would buy her some time, but they wouldn't buy her enough. Still, if Julian was to be believed, di Brazzo would see her dead if she turned over the jewels. Convincing him the paste items were real was a moot point. She was dead if she stayed and dead if she ran. She stopped and surveyed the room again. Damn it. Just damn it.

"What are you looking for?" Julian asked tentatively from the bed, where he'd had the good sense to stay, out of her way.

"Something to throw," Sophie ground out. She wanted to smash a nice, delicate porcelain shepherdess, but Julian's rooms were as austere as they came. "What am I going to do?" Sophie sighed and went to the window, leaning against the sash and looking down into the park. Some of the fire had gone out of her anger. She had to resolve the crisis facing her. Anger couldn't help with that.

"Are we still looking for things to throw?" Julian swung off the bed and approached her.

"No, I mean, what am I going to do about di Brazzo?" Sophie raked her hands through her hair.

Julian drew her to him. "Correction, my dear. The question is what are *we* going to do. I will not let you face di Brazzo alone."

The pronouncement stunned her. This serious side of Julian was quite unexpected and so unlike the witty, careless rake who had played strip piquet with her just that morning, divesting her of her gown with no gentlemanly qualms. "Why would you help me?" Even in her desperation she was skeptical. Perhaps this was all an elaborate ploy to chase her out of town and keep the diamonds for himself.

Julian smiled down at her. "Because somewhere between being thrown down on a sofa and losing the shirt off of my back, I've come to like you, my dear. These have been the best two days I've ever had."

Sophie laughed. "You're a horrible sap, Julian." But she pressed her head against his chest, her hands gripping the lapels of his coat. She let his arms wrap around her, enclosing her in their strength. For the moment, she was safe. For the moment, she had a champion. Julian Burke made her feel the closest she'd ever come to being invincible. Wrapped in his embrace, she could almost believe anything was possible.

Julian's member stirred against her skirts. With her cheek still on the fabric of his coat, Sophie smiled to herself. Nothing could be done about di Brazzo until tomorrow. This one last night was hers and she knew what she wanted. "Julian," she said softly, turning her face up to his, "take me to bed."

A wolfish grin spread across his face. "My dear, I thought you'd never ask."

Julian shrugged out of his coat and reached for the buttons on his shirt, but Sophie stayed his hand. "Let me," she whispered. "I wanted to do it this morning, but you were too quick." Sophie made fast work of the buttons. She pushed back the shirt and let her breath catch. From the firmness of his upper chest to the sculpted planes of his abdomen, Julian was all male muscle and hardness, so exquisitely put together a sculptor would have difficulty doing any better. "Julian, you're so beautiful." She was awestruck, even though she'd seen his naked chest before. She imagined she'd never tire of that particular view. No wonder the women of Vienna could talk of nothing else but Julian Burke.

"If you like this, wait until you see the rest," Julian teased. He stepped away from her and pulled off his boots. She reveled in the flex and play of his muscles as they tugged off the dusty footwear.

Julian's hands went to his trousers and the atmosphere around them was serious again. The playfulness of a few moments ago had evaporated, replaced by a sensual tension. Sophie had never guessed a man disrobing could be this stimulating. When Julian came to her, he'd find her more than ready for him.

His trousers were finally off. Julian kicked his feet out of them and strode toward the window to draw the curtain, treating her to an unadulterated view of him from all angles. His confidence in his own nakedness was a potent aphrodisiac. This was man who knew what a bedroom was for. She lay back on the pillows of the bed and waited.

"Sophie, you're trembling." Julian sat on the side of the bed. He ran a hand under her skirts, searching for the garter that held her stockings, his touch feather-light as he skimmed her private places.

"That's your fault," Sophie said, slightly more breathless than she'd have liked to have been. It was frightening how quickly he'd reduced her to a trembling pool of jelly and how much she liked it.

"Sit up and let's get this dress off you." Julian

deftly unfastened her gown in record time, petticoats and undergarments following their prede-
cessor to the floor.

Julian covered her, moving himself between her
legs, and she welcomed him. There was no sense
in any more games. They both knew what they
wanted, perhaps they'd even known last night that
such a moment was inevitable. His member
nudged her entrance, testing, looking for assur-
ances that she was ready. She was vaguely aware
of his arm reaching out to the console beside the
bed, searching for something. Then he drew back
from her and fitted a sheath onto his sex, his eyes
never leaving hers. She reached up and drew him
back to her, settling him where she wanted him.

This time, he didn't nudge. This time, he slid
into her and she took all of him, wrapping her legs
about him, pushing him on to the very core of her
being. Something inside her split and there was a
momentary pain. Julian stilled and for an instant
she feared he would leave her. She clung to him
with her legs, urging him to continue. He picked
up the tantalizing rhythm again and she was lost
to the pleasure of their united bodies.

The tempo of their dance increased until the
friction of his member against some secret part of

her was too great for her to bear. Sophie screamed and shattered into a thousand pieces of satisfaction. Julian was with her in the kaleidoscope of sensation, voicing his own pleasure, her name on his lips.

She lay in Julian's arms, letting her body slow from its furious pace. Neither of them spoke. It was enough to feel his body against hers, to know from the racing of his heart that he was as shaken by the experience as she.

After a while, Julian rose and went into the dressing room, returning with a basin of water and a washcloth. Sophie sat up, reaching for it. "Let me, Sophie," Julian said softly, pushing her hands away. "Just lie down."

He washed her in gentle strokes, far more comfortable with the act than she was. Even after such intense lovemaking, Sophie was swamped with acute embarrassment over the intimate attentions of his bath.

Julian set the basin and cloth aside and fixed her with a gray stare. "Why didn't you tell me?"

"It didn't seem important." Sophie pulled a sheet up to cover herself. "I wanted you. That was all that mattered." She hoped that would be reassuring to him. She had no expectations. In light of their situation, expectations seemed a bit ludicrous.

"I am honored it was me you chose. It is no mean thing to be the recipient of a woman's innocence. I am sorry I didn't guess."

"Don't be sorry. How could you have known? I gave you no reason to believe otherwise." She knew virgins didn't flirt outrageously or cup gentlemen through their trousers. But she did. Ironically, such shenanigans were probably the reason she'd been able to maintain her virginity for so long, given her line of work and the people she encountered. There had been other ways to satisfy them when the need arose.

Julian stretched out beside her. He pushed down the sheet. "You're too lovely to hide, Sophie." With a lazy finger he began drawing lazy circles around the areola of her breast. "So tell me, Sophie, how a girl becomes interested in stealing diamonds."

Chapter 8

Sophie shifted out of Julian's embrace, levering herself up on one arm. "The story is fairly ordinary in its beginnings. My father passed away, and his heir, a distant cousin, inherited our little estate. This cousin had a wife who didn't fancy sharing her home with me, so out I went."

"Your father was English?" Julian interrupted.

"Yes. My mother was French. DuPlessy is her name," Sophie explained. "It was easier to fit in over here with a French name. I worked as a companion to an English family in Brussels after the war. It was a good family with a lot of connections." Sophie paused here. This was where her story became more sordid. "You don't really want to hear all this, Julian."

"Yes, I do," he encouraged quietly.

"Well, one night at a ball a friend of the family asked me to help him retrieve something he'd left behind on a prior visit. I assumed he was telling the truth. I had no reason to disbelieve him. We went into the study and we took a book. It seemed harmless enough to me until he took me outside and showed me what was in the book. The book was hollow and there were some rubies inside. Of course, I was shocked. But he explained how these jewels really belonged to his mother's side of the family and how the host had tricked his mother's family out of them years ago.

"Then he told me about the opportunities to help people find lost things, how the war had displaced valuables like those rubies and how they'd fallen into the wrong hands."

Julian supplied the rest. "You came to Vienna to help restore lost items, then?"

"Yes." She was defiant now. "I did not steal anything. The items I took truly did belong to the people who hired me."

"Until now," Julian said firmly. "The diamonds don't belong to Count di Brazzo, no matter what he's told you."

Sophie bit her lip. "I know. This was to be the last job. I needed the money for my horse farm and a decent life in England. I suspected from the start he had not told me the whole truth."

Julian shifted to face her. He pushed a strand of hair out of her face. "The diamonds belong to the monarchy of England. I've been hired to bring them back. They were originally part of the royal treasury before the execution of Charles I. Much was destroyed intentionally by the council of state under the new government, but much of it was also discreetly looted and made its way abroad. Within time, people forget to be on the lookout for such treasures."

A quiet "oh" escaped Sophie's lips. There was so much she didn't know about Julian Burke. He was the king's man, a diplomat, a jewel thief, a great lover of women. What else comprised the sum of the man who lay beside her? There was no time to ask or to ponder that question. Julian was rolling her beneath him again and her body was ready for him, for a chance to return to that magical place where nothing mattered for a few moments of bliss. In Julian's arms she could hold the morning at bay.

Julian dressed efficiently in the morning light. There was much he wanted to have done before

Sophie awoke. He had loved her thoroughly in the night and now she slept deeply. No matter what happened this morning with di Brazzo, today would be their last day in Vienna. Sophie had to leave the city and he would protect her with his body, with his very name if need be. She had given herself to him and she was his.

In his dressing room, Julian threw a spare change of clothes into a traveling valise. He wrapped the box holding the king's diamonds in a clean shirt and placed it in the bottom of the bag. He packed up his personal items; razor and hairbrush. From his dresser drawer, he took out the wooden box containing his papers and tucked them into his coat pocket. There was another item in the box too, and Julian added it to his pocket. One never knew when a ring would come in handy. From the bottom dresser drawer he drew out his weapons; two pistols and a knife. There was powder and shot too. The next task was to write the necessary letters and get them delivered. With luck, St. Just hadn't left for Italy yet.

A half hour later, the notes were on their way a few blocks over to St. Just and his uncle. It was time to wake Sophie. Julian was reluctant to do it. She looked content as she slept. There was so much to face in the waking world. It would take all their wits to survive today.

Julian bent and kissed her brow, praying he wasn't waking her for the last day of her life. She stretched beneath him, her hair fanned about her like a halo.

"Good morning, angel," Julian whispered. His desire was rising but there was no time.

Her green eyes opened. She smiled drowsily at him and he savored the moment. In an instant her peace was gone. He could see recognition, and all they faced today, flooding back to her. "You should have woken me sooner."

"It is soon enough. I had business to take care of," he assured her. "There's a little bread and cheese for breakfast on the table in the other room." He left her to complete her morning ablutions.

She was fast, and they ate quickly. "We'll stop at your rooms first, Sophie. Grab anything of value you need— traveling papers, a change of clothes and anything personal you can't live without. All else can be replaced. We must move with speed and stealth. We cannot be hampered by luggage," Julian explained over the bread and cheese. "After that, we'll go to St. Just. He should be able to arrange safe passage for us."

Sophie nodded. "Do you think we'll make it?"

"Your meeting with di Brazzo isn't until eleven. There's a good chance we'll make it." There were a lot of unspoken "ifs" in his reassurance but there was no need to worry her needlessly.

Julian locked the door to his rooms with a sense of finality. Everything that mattered was on the landing with him. Beside him, Sophie sensed his mood—perhaps she even sensed all that he risked, not the least being his trust in her. "Thank you for doing this, Julian," she said quietly.

The streets were starting to fill with clerks heading to their work in banks and stores. Julian and Sophie were able to blend in a bit, in the event anyone was following them. They rounded the turn onto *Schonlanterngasse* and halted. They were too late.

"Oh my God," Sophie breathed in horror. "You were right." Her rooms on the second floor of the building had clearly been vandalized. Passersby stopped to stare and point at the broken windows and the open French doors leading onto her small balcony overlooking the street. The balcony was strewn with clothing and broken furniture. Shattered glass littered the street below.

Julian eased them back around the corner, pressing Sophie to the wall. "I'm sorry, darling.

They must have come in the night." He couldn't allow himself to think what would have happened to her if he hadn't caught her in his apartments. He stole a look around the corner, scanning the street. His eyes found what he was looking for—someone asking questions. A swarthy-skinned man with dark hair and poor clothing stood on the sidewalk near the building, stopping people as they entered. Julian could guess what he was asking them.

He took Sophie by the hand. "Let's get to St. Just." He needed the viscount's influence more than he'd anticipated. Di Brazzo's henchmen had destroyed her rooms and their contents, effectively trapping her in Vienna. She couldn't travel without papers. St. Just could get the papers.

Julian breathed a sigh of relief as they slid through the gates to the residence that acted as an unofficial British embassy in Vienna. St. Just ushered them inside a private room and locked the door.

"Thank goodness you're here. My eyes and ears on the streets this morning report only bad news. Di Brazzo has issued a warrant for Sophie's arrest. He's claiming he found the diamonds in her apartment."

Sophie clapped a hand over her mouth. "The paste set was in there."

Julian exchanged a sharp look with St. Just. He

saw immediately what di Brazzo was about. If he'd merely wanted the diamonds, he'd have happily taken the paste by mistake and foregone paying Sophie the promised reward. He wouldn't discover the deception until later. The paste set had been fooling visitors to the Tower for years. But the man couldn't let Sophie live to tell the tale. He'd issued the warrant in an attempt to flush her out and have the police do his dirty work for him. Getting Sophie DuPlessy out of the city would be impossible. All the roads would be watched. Julian thought of the ring in his pocket. Getting Sophie DuPlessy out might be impossible. Getting Lady Burke out would be a hell of a lot easier.

"What can I do, Julian?" St. Just asked.

"She needs traveling papers."

St. Just shook his head in protest. "I can get the papers, but police will be watching the roads. Papers won't be enough."

"I know. Make them out in the name of Lady Burke. Get me a special license and a gown of your cousin's."

Plans swirled around Sophie until her head spun. What was Julian talking about? "Those papers will be a fraud. They'll do no good if it can be proved they're a forgery." These men were mad. Julian was reorganizing the world with false names and alibis, and St. Just was standing there nodding as if it was perfectly acceptable behavior.

Julian paused and turned to her. "It won't be a lie, Sophie. We'll be married by special license at Karlskirche within the hour. I know it's not St. Stephens but it's too far. Karlskirche is only around the corner."

Sophie shook her head. "Wait. You can't marry me."

"Are you already married?" Julian inquired.

"No, but…"

"Do you have another idea for getting you out of the city before di Brazzo finds you?"

"No, but…"

An attractive young woman swept down the steps. "A wedding today, Julian? What will you think of next? You're a positive scandal." She laughed and moved toward them.

"Good morning, Emma." Julian bowed.

"Cousin, can you find something suitable for Julian's bride?" St. Just nodded in Sophie's direction, and Sophie found herself being led upstairs by a young woman who seemed as stubborn as St. Just and as mad as the completely insane Julian Burke.

"Here, this will be perfect." Emma pulled a soft green gown the color of celery from her wardrobe and held it up to Sophie. "How exciting to be marrying Julian by special license."

"It's not a real wedding," Sophie tried to protest.

"Julian doesn't do anything that isn't real," Emma argued, pulling Sophie's old gown over her head. "He's an English lord, you know, back home. Lord Julian. His brother's the earl but he gets the title as an honorific. You'll be Lady Sophie."

Sophie's knees nearly buckled at the announcement. Among his other careers, Julian was an English lord? She absently thrust her arms through the sleeves of the green dress, letting Emma arrange the skirts and find the matching shoes.

"Come sit. I'll do your hair up in a pretty style. Oh my, it's so long," Emma exclaimed as she pulled out the pins holding it in place. "Shall we leave it loose? You look like a medieval princess. We're lucky the dress fits so well." From somewhere, Emma produced a length of filmy, sheer material and fashioned it into an impromptu veil.

Emma chatted away helpfully and Sophie knew

she was doing her best to alleviate Sophie's nerves. But Sophie's thoughts were too far away to concentrate on the conversation for long. She wanted to talk to Julian, to tell him he needn't do this. There had to be another way. He couldn't possibly love her. That was the sad part. While he couldn't possibly love her, she could quite possibly love him. Even without a title, she could love him. The irritating, cool, sardonic rake was also a man capable of extreme tenderness and intense passion.

There was a knock at the door. St. Just poked his head into the room. "Emma, we're ready. I've a carriage waiting to take her to church." Good lord, it sounded like a real wedding day when St. Just said it like that. A carriage, a dress—one would be hard-pressed to believe assassins were searching the city for her.

"Wait." Sophie rose. "St. Just, can't you talk him out of this? It's madness." Panic tinged her voice.

St. Just flashed her a queer look. "You could do far worse than Julian, Miss DuPlessy. I would trust him with my life, and you can too. That's enough to build a relationship on, don't you think?"

He was scolding her. "I'm not a coward," Sophie retorted, gathering her skirts. She crossed the room to take St. Just's arm, her head high, her eyes flashing.

"All the same, Miss DuPlessy, you might need this." At the door, St. Just handed her a little gun reminiscent of the one she'd left behind in her ruined apartment. "Julian mentioned you know how to use one of these. I trust there's a pocket on Emma's gown?"

"You know I've had all my gowns made with a pocket," Emma reminded her cousin teasingly. "It's there on the right side, nice and deep. No one will notice it."

Sophie slipped the gun inside. "Are we expecting trouble?" She took St. Just's arm.

"One can never tell with Julian. I've found it best to always be prepared," the handsome viscount counseled.

Outside, a white, open carriage—a Viennese fiacre—waited with four matched grays. The viscount handed her up and followed her into the seat. He gave a shout to the driver and they were off. "I'm sorry Emma didn't have a white gown for you. I know it's all the rage these days. But you look lovely," he offered in the way of small talk.

"I hardly set store by such things." Sophie shrugged. Everything felt surreal. She was on her way to her wedding, sitting beside a viscount in a white carriage, dressed in a beautiful but borrowed gown, her gauzy veil fluttering in the light breeze. It would have been ideal weather for a real wedding.

Julian hadn't been joking when he'd said the church was right around the corner. Karlskirche was a handsome Baroque building, its dome dominating the neighborhood. St. Just handed her out and then reached under the seat. "I did manage these for you." He passed her a bouquet of white roses. "I grow them myself when I'm here in town."

"Thank you," Sophie offered humbly. The gesture touched her and it spoke volumes about this young man's friendship with Julian. Relationships of such quality were rare.

Sophie stepped inside the church, giving her eyes a moment to adjust to the dim interior and her nerves a moment to steady themselves. St. Just was beside her. "Julian is waiting at the high altar. Shall we?"

Sophie began the long walk to the high altar and its trappings. Vaguely, she was aware of walking in Baroque splendor; columns and gold gilt surrounded her. But she was only intent on the figure of Julian Burke, his dark hair smooth and combed, patiently, calmly waiting for her. He must have

raided St. Just's wardrobe for the occasion. He
was turned out in a dark blue morning coat and
gray trousers, a cravat neatly tied at his throat, an
emerald stickpin twinkling in its folds. He'd gone
to great efforts to provide the trappings of a proper
ceremony.

Two other men stood with Julian. St. Just nodded in their direction, familiar with them. Then the
priest began the rituals that would make Sophie
and Julian man and wife. Julian kissed her soundly
at the end. The two men came forward to congratulate them and introduce themselves; Andrew
Truesdale and Camden Mathison. There were papers to sign. Sophie signed her name in tight, neat
letters. Julian's signature was done in a great flourish. Lord Julian Burke. An official seal was put on
the document and it was done. They were bound
together in the eyes of the law. In the eyes of the
law, Sophie DuPlessy was no more. Sophie caught
Julian's gaze across the parchment.

He gave her a reassuring smile. "Everything
will be all right, Lady Burke."

The door to the church opened. Sophie realized
she hadn't noticed St. Just had left until he reen-
tered the building.

He strode up the aisle, reaching their side. "It's

done, then?" He glanced at Julian. "Then congratulations are in order, Julian." He shook Julian's hand.

"Thank you, Val, for all your efforts. Perhaps someday I can return the favor."

For a moment Sophie thought she saw a look of longing deep in St. Just's eyes. Intuitively she understood the bouquet of roses better. The viscount was a romantic for all that his dashing ways proclaimed otherwise, and unless she missed her guess, he was a romantic with a broken heart. However he was so terse when he spoke, Sophie thought she might have imagined the look after all.

"We need to go, Julian. The police are stopping everyone at the city exits."

Sophie looked nervously at Julian. "Perhaps a hat to hide my hair? Di Brazzo's men will recognize me."

Julian shook his head. "No. We have nothing to be guilty of. If we act guilty, we give them reason to be suspicious. We've made it so far."

Sophie took up her seat in the carriage, now miraculously decorated with white satin ribbon and posies of white flowers. She saw St. Just pass Julian a packet of papers and murmur the words, "Carefully, don't smear the ink. I sanded them heavily but the ink's still fresh."

Julian gave a curt nod. "Pistols at the ready, St. Just. Tell the others."

Only then did Sophie note that Truesdale and Mathison had mounted horses next to the carriage. They were joined by four other men wearing the uniform of the British cavalry. "A mounted escort, Julian?" she asked skeptically. This boded ill.

"It is suited to my station, dear," he said with a wink and a smile.

The trip through town went smoothly. They drew attention with their escort and the prettily decorated fiacre. Julian played the happy bridegroom to the hilt and threw gold coins to the children chasing the carriage.

Traffic slowed at the gate. The horses champed restlessly at their bits in a desire to be off. Sophie shared their frustration. Her hand clenched instinctively around the gun in her pocket.

Julian shot her a warning. "Don't pull that gun out unless I'm dead," he said in earnest seriousness.

"Don't say such morbid things!" Sophie hissed.

"Even then, remember you carry my name now. You'll be a rich widow."

"Don't even think it, Julian."

"That's my fiery angel. But it might help to look a bit paler. Officers have a soft spot for fragile women." Julian nodded in the direction of the man approaching them.

"Good day," the man said. He was dressed in the uniform of the city guard. "We're just checking traveling papers."

"Why is that?" Julian asked blithely, handing the packet of papers to him.

"An Italian count reported a great fortune in diamonds was missing. Sorry for the inconvenience." He scanned the documents. "Lord Burke, Lady Burke, you may be on your way. Felicitations on your marriage."

Sophie managed a smile, thankful for what little protection the veil gave her. She felt the carriage move forward slowly. She allowed herself to relax. They were nearly through. Then she heard it.

"That's her! Stop the carriage." There was confusion. She looked back to see di Brazzo himself and his men parting the crowd on their big horses. A shot rang out, chipping the side of the carriage.

"Get down!" Julian threw himself at her, forcing her onto the floor of the fiacre. "Keep driving," he yelled to the driver. "We've been cleared to pass. They are too late."

Real fear coursed through Sophie. She thought about St. Just, Truesdale and Mathison up there.

She heard other shots. A horse whinnied in agony. "Please don't let that be one of ours," Sophie prayed.

The carriage had stopped moving. That was a bad sign.

She felt Julian's hand on her arm. "Get up, darling." She sat up and saw the reason the carriage had halted. A city guard held the lead horse by the halter. St. Just was beside them, flanking the carriage. She glanced at Julian. He was unharmed, thank goodness. His eyes were the color of cold steel.

"Count di Brazzo, to what do I owe the pleasure of your disruption on my wedding day?" Julian's tone conveyed his dislike of the man.

"Your wife?" The count stared at Sophie in disbelief. She could feel his eyes boring through her, radiating menace. "She is none other than a thief who stole jewels from me. She should hang for her crime against nobility."

"I will not sit here and have my wife insulted." Julian's indignation was real. He turned to the officer holding the horse. "Take your hands off the horse. Is this the way Englishmen are treated abroad? We were told we were free to pass." Julian fixed the other guard with a steely stare, forcing him to intervene.

"I'm sorry, Count," the man stammered. "Lord and Lady Burke have been cleared to pass. Surely, you're mistaken."

St. Just drew his pistol and aimed it at di Brazzo with deadly intent. The nice young man who had given her a bouquet of white roses had transformed into a merciless warrior. "You are obstructing an agent of the crown. No one in England will convict me for shooting you."

Sophie sucked in her breath. This was all her fault. This was hers to solve. Julian could scold her later. She slipped the little gun from her pocket. Everyone was too busy staring at St. Just and di Brazzo. A quick shot near the horses would startle them. No one would be able to hold them back. "Brace yourself, Julian," she said quietly right at the last. Then she fired quickly, her gun hidden in the palm of her hand and tucked back into her gown before anyone was sure what they saw. In any case, the horses leapt forward, tearing free of the shocked officer.

The carriage sailed past the crowds and out into the countryside. Mathison and Truesdale closed ranks behind them, turning their horses to face any would-be followers.

They'd made it! Sophie tossed off her veil and

let out a whoop of delight, thrilling in the wind blowing her hair about her. She looked back to see Truesdale give Julian a salute and ride back into the city.

"I told you…" Julian began.

"Would you rather have had your friend shoot the count? This way was much simpler," Sophie interrupted, smiling her joy. It seemed that in leaving the city, her burdens had been lifted.

Julian couldn't stay angry with Sophie for long. The look of radiant happiness on her face, so much like the look that had first attracted him to her on the ballroom floor, was too hard to resist. He pulled his bride of two hours across the carriage and into his arms. He kissed her hard on the mouth. "You are a delightful minx, Lady Burke. Life with you will always be an adventure. I will have to learn not to underestimate you."

Sophie laughed up at him. "I was thinking the same thing about you."

Epilogue

Three months later, Tower of London

Julian and Sophie stood amidst a small, private gathering of family and friends in the Tower's jewel house. Among the group was King George IV and other members of the royal family. Julian's brother, the Earl of Dunsmore, stood soberly next to Julian. It had taken Sophie a little time to get used to the fact that Julian had a twin, an identical twin. They looked impossibly alike. But Julian was a born adventurer and Dunsmore was far more reserved.

There was a hushed silence as the king's brother, the Duke of Clarence, began the short ceremony. "Two centuries ago, a treasure was lost to

England. It recently resurfaced, and we knew we had to send the best to get it back. Julian Burke has returned triumphant. As of today, the diamonds have been restored to their rightful place." With a wave of his hand, he gestured for the curtain to be pulled back, revealing the diamonds. The group clapped politely.

Dunsmore leaned over to Sophie and Julian. "It looks like it always did," he whispered quietly.

"But those were paste," Julian said.

"I know. Still, rather anticlimactic," Dunsmore mused, "especially since we can't tell anyone about it. What do you think happened to the fakes?"

Julian smiled. "St. Just wrote from Italy to tell me he recovered them while visiting the count di Brazzo's palazzo in Florence."

"And he never knew he had the fakes?" Dunsmore queried. "Amazing. What else did St. Just have to say? Is he still wooing his way through the continent?"

"That appears to be the case," Julian replied obliquely.

Dunsmore snorted. "It's been two years. Do you think he'll ever come back?"

Julian shrugged. "He'll come back when he's found what he's looking for."

Beside him, Sophie squeezed Julian's hand. Now that she had Julian, she could imagine how empty her life would be without him. It pained her to think of the young viscount searching for a way to be whole. She could only hope that his time would come, that love would find him again.

"If we could have your attention once more." This time it was the king who spoke. "Julian Burke, come forward, please." Julian cast a curious glance at Sophie. She merely shrugged.

"For services rendered, you should be paid. But what does one give someone who has everything?" The little group laughed politely at the monarch's humor. "Burke has more money than what's good for him, has a wife far lovelier than he deserves. The one thing you don't have is a title, for what it's worth. We'll have an official ceremony later, but as of today, you are now elevated to the rank of viscount. You'll have to let me know which name you'll attach to it. You've got several estates already to choose from."

"That's easy." Julian fixed Sophie with a smile. "It will be Leighton, for the estate where my wife has started her horse farm."

Sophie beamed while those around her applauded. When she had set out to retrieve the jewels, she'd known the risks such a venture held. She had never imagined the rewards.

*   *   *   *   *

THE UNLACING OF
MISS LEIGH

Diane Gaston

When **Diane Gaston** was a little girl, she'd learn all the words to popular love songs. When she played, her dolls acted out tragic love affairs with the current heartthrob on TV or in the movies. She thought everyone in the world made up romantic stories in their heads to fall asleep at night. In her first career, Diane helped others craft their own happy endings. She earned Masters' degrees in both psychology and social work and became a county mental health therapist. She also experienced her own romance, getting married and raising a daughter and son.

Diane's dream job, though, had always been to write romance novels. One day she decided to pursue that dream and has never looked back. She is now writing full-time. Her Harlequin Historical books have won Romance's highest honours – the RITA Award, the National Readers Choice Award and the Golden Heart. Diane loves to hear from readers and friends. E-mail her at diane@dianegaston.com or visit her every Monday at the Risky Regencies blog and once a month at the Wet Noodle Posse blog.

Chapter 1

London, June, 1812

A thousand lamps blazed in the elms. Colonnades, fountains, cascades and porticos, while throngs of people of all sorts made up this night of masquerade in Vauxhall Gardens.

Amid this wonder, Margaret Leigh's heart raced. She was here to meet a gentleman, a man who would pay for her company.

"Are you certain you wish to do this, Maggie?" Her cousin's brow furrowed. "It is not at all proper."

She slanted him an amused look. "You are one to speak of propriety."

Henry had long been the scourge of the family.

A schoolmaster's son and a vicar's nephew, Henry ran off to join a theater company when he'd barely begun to shave. Now, there was little family left to condemn him, only Margaret and her younger brother.

Henry nodded and waved a hand. "To the devil with propriety, anyway. Life is too short not to seek enjoyment where we can."

Margaret released a nervous breath. "Well, I cannot afford either enjoyment or propriety at the moment."

Henry pursed his lips in sympathy. Wearing horns on his head and tight-fitting green trousers and coat, his expression looked nothing more than comical.

Margaret stifled a laugh.

Henry was dressed as Puck in a costume from Covent Garden Theatre where he performed small parts. For Margaret, he had borrowed a fairy costume—a gown of palest blush, its skirts fashioned from so many layers of silk net that she seemed to float as she walked. It was quite the most beautiful gown she'd ever worn.

"Here we are." Henry stopped at the supper boxes along the South Walk.

Margaret, an impoverished vicar's daughter, and her cousin Henry, an actor of no renown, were to be guests of the Duke of Manning. For the festivities, the duke had engaged several boxes joined together, decorated with flowers and swags of colorful silks. Already, the boxes seemed filled with people. Most of the gentlemen wore black dominoes, but the women wore a variety of costumes, from rustic milkmaids frocks to elaborate Egyptian princesses'gowns. The gentleman had arranged his rendezvous with Margaret to take place among the friends of the duke.

Margaret gave Henry a rueful smile. "If our parents could see us now."

Her cousin laughed. "I envision them collectively rolling over in their graves. I can almost hear your father." He made a dramatic gesture as if preaching from a pulpit. *"...I have written unto you not to keep company, if any man that is called a brother be a fornicator..."*

Tears pricked at Margaret's eyes. "You sound just like him."

Henry sobered. "My talent for mimicry."

Margaret's father had passed away of a sudden apoplexy not two months earlier and grief still overcame her at unforeseen moments. He'd been the last of that generation. They were orphans now, Margaret thought.

Henry's sympathetic look returned, but he quickly smiled and punched her on the arm. "I daresay your father would consider the Duke of Manning improper company for you."

"And his friend." The gentleman she was to meet.

The notorious Duke of Manning had run off with the Earl of Linwall's wife, set up housekeeping with her, and sired several children by her—the Fitzmanning Miscellany, the society gossips called them. In the supper box, the duke and his lady were easy to recognize, greeting their guests, both dressed in white wigs and colorful brocades that were fashionable decades ago.

Margaret turned back to Henry. "For a man and woman living in sin, they look very happy."

"They do indeed." Henry clasped her arm and stepped forward. "The rewards of impropriety."

They showed their invitation to the footman positioned at the entry to the boxes. As he admitted them, Margaret scanned the gentlemen in black dominoes. *His* would be lined in red, he'd written to her.

She glimpsed no red.

The words in his advertisement in *The Times* came back to her.

Seeking an educated lady of

genteel birth for companionship.
Gentleman of good fortune offers
generous compensation.

Margaret had answered the advertisement. She answered every advertisement for companions or governesses, the most common professions for a woman of her station. None yielded any results. When the gentleman mentioned in the ad sent a footman with a written response, Margaret's hopes surged.

And were immediately dashed.

The companionship the gentleman sought was of a different nature entirely. He sought a mistress.

Behind his rather witty response to her had been a sense of aching loneliness. Margaret wrote back to him, even though it was highly improper to do so. She sent a polite refusal.

He wrote back.

He wrote to her again and again, charming letters of persistent persuasiveness, witty words and despairing loneliness. Each time, she sent back a refusal, but soon the greatest pleasure of her day was seeing his footman arrive at the door with the now-daily letter, then reading its contents.

Eventually, the gentleman proposed a meeting for which he would pay her twenty pounds. He suggested this masked ball at Vauxhall as the location. Twenty pounds was almost as much as she could earn in a year as a lady's companion or governess.

She needed that money quite desperately.

Her cousin led her to a table of refreshments. She picked up a glass of claret in hopes it would settle her nerves.

"It will be an adventure," Henry said.

"An adventure," she repeated under her breath, downing the claret and taking another.

"Good God," cried her cousin. "There is Daphne Blane."

Daphne Blane was the darling of the London stage, a most sought-after leading lady and one who often was seen on the arm of a peer.

"How can you tell?" Margaret saw only a woman in a Grecian costume, with a gold mask covering most of her face.

"There is no mistaking her." Henry put down his glass. "I must greet her. She will be impressed that I am one of the duke's guests."

Without Henry at her side, Margaret's courage flagged. She ought to flee, run down the Grand

Walk to where the wherries waited to ferry guests across the river, hop into a hackney coach and return to Henrietta Street.

Instead, she took another fortifying sip of claret and looked for a corner in which to stand.

A young woman dressed as a shepherdess walked up to her. "Do I know you?"

God forbid anyone know her here, else she never would have come.

The masked young woman grimaced. "Oh, dear, that sounded rude, did it not? It is just you are near my age, I think, and if you should be one of my friends, I should be quite ashamed not to know it."

Margaret smiled. "I am certain you do not know me. I am Miss Leigh."

The woman offered her hand. "I am Justine Savard, the duke's daughter."

Savard was not the duke's surname, nor Lady Linwall's. Was Miss Savard the duke's daughter by another woman?

Her father *would* roll over in his grave.

Miss Savard returned her smile. "Are you here with someone?"

"I am with my cousin." Margaret inclined her head in Henry's direction. "He is Puck."

"He is your cousin? I wondered who was speaking with Miss Blane." Apparently Henry was not the only one to recognize the famous actress.

Miss Savard glanced around again, then caught herself and turned back to Margaret. "I fear my manners have quite gone begging." She looked apologetic. "I am expecting someone." Her color rose. "My sweetheart."

Margaret did not know what to say to this obvious confidence. "I hope he arrives soon."

"Oh, so do I." Miss Savard glanced around one more time. "More guests are arriving. Papa's friends. He and Lady Caroline invited everyone, I think. It is a shame his best friend could not attend. Papa and Baron Veall were schoolmates ages ago—"

"Baron Veall." The blood drained from Margaret's face.

"Do you know him?"

"No, I do not," Margaret said too sharply.

Her father's vicarage had been on land owned by Baron Veall, and one year the baron and his family summered in the great house there. Margaret had only encountered the younger son. One time.

She'd never forgotten him.

Miss Savard chattered on, "Well, the baron declined the invitation, but—it is the oddest thing—his son did not."

"His son?" Margaret squeezed the stem of her glass.

"His younger son, the captain."

Margaret's legs trembled.

"I pine to know why he accepted. My father would not tell me, but I had the distinct impression there was some negotiation—something clandestine—and I do love a mystery, as long as I can solve it." She looked thoughtful. "Perhaps it has something to do with Captain Veall's injuries. He was hurt terribly in the Battle of Fuentes de Oñoro a year ago—"

Margaret well knew this. She'd scoured the lists of injured and dead hoping not to find his name.

"He's been somewhat of a recluse ever since. My father called upon him once, but the captain refused to see him. Curious that suddenly he's attending this party." Miss Savard clutched Margaret's arm. "Oh, my goodness. There he is. Not Captain Veall. My sweetheart. I would know him no matter his disguise."

The man who captured her attention wore a

simple black domino and looked to Margaret indistinguishable from the others.

"Is he not handsome, my Mr. Kinney?" She gave
Margaret an imploring look. "Will you forgive me
if I abandon you? I am so eager to see him."

"By all means."

Miss Savard rushed to the man's side.

Margaret lifted her glass to her lips and
searched the guests, both hoping and fearing she
would see Captain Veall.

She'd been a little girl with hair in plaits and front
teeth missing. He'd been a few years older. She had
not even given him her name. He would never know
her now, even without her mask, but she greatly desired to discover the man he'd become.

Margaret finished her second glass of claret and
tried to determine which of the men in black dominoes might be Captain Veall. She walked back to
the refreshment table for another claret. The orchestra began to play in the Grove.

Behind her, a man's deep voice spoke. "Miss
Leigh?"

She froze, then turned. She'd almost forgotten
why she'd come.

The gentleman was tall, so tall he filled her vision. His domino, like his hair, was as black as the

night, but he swirled the fabric to show its red lining. His mask, unlike any of the others, covered one side of his face, not just the top half.

She felt robbed of breath. "I am Miss Leigh."

His eyes, a startling blue, appraised her. "I am the gentleman with whom you have corresponded."

"Sir." She curtsied.

Through the eyehole of his mask Margaret could see an angry red scar that the fabric did not entirely cover. Neither did it cover the drooping of one side of his mouth. The unusual mask was meant to cover his scars, she realized.

She lowered her eyes. "What do I call you?" He'd merely signed his letters *A Gentleman*.

"Call me Graham."

Her gaze flew back to his face.

The eyes. She remembered his blue eyes.

That long ago day in the woods when Bob and Hughy Newell threw their sticks and stones at a little girl too small to outrun them, a boy with those blue eyes had come to her rescue. Graham Veall had been her first, nay, her only hero.

"Would you walk with me, Miss Leigh?" His voice seemed to resonate deep in her soul.

It shook her. "You do not wish to stay at the party?"

"I only came for you." He pressed a purse into her hand.

Her payment. She swallowed.

He was letting her know she had already fulfilled their bargain. She could refuse his request if she wished.

But she wanted to be with him. He was Graham Veall.

"My pleasure, sir," she murmured.

His eyes creased at the corners. "Graham."

"Graham," she repeated in a stronger voice.

He led her through the porticos, away from the throngs of people, away from the music. They walked on a gravel path toward trees with fewer lamps and where shadows loomed ahead. Any trepidation Margaret felt about this meeting had vanished. This was Graham Veall walking at her side. She held his arm and savored the warmth of his skin beneath the silk domino.

"I thought it very likely you would not come, Miss Leigh," his voice sounded rusty from disuse.

"I needed the money." No use to pretend otherwise, she thought.

It crossed her mind to tell him of their prior connection, but she was too proud to reveal how poorly her father had provided for her.

His expression turned sympathetic. "Are you so in need of money?"

She lifted the purse. "This will pay to keep my younger brother in school one more year." She could not bear to think beyond that one year.

"It is for your brother?" Graham looked surprised. "How old is he?"

"Fourteen."

"Is his schooling so important?" He sounded incredulous.

Education was Andrew's joy; it was all he lived for. Even before Andrew was out of short coats, his thirst for learning had been evident. They'd been a family of scholars, so Andrew's talent was not surprising. Their grandfather and Henry's father had been schoolmasters. Margaret's parents had run a small boarding school in their home to supplement their father's church living. She and Andrew had always been surrounded by books and lessons and learning.

Until her mother died of influenza and her father could not manage the boarders alone. He'd used every spare penny to send Andrew to a good school, and Margaret had never begrudged the expense.

"My brother has a mind that begs for education.

Now I can provide it for him." She squeezed the purse.

Graham touched her arm and the warmth of his touch radiated through her. "I merely was surprised the money was not for yourself."

She returned a steady gaze. "Andrew's schooling is more important."

He tilted his head as if examining her anew.

Threading her arm though his again, he continued their stroll. The paths were now much darker, and from the deep recesses of the shrubbery came sounds of murmuring and laughter. Ever since the Newells had chased her, Margaret had hated walking through woods, but with Graham she would be happy to walk all the way to the hermit who inhabited the farthest reaches of the Gardens.

"Tell me more about your brother," he said.

She complied, telling of Andrew's love of physics, of chemistry and of all things mechanical. Graham asked questions and seemed to listen to her answers. Margaret could almost delude herself that he was a beau, instead of a man who'd paid for her company. Because he was Graham, she wished he was a beau.

As they walked on, two men burst from the shrubbery and stumbled onto the path ahead of them. Margaret jumped back, uttering a cry. Graham wrapped his arms around her and pulled her into the trees, his black domino cloaking them both. The two young men, deep in their cups, staggered by, talking loudly and apparently never noticing them.

Still, Margaret trembled under Graham's embrace.

"I would allow no harm to come to you," he whispered in her ear.

Her trembling came not from feeling again like that little girl clinging to the boy who rescued her, but from an acute awareness that he was a boy no longer. He was a man with a man's needs, and was willing to pay to have those needs met. His arms felt wonderful around her, his strong muscles holding her with such reassuring confidence. Her body was pressed against his, and it seemed that all his power and strength were melding with her.

Her breathing quickened, and sensation flared through her. She felt hungry for more, although she did not know precisely what made her ravenous. She only knew this moment must never end or she would surely perish.

Unfortunately he released her, but slowly, as if

as reluctant as she to break the embrace. Still clasping her arms with his strong fingers, he looked down on her, his blue eyes gleaming in the dim light, pleading for something she wanted desperately to give him, but not knowing precisely what it was he desired. He lowered his head and Margaret's excitement grew. She rose onto her toes.

The sounds of more revelers came near. He again enveloped her in his domino. "We will walk back to the supper boxes," he rasped.

Her disappointment was crushing.

They walked in silence, and Margaret searched her mind for a question she could ask him, a question that was not *Why did you release me*?

"Why did you advertise for a mistress?" she finally asked.

She felt him stiffen. "Isn't it obvious?"

Obvious? It was inconceivable that this virile man could not have any woman he wished. He was tall, well-formed, and as darkly handsome as any hero in a Minerva Press novel. What woman would not seek his bed?

"No, it is not obvious."

The path was growing lighter, although their surroundings still seemed leached of color. Only his eyes remained sharply blue. And pained.

He stopped and gestured to his mask. "I am disfigured."

"What could that matter?" She reached up to his mask.

He seized her hand and roughly thrust it aside. "Do not remove it!"

She jerked away, alarmed by his violence.

He lowered himself onto a bench nearby and sunk his head in his hands. Margaret sat next to him and placed the purse in her lap.

She pulled one of his hands into both of hers. "I am sorry."

He straightened, but averted his face.

It was his unhappiness for which she was sorry. Sorry for his shame at his appearance, and so sorry for her foolish boldness.

He glanced at her and away again. "I should not have come." He picked up the purse and gave a dry laugh. "At least you have the money."

"And it will be well spent." She gently squeezed his hand.

"On your brother."

She smiled. "On my brother."

He examined her face so intently, it was as if his gaze permeated every part of her. "What else do you want?"

She blinked. "What else?"

His gaze did not waver. "If you could have your heart's desire, I mean. What would you want?"

Her heart pounded. Some hopes were best abandoned, like the hope that he would again put his arms around her.

She said instead, "I should like to send my brother to Cambridge."

He laughed.

She felt wounded. "It is nonsensical, I agree. No lady's companion or governess can afford Cambridge."

"That is not why I laughed. I expected you to want a house or carriage or jewels." He caught her gaze again. "Is there no patron to help your brother?"

"No one." She smiled wanly. "There is only my cousin, but he hardly earns enough to hold himself together. He is an actor. I am staying in the boarding house where he lives, until the actress whose room I'm in returns." A few days from this. "Perhaps you saw my cousin. He is dressed as Puck."

"I did see him," he answered absently. He was silent for a long time before piercing her with another intent gaze. "Miss Leigh, I will send your brother to Cambridge."

She blinked. "Why would you do that?"

He shrugged. "Because I have the wealth to do so."

She did not understand him.

He glanced away and back again. "I will do it. I will pay for Cambridge, but I will also pay you. An annuity for life, if—"

She held her breath.

His eyes bore into her. "If you agree to my original proposition."

Everything around her blurred. "To be your mistress?"

"For at least two months," he added. "Cambridge, an annuity so you will never have to be a lady's companion. All that for two months of your life."

She gaped at him.

"I live very privately. No one will know where you have spent those two months. I give you my word. I will trouble you no further afterward. You will not even know who I am. No one will know. Your reputation will be unsullied."

She must be lost to all propriety, Margaret thought, because it was not her reputation she thought of. She thought only of how short a time two months could be and how very much she owed him already.

He'd saved her life that day when Bob and Hughy were carried away with their mischief. They'd driven her to the ground, their laughter maniacal as their rocks and sticks struck her over and over. Graham had run to her rescue. He'd fought them off. He'd saved her and remained the hero of her heart ever since.

"I will do it," she whispered, thinking now of his arms around her and how his body felt against hers. She made her voice stronger. "I will be your mistress."

Chapter 2

Three days later, Graham Veall tugged at the cuffs of his shirt and tried not to look at his image in the mirror.

"Coward," he said aloud.

He forced his gaze upward.

Even with the mask in place, he looked like a miscreation. He snapped his eyes shut and again heard the sounds of battle, the thundering of horses' hooves, the clang of the Frenchman's sword against his own. Again he smelled the pungent odor of gunpowder, of soldier's sweat, of spilled blood. Again he saw the Frenchman's wild eyes and bared teeth and the sight of the gleaming sword right before it sliced into his face.

Breathing hard, Graham opened his eyes and

pressed his palm against his masked cheek. The mask was a cleverly tailored bit of silk and batting that fit snugly against his skin and covered all but a peek of the carnage the Frenchman's sword wrought.

Graham pressed his lips together.

Below stairs a woman waited, a woman any honorable man would send back to London. Any honorable man would forget this insane, impulsive idea that had overtaken him one lonely afternoon.

But he would not send her home.

He might be robbed of a face, but he'd be damned if he'd forego every pleasure in life because of it. He wanted company. He wanted conversation. He wanted to hear a woman laugh, to smell her hair, to feel her bare legs wrapped around his. He wanted the pleasure of plunging into her body, of feeling her release, of spilling his seed inside her.

Even if he must pay for it.

Miss Leigh was more than he'd dared hope. She certainly possessed all the charm her letters promised. Old enough not to be *missish,* obviously intelligent, she'd appeared to have more to converse upon than society gossip from *The Morning Post.* He knew little else of her except that the eyes beneath her mask had been a warm brown and her lips invitingly full. She'd not jumped at the chance to take his money and, in his opinion, her hesitation showed a discernment that gave her credit. But she also had not shirked when he cast out the lure that secured her agreement.

A younger brother in need. Admirable indeed.

This enticement alone would have been sufficient to secure her agreement, he'd have wagered, but adding the annuity assuaged his conscience. The least he could offer a respectable young woman was a comfortable income for life. It would pose him no hardship. He could well afford both Cambridge and an annuity.

While still in leading strings Graham had inherited a vast amount from an uncle who'd made a fortune in the East India Company. Unlike most younger sons, Graham's desire to purchase a commission in His Majesty's army had not been made for financial reasons, but for the vainglorious notion that his country needed *him* to vanquish Napoleon.

Well, he must leave victory to Lord Wellington now. All Graham had done was lose half his face and all of his idyllic future.

He twisted away from the mirror and strode out

of his bedchamber down the stairs to the drawing room where he'd kept Miss Leigh waiting for nearly half an hour.

Through the cracked door, he saw her looking out the window, hands clasped in front of her.

He entered.

She turned and curtsied. "Sir," she said, her voice breathless.

"It is Graham," he corrected, remaining just inside the doorway.

Light from the window illuminated half her face, leaving half in shadow. Nature's cruel mockery, no doubt, of the image he'd just seen in the mirror. Unmasked, she was prettier than he'd imagined. Her eyes were large for her face, and her nose strong. Both seemed perfectly balanced by those lush pink lips. He liked that her hair was the color of nutmeg and that she was taller than most women he knew.

What will it be like to bed a woman as tall as she?

He released a breath. Curse him for thinking such thoughts within moments of their reacquaintance. Even a woman whose company he purchased deserved better.

He glanced around the room. "Did not Coombs bring you tea?"

"Coombs. He was the man who brought me your letters." She gazed at him. "He offered tea. I declined."

Graham took a step forward and gestured to the area near the fireplace "Do sit, Miss Leigh."

She obediently crossed the room and sat on the couch, leaving enough room for him to sit next to her if he so chose. He almost smiled. No, she was not missish, but he sensed she was not entirely at ease either, no matter how much she might wish he'd think so.

He walked over to a cabinet. "Would you prefer something stronger than tea? Sherry, perhaps?"

Her tense mouth seemed to relax. "Yes, thank you. Sherry will do nicely."

Graham poured her sherry and a brandy for himself. Handing her the glass, he chose the nearby chair.

She took a sip. "I did not expect you to be wearing your mask."

By reflex he touched it. "Did you fear I would inflict the horror upon you?"

A tiny line appeared between her eyes. "I thought the mask was merely for the masquerade."

He twirled his brandy glass. "I am in a perpetual masquerade." Downing its contents, he leveled his gaze at her. "The mask remains."

She waved her fingers in a gesture of unconcern and more calmly sipped her drink. "This house seems quite comfortable."

It was a hunting lodge within easy riding distance of London, borrowed from the Duke of Manning with the promise that His Grace would never call. His Grace had only broken the promise once, and Graham surmised his father had sent his friend to check on his welfare.

"It is suitable." He rose and poured himself more brandy. "Have you seen its rooms?"

She shook her head. "Coombs gave me a moment to refresh myself in my bedchamber and then showed me to this room."

He downed his second glass of brandy and extended his hand to her. "Come. I'll give you a tour."

She placed her bare hand in his, skin against skin, and his body flared in response. By God, he was desperate for a woman. He felt like ravaging her on the drawing room carpet.

His eyes met hers for a moment, and he fancied she'd read his thoughts.

"I will show you the library first." He forced his voice through a suddenly constricted throat. "I added some books I thought you might enjoy."

Her brows rose. "You did? What sort of books?"

He shrugged. "Novels mostly. *The Wild Irish Girl. A Tale of Youth. Self-Control.*"

Her eyelashes fluttered, and amusement tugged at those moist kissable lips. "Oh, dear, where shall I start? With *The Wild Irish Girl?* Perhaps not with *Self-Control.*"

He frowned. "I meant no message. The titles were recommended to me as ones a lady might enjoy."

Her smile wavered. "I was merely jesting."

They entered the library, and he pointed out the new editions.

She ran her finger along one of the shelves. "If I finish the novels, I shall delve into *The Gentleman's Magazine* or *The Sportsman's Dictionary.*"

This time he recognized her humor. "I fear this is a rather masculine residence." He gestured to the door. "Allow me to show you the drawing room. There is a pianoforte there, which might have more feminine appeal."

After a peek at the drawing room, he showed her the dining room and led her down to the kitchen.

As they approached, he heard the banging of pots and pans. "Did you bring a maid with you?"

She laughed. "I have no maid."

"Mrs. Coombs will be available to you, then. She is both cook and housekeeper, so our meals will be simple fare. She and Coombs are the only servants in the house, and their rooms are on this level." In other words, they would have plenty of privacy above stairs.

"I am accustomed to simple fare," she replied. "And to tending to myself."

Mrs. Coombs, busy preparing dinner, greeted Miss Leigh in a friendly tone, "I will be at your service, miss."

Graham appreciated Mrs. Coombs's tolerance of his unusual plan. He'd known her for years and had expected her to have a different view of propriety from a typical London servant.

He explained to Miss Leigh, "Coombs was my batman in the army. Mrs. Coombs followed the drum."

Margaret gave the older woman a respectful look. "How very brave of you, Mrs. Coombs."

"'Twas an adventure, that much I will admit," she answered.

Indeed. Mrs. Coombs had seen things no woman should see, including a man with half his face sliced away.

"I will show you above stairs," he said.

Graham offered his arm and escorted Miss Leigh back to the hall and up another flight of stairs to the bedchambers.

There were four, and some attic rooms above those. He showed her the two smaller bedchambers first, before leading her to the room connected with his.

He stopped by her door. "You have already seen your room. I hope it is to your liking."

She looked into his eyes. "It is perfectly comfortable." Her gaze shifted to the next door.

He walked over and opened it. "This is the room I use."

She merely nodded. Their gazes connected in a moment that stretched far too long, a moment that left him too much time to think carnal thoughts, such as how he might drag her into his bedchamber and urge her to fulfill the implied part of the bargain.

But if bedding had been all he wanted he could have purchased a woman for as many nights as he desired. He'd always found the idea of going to a brothel distasteful, however. He desired so much more than mere physical release.

Graham glanced toward the door to her bedchamber. "Shall I leave you until time for dinner?"

"Leave me?" She sounded surprised. "Here?"

He lowered his brow. "Well, not here if you do not wish it. You may go to any room you desire."

She glanced away as if in thought, then faced him again, looking directly into his eyes. "Then I should like to see your bedchamber."

Chapter 3

Margaret's heart pounded at an alarming rate, although she had no wish to let it show. "Your bedchamber is the only room I have not seen."

He opened the door and extended his hand for her to enter. She crossed in front of him, and that flash of awareness she'd felt at Vauxhall swept through her, fueling her excitement.

His bedchamber was neat and orderly, with few personal items in view. It made her sad that so little of *him* possessed the space. Her eyes riveted on the bed, so neatly made it looked as if he had never slept in it.

"It is the least interesting room in the house," he remarked.

His self-deprecating tone gave her pain. "Perhaps

it interests me. I am to spend time with you here, am I not?" Her pert words surprised her, and she finally understood her cousin Henry's choices. To forego propriety and do what one wished was liberating. "That is our bargain, if I understood correctly."

He leaned against the doorjamb, his arms crossed over his chest. "You understood perfectly."

She forced herself to walk over to the bed where she wrapped her fingers around the mahogany bedpost and leaned her cheek against the cool wood. "I have thought a great deal of this, sir."

He walked toward her. "Call me Graham."

She blinked and averted her gaze. "I seem to have difficulty using your name." She'd always thought of him as Graham, since she'd been a little girl. To speak his name now felt like revealing who she was.

His eyes penetrated as he came closer, so close his scent surrounded her, all soap and bergamot. "Would it help if I called you Margaret?"

She'd signed her name to her letters Miss Margaret Leigh. Her name on his lips felt intimate. "I should like that."

His gaze drifted from her face to the bed.

She gripped the bedpost tighter. "I am not sorry

for my decision…Graham. I have no expectation of marriage in my situation, so this may be my only opportunity to—to—" She was not yet so bold that the words came easy. "To bed a man."

He took a step back. "Your only opportunity?"

She felt her face flush and she lowered her head. "Well, I am a vicar's daughter and—"

His voice rose. "A vicar's daughter?"

Her gaze flew back to his face. Had she revealed too much? Would he recall that the vicar that summer had been Reverend Leigh? "He died, so there is no worry."

He scraped a hand through his hair. "Good God. A vicar's daughter and a virgin."

Her brow furrowed. "What did you think I was?"

He shook his head. "I did not think you devoid of experience. I did not expect a virginal vicar's daughter to accept my proposition."

She felt her cheeks burn. "Why does this matter to you?"

His eyes flashed. "Do you think I wish to deflower a vicar's daughter?"

He might as well have torn Andrew's academic gown off his back, but even worse, he dashed her hopes, her romantic dreams.

She placed her hands on her hips. "I have no

idea whom you wish to deflower, but if you had such specific requirements, you should have listed them in your advertisement." She pretended to read. *"Seeking an educated lady of genteel birth for companionship. No virgins or vicar's daughters need apply."*

"Very humorous." His face, the half of it she could see, had turned red and his voice was angry. "This changes everything."

She advanced on him. "Why? Why does this change everything? Am I not still the woman who would share your bed so her brother might have a bright future? How has being a virgin and a vicar's daughter changed me?"

He leaned down to her, his face only inches from hers. Even in the emotion of the moment, she glimpsed the scarring visible from a gap in his mask and even through her fury, her heart lurched. She wanted to soothe his injured cheek.

She wanted to slap him across the other one. She was shaking with anger, but very much alive.

With an audible release of breath, he moved away and turned his back to her.

She pressed her fingers against her temple. "I ask only that I might stay the night." The emotion was drained from her voice. "The room in my cousin's boarding house is no longer available to me. I must make other arrangements." She'd already sent the money given her at Vauxhall to Andrew's school. She had precious little coin left.

He spun around to face her. "Do you think I would toss you out in the street?"

"You advertise for a mistress, do you not?" She glared at him. "How do I know what else you might do?"

He took a menacing step forward, but she stood her ground. At least she would not let him see how desolated she felt.

He was so close she felt the warmth of his breath on her face. He placed his fingers on the tender skin of her neck, his thumb caressing. "A test, Margaret." His voice dropped to a whisper.

He slowly brought his lips to hers in a gentle kiss, then his arms wrapped around her and the kiss deepened into something more, something unexpected. Her mouth parted in surprise and he took advantage. She felt his tongue against hers and suddenly she was crushed against him, his hands now at her hips pressing him against her.

She wound her arms around his neck and slipped her fingers through his hair. She'd never known a kiss could feel like this, so all-consuming, so glorious.

He widened his stance and held her even closer. His hands moved over her back, her waist and, wantonly, her derriere. She sighed. Her fingers played in his hair and caressed his neck. His lips broke away and then captured hers again every bit as hungrily. She did not wish him to break off this kiss. She put her hands on both sides of his face to hold him there.

He pushed her away, looking as alarmed as she felt.

"Did I hurt you?" she asked.

He was breathing hard. "I dislike being touched on my face."

He had not minded where her fingers touched him otherwise.

He took another step away from her. "You needn't dress for dinner, unless you desire it."

The change of subject was jarring. "Am I to stay for dinner?"

His blue eyes seemed to pierce into her again. "For dinner and more. You have convinced me that this arrangement may indeed suit us both."

Her irritation fled. "The kiss was the test?"

"Yes." His gaze was warm.

Dinner was a pleasant affair, more pleasant than any meal Graham could recall since he'd returned from Portugal. Those first dinners with his family were ones of pitying glances and oversolicitousness. They'd nearly driven him mad.

In spite of his abominable behavior earlier, Margaret conversed easily, with apparently a great deal less discomfort than his own. She displayed a curious mind and a brave one. She asked him if he had been in the war in Portugal, a backhanded way of asking how he'd been injured, no doubt. No one else had dared ask about Portugal.

He avoided speaking of the battle, confining his discourse to the people, the land, the architecture. Before he knew it, Coombs had brought in dishes of strawberries and cream for dessert.

When Coombs returned to remove this final course, Graham told him, "We will have tea in the drawing room." He stood, but looked down on Margaret. "If that pleases you."

"Of course." She took the hand he extended to her.

The warmth of her skin threatened to unleash the passion he so carefully kept at bay. The sky outside was only beginning to fade into dusk. Alone, he might have sat in the library with a bottle of brandy waiting for darkness to fall, but he could not merely drink his way to bedtime while she watched.

They entered the drawing room where the sofa and chairs were so cozily placed that knees could touch. She chose the sofa; Graham, a chair. He did not trust himself next to her.

Coombs entered with the tea tray, and when he left, Margaret poured.

She handed Graham a cup. "How long have you stayed at this house?"

He'd spent about three months at the family's estate, first feverish and in bed, later driven to distraction by his mother and sisters fawning over him, and his father and brother laboring to cheer him up. None of them had been able to look him in the face, even though he kept his disfigurement covered.

"About nine months," he replied.

"Nine months!" her eyes widened. "That is a long time. Have you been alone all that time?"

"With Coombs and his wife."

She shook her head in disbelief. "That is a long time to remain in such solitude."

He gave a wry smile. "Hence my hatching of the plot to solicit companionship."

She nodded. "I quite see now. You were lonely."

His laugh was mirthless. "That is wrapping it in a pretty package." He sipped his tea and searched for something besides his loneliness to discuss. "The letters I received were quite diverting."

She lowered her eyes, showing long thick lashes. "Was I the only one to think you were seeking a lady's companion?"

"The only one." Hers had also been the only letter that had not overtly addressed both seduction and remuneration, the only letter that piqued his interest.

She looked thoughtful.

He gazed at her. "I could not resist clarifying the matter for you. To my surprise, you wrote again."

Sympathy seemed to pass through her eyes, gone so fast he was uncertain he'd seen it. He finished his tea and pined for brandy. "I am afraid your refusals only increased my determination."

She smiled. "Until you discovered what would win me."

He glanced away. He had exploited her unselfish spirit.

She leaned forward and put her hand on his knee. "Do not be cross. As I said before, I do not regret my decision."

Her touch roused thoughts of sharing her bed and the delights they could create beneath the covers.

She put her hand back in her lap. "Even a spinster wishes to experience life."

"A spinster?" It seemed the wrong term to describe her, especially when his body ached for her.

She blushed. "I am three and twenty and have no prospects for marriage. As I said, this might be my only chance."

Graham slanted a glance toward her. "Are you certain you are a vicar's daughter?"

She laughed. "Yes. I am afraid I am."

"There is something of this that makes no sense." Mere curiosity did not explain it, nor sacrifice for a brother.

She looked down at her tea.

There was something she was not telling him, he was certain of it.

"Shall I play the pianoforte for you?" she asked.

"Only if you wish to." He thought of pressing her for the whole truth. He, however, had no intention of explaining himself to her. He would not tell her he was the younger son of Baron Veall, nor what his regiment had been, nor how his face had been slashed nor how he'd almost died of fever. Better they not truly know each other. Better that this interlude feel like a dream, allowed to fade upon wakening.

She cleared her throat. "Shall I read to you?"

"No." His mind could not attend a book.

She glanced away and back. "Would you desire to play cards?"

"No, please." He could not concentrate on cards. His mind was filled with thoughts of bedding her.

She averted her gaze again and sipped her tea. The silence between them stretched on.

He forced himself to speak. "Forgive me." He could not tell her what consumed him—the thought of undressing her, of running his hands along her bare skin, of plunging inside her and at last feeling release. "I am unused to entertaining."

"I thought I was to entertain you." She peered at him. "What did you do in the evenings when you were alone?"

Besides drink? he wanted to say. "I sometimes took walks outside. When it became dark, that is."

"You walked in the dark?" Her lovely brown eyes widened.

He frowned. "I do not go out in daylight."

"For fear you will be seen?" She put down her teacup. "That is nonsensical, Graham. Is it not an injury you have, nothing more? It cannot be so dreadful that you must hide in the dark."

"I will not speak about my injury," he said through clenched teeth.

"I am persuaded that you ought to talk about it,

Graham," she spoke earnestly. "You have altered your whole life around it."

"Out of necessity," he snapped. "Do not presume to advise me on what you know nothing about."

Her eyes were full of concern. "I want to know of it, Graham," she said in a quiet voice.

He stiffened. "You want me to remove my mask."

She nodded. "How else am I to understand?"

"I do not require your understanding," he roared. "I will not show you the monster beneath the mask. There will be no display of horror here, and if you intend to harp upon this subject, you may return to London in the morning." He stood. "Play the pianoforte. Read. Do as you wish. I am retiring for the night."

Graham stormed out of the room without looking back. He did not head for his bedchamber, however. Instead, he strode to the door at the rear of the lodge and out into the cool evening air. It was not quite dark, but he hardly cared who saw him.

Except the young woman standing at the drawing room window watching his retreat.

Chapter 4

Graham walked until he returned to his senses. By that time, night had fallen and only a sliver of a moon lit his path back to the lodge.

His disfigurement set him apart from other people. He well knew that, but he ought not to have vented his spleen at Margaret. She had never heard the gasps of horror when people saw his face. She'd never seen the disgust on their faces and how they quickly turned away. Graham could not bear for Margaret to turn away.

He groaned. This cabbage-headed plan of his to alleviate the dreariness of his life was nothing more than a sordid manipulation. He wanted her in bed and he'd figured out what to offer her that she could not refuse. How dishonorable of him.

Setting his chin, he resolved to give Margaret the funds for Cambridge and the annuity, then set her free.

Such altruism did not lift his foul mood as he walked back in the house and up the stairs to his bedchamber.

He closed the door, peeled off his coat and kicked off his shoes and stockings. Coombs had turned down the bed and left a lamp burning. Graham caught his image in the mirror, as he untied the lacings of his mask and pulled it off so he could splash cool water on his face.

He'd just put the towel down when the door opened. Clapping his hand over his scars, he spun around.

Margaret stood in the doorway that connected their two rooms, looking like an angel come to earth in her white muslin nightdress with her hair loose about her shoulders.

He turned away from her and grabbed his mask. As he fumbled for the laces, he heard the swish of her skirts and felt her fingers take the laces and tie them.

"Have I positioned it correctly?" she asked.

He adjusted it. "Yes." He turned to her more slowly. "You did not have to come. I will require nothing of you, Margaret."

She looked up at him. "I had to apologize once more." She lifted her fingers to his mask, but lowered them again. "It is your right to hide beneath your mask if you wish."

He checked the laces to make certain they were tight enough.

She licked her lips, and he felt desire pulse through him once more. It must have taken a great deal of boldness for a virginal vicar's daughter to agree to bed a disfigured stranger.

"I came here to make you happy," she said. "Not to cause you distress." The rapid rise and fall of her chest, distracting in itself, suggested she was not as calm as she sounded. She touched the cloth of his shirtsleeve, and he felt it as if she'd caressed his skin. "May we not simply... proceed?"

He gazed down at her inviting lips. "Are you certain of this?"

"Yes," she breathed.

"Do you know how to take care of yourself? To prevent a child?" He would not compound the cost to her by creating this complication.

She lowered her head. "The actresses in my cousin's boardinghouse taught me what to do."

He still hesitated.

She took a step back and untied the ribbons of her

nightdress. She pushed the white fabric over her shoulders and let the gown slip down her body to the floor. His gaze wandered over her, slow and savoring. Her skin glowed like candlelight on silk. From her luxuriantly full breasts to her narrow waist and long slim legs, she reminded Graham of the painting he'd seen in Florence when on his grand tour.

Venus Rising from the Sea.

He gazed into her face, and her eyes pleaded. "Do I please you, Graham?"

"You please me," he said, his voice so low he hoped she'd heard.

Her eyes darkened, and she stepped forward to undo his shirt's buttons and lift it over his head. Her eyes flickered with pain when she saw the marks on his chest, more of the Frenchman's handiwork.

"As you can see," he rasped. "I am not pleasing."

She glanced into his eyes. "You must have been terribly injured."

He stroked her unmarked cheek. "Not enough to kill me."

He'd often cursed the fate that spared him, but at this moment he was glad to be alive, to be with her.

He lifted her into his arms and carried her to the bed, his muscles trembling, not with the effort, but with a struggle for restraint.

He lay her carefully on the bed and climbed in beside her. "I will be gentle with you, Margaret. I promise you."

She smiled and combed his hair with her fingers. "You said you would allow no harm to come to me."

His words at Vauxhall. "I meant it."

He pulled her towards him, kissing her with all the pent-up need inside him. She melted into him, putting her arms around him, holding him against her. His hand slid down her back and her skin was as smoothly perfect as he'd anticipated.

His arousal pressed painfully against his trousers. He reached down to unbutton them. She helped him pull them off, his drawers with them. He saw her gaze at his male organ, so hard with desire, he felt as if he would burst. She did not shy away, and it made him inexplicably proud of her. She had more courage than he. She'd had the courage to enter his room

He was determined to take her slowly, to make this first time one of pleasure for her, not pain.

"This is new to me," she whispered.

"You make it feel new to me as well," he murmured back.

His lips captured hers again. He stroked her

gently with his fingertips, fearing that contact with his whole hand might loosen the binds he kept tight on his passion. She gasped as his fingers explored her breasts, and he gently rubbed their tips over her nipples. Then his fingers slid down to between her legs.

"I will make you ready," he murmured to her.

"Yes," she responded, her voice thick.

She was warm and moist for his touch, and his fingers easily eased inside her. A low moan escaped her lips, and she arched her back, but never pulled away.

There was a pounding in his head that told him to simply mount her and seek his release, but he fought it and focused on pleasuring her, determined she should not regret the decision she had made to come to him.

Margaret gasped at the sensations his fingers created. She knew so little of lovemaking; she'd never imagined a man could touch her so and bring such exquisite pleasure. The sensations grew more intense—not painful, but something akin to demanding.

She clasped his hand, stilling it. "Wait, Graham."

He withdrew his fingers. "Did I hurt you?"

She shook her head. "Not hurt. Not precisely. I—I do not know how to explain."

He held her close. "No need to explain."

She wished she could put it into words, but it was all so new, so profound. One thing she knew, she needed his arms around her at this moment, needed to calm herself, to assimilate the experience.

"Do you wish me to stop?" he asked.

She could tell he was trying to keep his tone mild. "No, do not stop." She thought she might perish if she did not have the yearning growing inside her fulfilled.

He lay on his side, the masked part of his face pressed against the bed linens. She could almost envision how he might have appeared without the injury. His dark good looks took on a rakish appearance with the shadow of a beard on his face. Lifting a finger, she drew it from his cheek to his chin, careful not to touch the mask, lest he become angry again.

He lay still while she explored the contours of his muscles with eager fingers. She slid her hand over his shoulders and down his chest, thrilling at the feel of his skin, the wiry hair that peppered his chest. The scars beneath her fingers made her wish to weep. Battle must be a terrible thing to so mar his body. She felt his muscles tense as she traced the scars. She did not want to distress him.

She moved her hand lower, wondering if she dared touch the male part of him.

She dared.

He groaned when her fingers closed around him.

The actresses explained how a man's male member grew hard when desire overtook him. Margaret felt a surge of power knowing she had caused his arousal.

His own hand closed around hers and she felt as if she'd made another misstep, but he said, "My turn now."

He touched her body like she'd touched his, this time caressing her with a firm touch, not mere fingertips. He eased her onto her back and rose above her, both hands kneading her breasts.

The sensation shot all the way to the apex of her legs and she heard an urgent cry escape her lips. The need she did not quite understand grew stronger. Then he did something equally as wondrous. He placed his lips upon her nipple and tasted it with his warm tongue.

Her back arched and she dug her fingers into his skin.

She'd had no idea a man would want to do such

a thing, nor want to touch her so intimately. She wanted to cry out with joy, so glad she'd given herself this chance to be loved by Graham, even if only temporarily. The memory of his touch—his tongue—would last for a lifetime.

"I think it is time, Margaret."

She would also remember the sound of her name on his lips.

"Yes." She almost laughed, more than ready for the grandest mystery of all.

He gently spread her legs. With a mixture of fear and need, she forced herself to relax. He began to ease himself inside her, stopping suddenly to whisper in her ear, "This may give you some pain."

He pushed, one hard thrust that made it seem like something tore open inside her. She felt a sharp pain and cried out.

He held her in his arms. "I am sorry."

She stopped him from withdrawing, pressing her hands against his buttocks. "Don't stop."

It seemed all the permission he needed. He began a rhythm with which her body seemed already familiar, meeting his every thrust, growing her excitement until she could not think. She was lost in the sensation, in the pleasure, in the delicious need. She heard their excited breaths, felt their bodies moving against each other. She saw him above her, as lost in the moment as she. They were joined. They were one, sharing the need and sensation and pleasure. It was exhilarating. It was unforgettable.

Faster and faster they moved, until something changed for both of them; she could feel it. Pleasure burst through her, waves and waves of pleasure that washed over her. His muscles tensed, and she realized he'd spilled his seed.

Coming down from the intensity of that shared moment reminded Margaret of a feather floating to earth, slow and languorous.

Graham slid from her. The break from their joining was jarring, a loss from which she could not imagine recovering. Unbidden tears rolled down her cheeks.

He rose on one elbow. "By God, I did hurt you."

She shook her head. How was she to explain it to him, all that she felt, all that seemed now altered inside her? "I am not hurt. Far from it—" She squeezed her eyes closed for a moment, before gazing back at him, so handsome, even if half shrouded. "I did not expect it to feel like that."

She was no longer merely Margaret, because he was now a part of her. Two become one.

He stroked a stray lock of hair off her face. "I swear I will make it better for you next time."

She snuggled next to him, laying her head against his heart. "You cannot possibly make it better."

He held her tight. "There was pain, I know it. There will not be pain again."

The pain had been fleeting. It marked the moment of change in her. She was forever altered, forever a part of him. "It was a mere trifle."

He stroked her hair again and looked so concerned that she searched for a way to reassure him that to worry was misguided. Celebration seemed more in order.

He rose from the bed and walked over to the tallboy that held his washbasin and pitcher. He poured some clean water on a cloth and brought it over to her.

"The linens can be laundered," he said. "There will be fresh ones tomorrow."

She clasped his hand and pulled him back on the bed so that she was underneath him again. "Do not bring me too much reality," she whispered. "I want nothing to spoil this lovely dream."

She reached up to kiss him, and soon the dream was alive again and the changes inside her were etched even deeper.

Chapter 5

The dream lasted into the morning and through the next days and weeks. Margaret tried not to think that it would come to an end when the two months were done.

Their nights were filled with loving. Margaret had not believed anything could bring more pleasure and happiness than that first coupling, but each night Graham proved her wrong. He was a generous lover, this hero of her childhood, this man she adored.

Their daylight hours were an idyll of another sort, consisting of long conversation, of reading to each other, playing savage games of piquet, or singing the silliest songs they could think of, while she played the pianoforte.

They took long walks. She'd even coaxed him out into the sunshine and fresh air. They walked through the garden and the wooded area nearby. The rare person they encountered took Graham's appearance in their stride, probably hearing of his injuries and mask and not being surprised by them. He was not as fearsome as he thought; Margaret was pleased she'd been right about that.

A crack in the fragile shell of their dream-like existence occurred when Graham's man of business called with the papers that set up a trust to pay her brother's expenses to Cambridge and her annuity. She'd gasped at the amount Graham had given her. She would be able to live in comfort wherever she wished. Neither the trust nor the annuity could be rescinded, even if Graham changed his mind. Andrew's education and her future were secure.

Seeing the papers, however, reminded Margaret that the bargain she'd made with Graham was for a period of two months. And the end was rapidly approaching. The thought cast her in the dismals the whole day, and she could not explain her mood to Graham.

On the morning after the man of business had called, Margaret woke at dawn with a very unsettled stomach. Not wanting to rouse Graham, she slipped out of bed, wrapped herself in a robe, and made her way down to the kitchen where the indefatigable Mrs. Coombs was already busy preparing breakfast. The smells, usually intoxicating, made her retch.

"You are up early, miss," Mrs. Coombs said cheerily.

"Will you check if I am feverish?" Margaret asked. "I feel unwell."

Mrs. Coombs placed her palm against Margaret's forehead and then against her neck. "No fever. What is troubling you?"

"I feel nauseous."

Mrs. Coombs brows rose. "Indeed?" She lowered them again to peer at Margaret. "Tell me, miss. When did you last have your courses?"

Margaret's mouth dropped open in sudden understanding. "Before I came here."

"I suspected as much." The woman crossed her arms over her chest. "I'd say you are not ill."

She blinked. "I am not ill." Warmth spread throughout her and she pressed her hand to her belly. "I am with child."

"My guess," said Mrs. Coombs.

Margaret hugged the idea around herself. "A

child," she whispered. She shook her head. "No, it is impossible. I was taught how to prevent it."

Mrs. Coombs leveled a look at her. "There's no preventing a baby that wants to be born."

"A child," she whispered again. *Graham's child.* What could be more wonderful? A child to watch grow. A child to love, to help against the desolate loneliness of losing Graham.

Mrs. Coombs cut her a slice of bread. "Here. Eat this. It helps to have something in your stomach. Chew it slowly."

Margaret chewed very slowly. "I feel better," she said as she finished the bread. Indeed, she felt joyous. "Thank you so much."

Mrs. Coombs nodded in satisfaction and turned back to her work.

Margaret paused before walking out the door. "Mrs. Coombs, do not tell Graham of this."

The older woman looked up. "I do not keep secrets from him."

Margaret walked over to her. "Please, I beg you. Do not say a word to him of this. It—it is my news to tell." *Or not tell.*

Mrs. Coombs put her hands on her hips. "Very well. I'll not volunteer a word." She shook a finger at Margaret. "But if he asks me, I'll not lie to him."

"That is enough." Margaret gave the woman a hug. "Thank you." She again started for the door.

Mrs. Coombs called after her. "I'll leave a tin of biscuits in your bedchamber. Let me know if that does not do the trick."

Margaret smiled. "You are an angel."

Keeping the secret was not as easy for Margaret as she supposed it would be. She tried to hide her queasiness and her sheer preoccupation with the fact that Graham's child was growing inside her. She was quieter, and the change in her took away some of the ease between her and Graham.

This morning, Margaret had been fighting nausea when Graham reached for her to make love with her as he had so many mornings before.

He broke off abruptly. "What is this, Margaret?"

She sat up. "I do not know what you mean."

"Do not play the innocent with me." He pulled on his shirt. "Something has changed."

She seized his hand and held it against her cheek. "Nothing has changed, Graham. I—I merely feel a little unwell this morning and I did not wish to trouble you."

"Unwell?" He felt her forehead.

"Not feverish," she said. "Unwell."

He gave her an intent gaze. "Have you felt unwell the last few days?"

She could not meet his eye. "A little."

"Then why not tell me before?"

"I did not wish to ruin things."

He took his hand away. "Hiding it was meant to improve matters?"

A child had not been part of the bargain he'd made with her. She was afraid to tell him of it.

"Graham, I have felt a bit queasy in the stomach. I presume it came from something I ate."

He peered at her. "Queasy in the stomach."

She made herself return his gaze. "It is nothing."

He gave her a skeptical look and turned away to dress. She watched him remove his mask, his back carefully to her and the mirror angled so his reflection did not show. After washing and shaving, the mask went back in place and he put on his clothes, all the while avoiding looking at her or speaking to her.

Margaret held her breath as a wave of nausea hit her. At the moment, all she could think of was her tin of biscuits. She found her nightdress and crossed the room to her bedchamber and the bed she never used.

And her tin of biscuits.

He appeared in her doorway. "I'll be down in the dining room."

She quickly hid the tin. "Will you tie my stays first?" It was the one part of dressing she was unable to do on her own and it had been part of their morning ritual for him to help her.

Unlike other days, he did not enter her room. Instead he remained in the doorway as she hurriedly put on a clean shift. She stepped into her stays and positioned the garment, then she walked over and presented her back to him.

When he'd performed this little task for her before, it had been a lovely, intimate moment between them. Not this day. His hands were efficient at tightening the laces, but there were no lingering caresses, no murmured words in her ear. She felt his fingers tying the laces in a bow, but instead of a fond sweep of her shoulders, he merely stepped away and was gone.

She leaned on the doorjamb as another wave of nausea washed over her—and an encroaching fear that the idyll's end had already arrived.

Graham sat across the table from her, watching her nibble on a piece of toast. His appetite was no better than hers, but that only convinced him that matters had indeed changed between them.

Only two weeks were left of the two months they had agreed upon. He had hoped to ask her to stay longer, but now he wondered if he'd been blind to how things stood between them. Now he felt she might at any moment ask if she could leave early.

He could stand the silence between them no longer. "I have matters to attend to in the library."

He did not wait for her response, but strode out of the dining room to the library, where he drew the curtains to block out the light. He found a bottle of brandy and a glass and sat behind the desk in the dark. He had finished half the bottle before the door opened.

She was silhouetted in the doorway. "What is this, Graham? You are sitting in the dark?" She marched over to the windows and opened the curtains. The sunlight he'd blocked out came flooding back like a triumphant army.

She turned to him and saw the bottle. "You are drinking? It is only nine-thirty in the morning."

He lifted his glass. "In the dark, it might be any hour."

She walked up to the desk and picked up the bottle, measuring how little remained. "This is nonsensical. You are succumbing to a fit of depression merely because I felt a little unwell this morning."

He defiantly drained the contents of his glass. "Do not turn tables on me. You are the changed one, Margaret. You have been different ever since the money I promised you came into your control."

Her chin shot up. "The money? You think I changed because of the money?"

He let his eyes bore into her. "Possibly. I cannot undo it now. The money is yours."

She returned his gaze with a wounded expression that was quite effective. He almost believed in it.

"Oh, Graham." She twisted away from him, walked back to the window and gazed out on the garden where she had taught him he need not hide in darkness. She turned back to him. "I admit reading the papers and recalling that I would receive money for—for our time together did sober me." Her arm swept the expanse of the nearly floor-to-ceiling window. "It was a bit like opening the curtains. It let the outside world back in, the reality. I did not much like being reminded of it. The money itself was not the cause."

He poured more brandy, not because he wanted

it, but because he needed to be numbed. "If not the money, then what has changed you?"

She turned away again.

"You are hiding something from me, Margaret. I am convinced of it."

She looked over her shoulder at him. "Are you the only one who is allowed to hide, Graham?"

He gave a dry laugh. "Me? I have been honest with you from the beginning. Have you been honest with me?"

She swung around to him. "Honest? Perhaps. But you have hidden yourself from me just the same. I am not to know who you are. I am not allowed to see what you look like."

He stood. "Back to my face again, are we? I ought to have known. You will not be satisfied until you unmask me."

She took a deep breath, as if attempting to muster courage. "I will make another bargain with you. Reveal yourself to me, and I will tell you what I have kept hidden."

He met her gaze and held it, like one cat staring down another before lashing out with its claws.

It would serve her right to see him as he really was. She would finally understand the choices he made. There would be no chance she would stay, but he'd always known that.

Without any warning, he pulled off the mask.

He heard her swift intake of breath. Saw her eyes widen. But she did not flinch. She did not turn away. Instead she walked closer to him, so close they were inches apart. She raised her hand and touched the jagged scars that crisscrossed his cheek. With her finger, she traced the scar that caused the drooping of his eye and the one that pulled at the corner of his mouth.

He forced himself to endure her touch. The sunlight was bright enough to illuminate every detail. None of it was hidden from her now.

He braced himself for platitudes. *It is not so bad, Graham. Perhaps the scars will shrink, Graham.*

She was silent.

Finally she stepped back. He realized he was still gripping his mask in his fist. He lifted it to put it back in place.

She seized his hand. "Leave it off, Graham. Sit with me." She led him over to the sofa, also bathed in sunlight.

He did not mind that the light made her skin glow and her hair, worn tied back in a ribbon, shine with gold, but that same light revealed the monster he had become.

She still did not look away from him when she sat with him. She continued to grasp his hand.

"Now my secrets," she whispered.

She told a story of her childhood, of being chased through the woods by two boys, of falling and being pummeled with sticks and stones until another boy came to her rescue.

"By God," he said. "I remember it. It was me. I had my father see that the boys were given a severe dressing down." He gazed at her. "You were that little girl."

She nodded. "I needed you that day and you needed me when we met at Vauxhall. That is why I agreed to your proposition."

"You knew who I was all along? Did someone put you up to this? The duke?" That he could not tolerate. It bore too close a resemblance to pity.

She squeezed his hand. "Not at all. I discovered by accident that Captain Veall would also be a guest at the party. When you gave me your first name, I knew you were Graham Veall."

He frowned and averted his gaze.

"Do not worry," she said. "I will keep our association as secret as if I never knew you. I give you my word."

He sat back and rubbed his forehead. She had known all along who he was.

His eyes shot open and he leaned towards her. "This is not the cause of your withdrawal from me. You have known this from the beginning."

She glanced away.

He took her chin in his hand and made her face him. "You are hiding something else."

Tears glistened in her brown eyes, making them appear even more luminous. "Oh, Graham," she gasped. "I think I might be carrying a child."

He gaped at her, speech failing him. This he did not expect. A child. *His* child, growing inside her.

"I—I do not know for certain, so I did not want to tell you. You must not be concerned, though, because you have given me more than enough to support a child. And I am happy about it." A tear rolled down her cheek. "Very happy."

She was carrying his child inside her.

She took a shuddering breath. "I did what I was taught to prevent it, but it didn't work. But I am content. This will most probably be my only chance to have a baby, but I need not burden you with any of it."

"Burden me?" he managed to utter. "I am not that sort of monster, Margaret."

"I know you do not want a child. But I do so very much want one. Want *this* one."

He scraped a hand through his hair. "Good God. I did not want to walk outside in the daytime. Or to remove my mask. I've done those things." He took her face in both his hands. "I did not want a woman to love, merely a woman to make love to, but you changed everything."

"I do not understand."

He released her and looked away, covering his scars with his hand. "It is no use. There's no chance. I cannot be a husband. A father. What woman would want to look upon this the rest of her life?" He pointed to his scars. "I'd frighten my own children."

She stared at him. "Graham, what are you saying to me?"

He gazed upon her. "I'm saying if I were not some monstrosity best reserved for a display of oddities, if I had met you before, I would marry you and consider myself the most fortunate of men. I would adore any child you bore."

She gaped. "Are you proposing marriage, Graham?"

He turned away. "How can I propose marriage to you?"

She laughed softly. "Place an advertisement in *The Times. Seeking a once-virginal vicar's daughter for marriage. Gentleman of good character offers happiness and a great deal of pleasure.*"

She touched the mangled side of his face and brought her lips to his.

Epilogue

London, February, 1818

Graham walked in the door of his London town house, shaking the rain from his topcoat. Coombs helped him with the garment and took his hat and gloves.

"Thank you, Coombs." Graham headed up the stairs. As he neared the top step, he pulled off the mask. "Anyone at home?"

"Papa!" came an excited squeal.

A little girl with nutmeg-colored hair and brown eyes ran into the hallway. Behind her was a blue-eyed little boy still in a short coat. "Papa," he cried, mimicking his sister's exact tone.

Graham crouched down to catch them both in

his arms, these perfect children of his. His daughter flung her chubby little arms around his neck and kissed his cheek—his scarred cheek.

"I missed you so much, Papa!" she cried.

"I missed you, too," his son said.

He laughed. "I missed you the most." He kissed them both on their smooth, unmarred little faces. Still holding them, he glanced at the doorway to the drawing room.

His wife stood there.

Even after nearly six years, Margaret's beauty still took his breath. Carrying their children, he walked over to her and leaned down for a long lingering kiss that made him wish it were time for the children to be tucked in bed.

As his lips left hers, she whispered. "I missed you the most."

He smiled, but knew she was wrong. Everything worth possessing was here in his arms now. His wife. His son. His daughter. This was life itself.

And he'd almost missed it all.

* * * * *

NOTORIOUS LORD, COMPROMISED MISS

Annie Burrows

Annie Burrows was born in Suffolk, to parents who loved to read. Her home was always full of books and every Saturday they went to the local library to stock up on more!

Her love of stories meant that when she was old enough to go to university, she chose to study English literature. She wasn't sure what she wanted to do beyond that, but meeting a handsome student of maths, who was also the owner of a very powerful motorbike, helped her make up her mind. She married him and followed him to Manchester, where he earned his doctorate.

For many years Annie felt it was important to stay at home to raise her two children, but one day, when the youngest was at senior school, she began to wonder if all those daydreams that had kept her mind occupied whilst carrying out mundane chores would provide similar pleasure to other women. Her first attempt at working one of her storylines into a manuscript that she could send to publishers took almost two years, mainly because she kept tearing it up and starting all over again. Fortunately, Mills & Boon eventually accepted another one of her manuscripts, and *His Cinderella Bride* was published in September 2007.

Chapter 1

Viscount Maldon ran a finger round the inside of his neck cloth, uncomfortably aware that by entering this place, he was putting his neck in a noose. He should have had a stiff drink before coming out. Everyone knew they did not serve anything stronger than lemonade in Almack's Assembly Rooms. And lemonade was not going to do a thing to steady his nerves.

The dancing was already under way, and the lobby was currently deserted, so nobody had noticed him yet. But once he set foot in that ballroom, there would be no going back. He would be at the mercy of every girl that men who could afford to be choosy had already passed over. The fat ones, the ones with annoying laughs, or bad breath, or, heaven forbid, facial hair…

Breaking out in a cold sweat, Viscount Maldon veered sharply away from the entrance to the ballroom, and ducked into an alcove that was partially screened by the luxuriant foliage of a potted palm. A man required nerves of steel to walk, unarmed as it were, into the all-female domain of the marriage mart!

How had Acton ever thought he could do it?

"You have got to show your creditors you mean business." The family's elderly man of business wheezed as he pushed a piece of paper across the desktop with his gnarled forefinger. "Merely setting foot in Almack's will send out a clear-enough message. But if you can manage to secure a dance with one or more of the females on this list whilst you are there…"

Viscount Maldon had meekly pocketed the list. He had taken it home and studied it. He had learned all the names on it by rote.

So there had been no need to put it in his breast pocket before setting out tonight. He had been somewhat surprised, when he had given his appearance one last critical appraisal in the mirror, that it had not distorted the fit of his cutaway coat: it felt like a ton weight against his heart.

But he looked just as he always did. His spare frame elegantly covered in well-tailored clothing, his fair hair tidily clipped and neatly brushed. Only the clouds dulling his gray eyes might have given those who knew him well a clue that something troubled him.

The list, that was what troubled him. The list of all the women Acton had ascertained might be prepared to accept his suit.

"You are not free to gad about like a younger son with no responsibilities, now you have come into the title," Acton had lectured him. "It is up to you to save the estate, and marrying well is the most effective way of going about it."

Marrying well! He grimaced. Pursuing some unattractive female for the sake of her dowry was not his idea of marrying well.

But men with their pockets to let did not, as Acton had querulously pointed out, have the luxury of choice.

Surely, Viscount Maldon thought mournfully, amongst all the eligible maidens upon the list Acton had given him, there must be one who was not too repulsive? At least, not too repulsive to dance with.

He *had* to demonstrate that he was the man to sort out the muddle his father had created and his brother compounded, with their reckless gambling. It had to be done some time, and, since he had got this far, it might as well be tonight.

Having talked himself into accepting his fate, Viscount Maldon peered through the foliage, towards the open door of the ballroom, and took his first real look at the assembled throng. By some cruel irony, the first face he recognized, amidst the swirling mass of humanity, belonged to Acton's first choice.

Dressed entirely in white, Miss Harriet Millbury was bouncing through the steps of a cotillion on the arm of an elderly earl, a muddy-complexioned man, who everyone knew was in search of a third wife to provide the heir his first and second wives had so signally failed to produce.

Looking at her, he was put forcibly in mind of a ship in full sail, bobbing along on the waters of the Thames in a stiff easterly breeze.

Repressing a shudder of revulsion, he shrank further back into the recess behind the potted palm. Plenty of men might find Miss Millbury quite attractive. Larger women, so he'd been reliably informed, provided a softly cushioned ride.

But then, it was not only big women he had an aversion to. The second name on the list filled him with even more trepidation. He had met Miss Framlingham at a house party not long after she had emerged from the schoolroom. She had pale eyes and long features that had instantly put him in mind of a particularly irritable goat his great-aunt had kept. Her temper might not be as unpredictable as her face led him to believe, but since this was her third season and she was still single, despite her temptingly large dowry, there was definitely something about her that put men off.

He took a deep breath, reminding himself that he need not actually propose to anyone tonight. He was only here, in London for the season, to buy himself a breathing space. He was only here, in Almack's tonight, to demonstrate that he was following the sensible course that his man of business had recommended.

He shut his eyes tight, concentrating on the task of breathing in and out, which had, just for a moment or two, proved unaccountably tricky.

Only when he felt reasonably confident that he could enter that ballroom without betraying the repugnance he felt at the course he was about to take, did he throw back his shoulders, open his eyes and turn his head deliberately towards that fateful portal.

Where another female caught his eye.

What drew his attention to her was not her face, for he could not see it, but the fact that she was sidling, yes, positively sidling out of the ballroom, and was currently backing stealthily—straight towards the very potted palm he was hiding behind.

Keeping her eyes fixed on the ballroom from which she had just emerged, she was feeling her way backwards with her feet. It was clearly not easy The nearer to him she came, the more she bent over from the waist, with her arms stretched out as though for balance. The irregular method of movement caused the fabric of her evening gown to slither over each buttock alternately, molding the flexing muscles like the caress of a lover's hand.

The unprecedented sight exerted a hypnotic effect upon him. It only occurred to him much, much later, that he could have coughed, or given the young lady some other warning that her deliciously rounded derriere was on a collision course with his thighs. But at that moment, movement of any sort was quite beyond him. Even if his innate sense of chivalry had come into play, he excused himself later, the alcove was too small to permit him to step to one side. And so he simply stood there, transfixed, his mind capable only of anticipating what those twin globes would feel like when they finally made contact.

Satin cushions. He inwardly groaned when the moment came. Firm, yet yielding, and utterly, perfectly formed...Who could have foretold that coming to Almack's could have resulted in an encounter of such exquisite sensuality?

A tide of crimson surged up the back of the girl's neck, telling him that she was aware it was a person, and not the wall, that she had just backed into. Her whole body stiffened; she straightened up and drew in a sharp breath. The kind of breath that all too often—he knew from his experience with his sisters—presaged the utterance of the kind of ear-piercing shriek that was the very last noise any female ought to be making in the entrance lobby of Almack's.

And he did what he would have done to prevent any of his sisters from making an exhibition of herself. He clapped one hand over her mouth, effectively silencing her scream before it began, and, as a further precautionary measure, flung one arm about her waist, pinning her arms to her sides so that she could not go dashing off and accusing him of, well, at the very least, of cowering behind a pot plant like some kind of maladjusted schoolboy!

"Think twice before you do anything that might be construed as causing a scene, miss," he murmured softly into her ear, a delicate, shell-like structure, he noted absently, entirely devoid of ornament. "Just calm down, and then—" He winced as she kicked him in the shins. Though her feet were shod only in dainty satin slippers, she had a kick like a mule. So he tightened his hold, pulling her close and spreading his legs so that she was in no position to kick him again.

"Hold still!" he hissed into the cap of dark, sweetly scented curls that were tickling his nose, when she began wriggling like an eel. He had saved his shins, but oh Lord! That softly cushioned rear, rubbing so energetically against his loins, was proving far more dangerous.

The sight of her bottom had been interesting. The feel of it, delightful. But the wriggle…damn but that was beginning to make him downright uncomfortable. His breeches were not cut to deal with that amount of strain.

He was almost grateful when she stamped on his foot, giving him a valid reason for letting her go. Muttering an oath beneath his breath, he braced himself for the aftermath. She was bound to slap his face—or worse, faint—if she did not simply run screaming into the ballroom, complaining that there was a pervert lurking behind a plant in the lobby, grabbing unwary females.

Thus putting an end to his career as a fortune hunter before it had even begun.

A liberating sense of succumbing to the inevitable washed over him. Perhaps a short spell in debtor's prison would not be so very bad. He could even see himself surviving a lengthy spell of incarceration. Somehow. For it would not be a life sentence. No, he could get out of prison. An unhappy marriage, though…

And that was when he realized that the girl, far from running, or fainting or screaming, was standing ramrod straight, exactly where he had released her.

As though frozen to the spot.

"Please," he implored her in an urgent undertone. "Just run along now, there's a good girl."

As though his words had released her from a spell, she whirled round, to glare up at him through narrowed green eyes.

"You cannot make me!" she said.

Extremely quietly.

Viscount Maldon was impressed. The girl had enough sense to realize that the last thing either of them needed was to draw attention to their encounter.

But if she did not want to be compromised, why was she not taking this opportunity to flee from him?

"What game are you playing?" he asked, his curiosity thoroughly roused.

"I am not playing!" she retorted.

"Then what are you doing?"

"I should have thought it was obvious, I am doing the same as you."

He doubted very much whether she had a list of prospective suitors in her pocket, particularly since the voluminous gown she wore did not appear to have any pockets.

When it became clear to her that she was a complete puzzle to him, she rolled her eyes in exasperation and explained.

"Hiding!" She then placed her hands on her hips. "And if you were a gentleman, you would remove yourself. At once!"

He glanced warily in the direction of the ballroom before shaking his head. He was not ready to step out from behind the pillar that supported the potted plant. Not in any sense!

"Not a chance." Then he folded his arms across his chest in what he hoped was a forbidding manner, and added for good measure, "Besides, I was here first."

She gasped. "Not only are you clearly *not* a gentleman, but—" she paused, and he could see that she was reaching inside herself for something suitably cutting to say that would slay him on the spot "—you are a coward! Yes, and, and—" she ran her eyes up and down his person, as though seeking inspiration. "A puny one," she flung at him in triumph, "at that!"

"Puny!" He drew himself up to his full height, and threw out his chest. "I am not in the least bit puny. I may be slender, but," he pointed out, "what there is of me is exceptionally muscular."

"Huh," she replied, rubbing at her arms. "You could not hold *me* captive for long!"

"Indeed not," he replied with an unholy grin, recalling exactly why he had let her go. Simply recalling how arousing that wholly unexpected tussle had been was making his breeches grow tight all over again. Just when he had begun to think her sharp tongue might serve as an antidote to the power of her lush curves. "It is not at all the sort of activity the patronesses encourage within these hallowed walls."

"No." She shuddered. "All the groping and lusting is supposed to occur on that dance floor—" she grimaced, turning to peep through the fronds of the palm "—in full view. And in there, I have not the liberty to kick anyone in the shins." She finished wistfully, "I have to be polite to elderly widowers on the lookout for a nanny for their six motherless children, and smile at all the grubby fortune hunters with roving hands and a desperate gleam in their eyes."

Until that point, the insults she had been flinging at him had bounced straight off. But that one found its mark.

"Don't you think, perhaps you are being a little harsh?" he argued. "I mean, possibly fortune hunters look desperate because they *are* desperate. Perhaps they are on the brink of utter ruin, through no fault of their own. Perhaps the last thing they wish to be doing is looking for a bride. Can you not imagine what a young man might feel like, having been raised in expectations of living life as a carefree bachelor, to be suddenly confronted by the choice between debtor's prison or marrying without affection, without respect, without any criteria other than that his bride should have money?"

"I would not be a bit surprised," she observed thoughtfully, glancing over her shoulder at him, "to learn that it might make them feel like hiding behind a potted plant. But—" she whirled round to face him fully, her expression turning mutinous "—they do not have to be quite so oily and insincere, do they? Telling me I've captivated their hearts after only one turn round the dance floor! Do I look like a complete imbecile to you? Do I?"

He had already decided that this young lady had a mind like quicksilver. And yet, some devil in him had him drawing out his quizzing glass and inspecting her from head to toe. Her gown, he noted at once, had not been made by a London modiste. The billowing effect that had made her stealthy retreat from the ballroom so utterly entrancing was entirely due to its poor fit. Her figure, he had already determined, was perfectly proportioned to fit in his arms. And her face…well, the nose was a little short, the mouth a little too wide, and her eyes were shooting the kind of sparks that denoted a fiery temper. And yet, the combination of less-than-perfect features somehow rendered the whole remarkably attractive.

"Just tell me one thing," he said, "and then I will give you my honest opinion. Are you an heiress?"

Her eyes narrowed, her whole face scrunching up in a way that put him in mind of an angry kitten. "What has that to do with anything?"

"Well, only that if you are, I would say you have entirely captivated my heart, too. I would propose on the spot."

Her mouth dropped open. While she was sputtering, trying to find some suitably withering comeback, he went on languidly, "You know, for a man who has to marry money, you, sweet kitten, would seem a veritable godsend. If a man had to choose between the massive Miss Millbury, the frosty Miss Framlingham, or you, I am certain he would be foolish to do anything but fall head over heels in love with you."

"F-fall in love with my money—my hypothetical money, you mean."

"You have no money?"

She looked uncomfortable. "I think one of my aunts must have exaggerated my worth somewhat, thinking I would wish to be a social success. They probably meant well when they described me as coming from the wealthiest family in our town. But it is only a small town, you know, populated with simple country folk for the most part."

"But you must have good connections, else

you would never have been admitted within these hallowed portals. I am sure," he said gently, "that you will meet a man who will value you for yourself, in time." He ran his eyes slowly over her figure with such lazy speculation her face went scarlet. "You are definitely worth a second look."

"I am *never* going to get married," she declared with some vehemence.

"Ah!" he grinned at her. "A kindred spirit. I felt exactly as you do, until circumstances removed the luxury of choice. How would you feel about coming to some form of compromise?"

"Compromise?" she gasped, taking such a hasty step backwards that the pot rocked on its stand.

He grabbed it, steadied it, and explained. "I was only going to offer to share my hiding place with you. Come now, kitten," he said, holding out his hand. "Tell me your name, and let us be friends."

Her only response was to scowl.

"Katherine!" came an outraged screech from beyond the potted palm.

Looking over her shoulder, Viscount Maldon saw a tiny woman—clad entirely in garments of such a virulent yellow, he could practically taste lemons—making straight for their alcove.

"What on earth are you doing in the corner? *With a gentleman?*"

Katherine—well, at least he had learnt his lovely companion's name—went a deeper shade of crimson and gripped her reticule as though she had to have something to cling to. Though her mouth opened and shut, all that came out was, "Aunt Twining!" on a kind of despondent gasp.

He wondered which she was finding the more difficult. Trying to repress the urge to inform her aunt that he was *not* a gentleman, and risk having to explain exactly how she had made that assessment of his character. Or coming up with a valid reason for being ensconced in close physical proximity with a man who was a complete stranger to her chaperon.

So Viscount Maldon extended his hand through the palm fronds to shake that of the elderly lady who was practically dancing on the spot in consternation.

"You must be Katherine's chaperon! So pleased to make your acquaintance. Allow me to introduce myself. Tarquin Fortescue-Simmonds. Viscount Maldon." His bow being somewhat impeded by the palm fronds, he stepped past Katherine and out into the lobby. While the lemon-clad chaperon was still wondering how on earth she ought to deal with a situation that no book of etiquette gave any guidance about, he plowed on, "It is such a pleasure to meet a fellow botanist in a place normally so devoid of the true intellectual." He gave her his most dazzling smile. The one that rarely failed him when any of his own aunts were on the verge of giving him a well-deserved trimming.

"Is it?" she asked, completely bewildered by his sangfroid, at a moment when she must have expected him to be uttering excuses.

"Oh yes, quite remarkable. So remarkable in fact, that I am afraid we got rather carried away by our discussion of what ails this particular specimen of um…" he trailed one of the fronds of the palm through his gloved fingers "…Vertiginous Veridium."

From within the alcove, he heard Katherine utter something that sounded remarkably like a snort of suppressed laughter.

And then, apparently unwilling to be outdone by his execrable example of half-forgotten schoolboy Latin, she opened her reticule, produced a pair of spectacles and hooked them over her ears. The effect was startling. In an instant, she turned from a lovely, lush young wood nymph, into a rather owlish-eyed and frumpy-looking provincial.

"It is a rather puny specimen, for its type, Aunt Twining," she explained, bending to peer closely at the very frond he had just drawn attention to, her slender fingers trailing over some streaks of brown amidst the greenery.

"We were discussing what particular form of blight has struck it, and whether it will recover. I am afraid we rather forgot about the impropriety of entering any sort of discussion, without a proper introduction, in the heat of our exchange."

"Heat?" The aunt was looking from one to the other of them in complete bewilderment.

"Yes, I am afraid we disagree as to the root cause of the problem tonight. You see, I believe that a case of Impecunious Vulgaris can be easily cured by an application of Matrimonium Ingratus, whereas, if I am not mistaken, your delightfully frank niece believes that this is the very last solution to apply to any kind of plant."

"Indeed it is," Katherine replied, "but in this particular case, I believe the problem is only that of position." She indicated the alcove with a magnificently disdainful sweep of one gloved hand. "Nothing could thrive in such an unhealthy spot."

"You may be correct," he conceded gravely. "Certainly, there is something of a chill to the air, which could shrivel the most rampant of foliage."

To his shocked amusement, she could not help taking just one, swift glance at the front of his breeches, then coloring guiltily when he caught her looking.

"Well, my dear," her aunt twittered, saving either of them the necessity of digging themselves in any deeper. "I never knew you were so knowledgeable about plants. Very commendable, I am sure, but you know, you really should not draw apart with a gentleman, no matter how fascinating your discussion. Especially not to contradict him. Not the thing at all!"

"I assure you, I do not mind in the least," Viscount Maldon put in, when Katherine's hitherto ready wit appeared to have deserted her. "It has been refreshing to meet with such an original— dare I go so far as to say, unconventional—young lady as your niece. In fact, it would give me great pleasure if you would grant me permission to escort her onto the floor for the next dance. Then he enquired of Katherine, "If you are free?"

"You have not been properly introduced!" twittered the aunt in the manner of an overgrown and entirely flustered canary bird.

"Viscount Maldon," he repeated, executing a graceful bow.

"Miss Katherine Malahithe," replied his worth adversary, dropping him a regally disdainful curtsy.

Viscount Maldon held out his arm, and Katherine, having shown all her teeth in a parody of a smile, rather ungraciously laid her hand upon it.

His entrance, just as he had feared, caused something of a flutter amongst the other occupants of the ballroom. Yet somehow, with Katherine on his arm like a shield and her chaperon bringing up the rear, the whispers had no power to hurt him.

Though Katherine, judging by her expression when she faced him in the set that was forming, had overheard quite enough to have formed a correct impression of his financial straits.

"You are one, are you not?" she accused him, in an undertone. "A grubby fortune hunter!"

"I believe," he replied, when the movements of the dance permitted him to reply without risk of being overheard, "in the precepts laid down by Beau Brummel. I bathe daily and," he explained loftily, "my linen is always spotless."

Katherine was only nonplussed for a moment. With that swiftness of wit he had come to expect, she replied, "Very well. I acquit you of grubbiness. But I should just like to point out," she said with a smile that could have curdled milk, "that your technique for catching heiresses falls lamentably short of the mark. You will never be successful, if you mean to spend the entire season lurking behind plant pots."

"You have discovered my fatal flaw." He smiled as he twirled her under his left arm in the execution of a particularly complicated step. "The prospect of matrimony sends me into such a quake that were it not for half a dozen younger sisters, all relying on me to provide them with some kind of dowry…" He sighed mournfully, causing Miss Malahithe, contrarily, to look as though she was about to burst out laughing.

The figures of the dance separated them, but when they drew near again, he leaned in and whispered, "Are we half way through the dance yet? Or must I wait until the very end before persuading you that you have entirely captivated my heart?"

At that, she did burst out laughing, drawing several disapproving looks in their direction.

"You are the most insincere, preposterous…"

"But not grubby. You have to admit I am immaculately turned out," he interjected.

"…impossibly exasperating man I have ever met," she finished. "It would serve you right if I accepted a proposal from you this very minute."

"I have not made one!"

"But if you did, and I accepted, I suspect you would run screaming from the ballroom and throw yourself into the nearest river."

He looked pained. "I have never, and will never, do anything so unmanly as to utter a scream. I might," he admitted, "retire to some secluded spot and shed just one or two tears. Into a handkerchief."

"A silken one, no doubt," she riposted in a withering tone, "since you are clearly as vain as a peacock!"

"You wound me—" he sighed tragically "—by reminding me that all my silk handkerchiefs have had to be pawned."

The music reached a crescendo. The dance was over. Miss Malahithe and Viscount Maldon stood quite still for a moment or two, regarding each other as though neither were quite sure just what they were doing there.

"Thank you," he said, coming to himself with a start. Taking her hand, and pressing it, he said, "I did not think I could do this." When she looked a question at him, he explained, "Making up to women I do not like." When her expression turned stormy, he hastily put in, "But I do like *you*, Miss Malahithe. Oh, do not look so alarmed. You are not in any danger from me." He patted his breast pocket absently. "You are not on my list, you see."

"List?"

He took her arm, and turned her in the direction of the chaperon's bench. "All fortune hunters worth their salt arm themselves with a list of the heiresses most likely to succumb to their wiles."

Miss Malahithe wrinkled her nose in disgust and averted her face. When they reached the chaperon's bench, though she thanked him mechanically for the dance, her face was so devoid of expression that Viscount Maldon felt as though some of the lights in the ballroom must have been snuffed. He stared at her, nonplussed, as she dwindled from a vivacious, amusing companion, into a dowdy dumpling, merely by sitting down, hanging her head and hunching her shoulders.

Feeling rebuffed and bewildered, Viscount Maldon made for the exit.

And immediately cheered up.

He had done enough to persuade Acton he was following his advice. He had gone to Almack's and danced. The fact that it was not one of the females on that damnable list that he had danced with filled him with a rebellious sense of satisfaction.

And a sense of anticipation too.

He was looking forward to furthering his acquaintance with the completely unconventional Miss Malahithe. He was going to thoroughly enjoy provoking her into showing her claws, unleashing the personality she seemed so determined to conceal from every other man.

Oh, yes! He grinned, sauntering down the steps and out into the night air. Teasing her out of hiding would be like opening a window and breathing in fresh air, whenever his personal prison walls crowded in on him too oppressively.

Chapter 2

Katherine scanned the ballroom surreptitiously while her aunts greeted some of their acquaintances who were lingering just inside the entrance. She had not seen Viscount Maldon for three days, and if he was not here tonight—she sighed—she would be in for yet another evening of suffocating boredom.

Viscount Maldon might make her by turns, furious, exasperated, shocked or amused. But never—she smiled to herself—no, not once, had she experienced a minute's boredom in his company.

She was glad now that she had not carried through with her decision, made in the wake of that dreadful first meeting, never to speak to him again. After spending a sleepless night going over every second of the humiliation he had inflicted on her, she had decided that the only way to deal with a man like that would be to freeze him out with that icy civility she had seen her aunts employ to such devastating effect on encroaching persons.

But he had ruined her attempt at frosty manners within seconds of their next meeting.

"Good evening Miss Malahide," he had said, bowing over her hand.

"Malahi*th*e," she corrected him, annoyed that the interlude which had so shocked her had been of such little account to him that he could not even remember her name.

"Oh?" he had raised one eyebrow, a mocking gleam in his eyes, "Why is it then that whenever I think about you, the connotation of hiding springs to my mind?"

"The one hiding was you, I believe, Viscount... *Walden,*" she retorted, deliberately getting his name wrong, just to demonstrate *she* had not been thinking about *him* at all.

He shook his head, clicking his tongue in rebuke. "Come, come, kitten, you can do better than that. You must have heard the gossip about me. Doting mothers warn their daughters, in thrilled accents, to beware of me lest I am tainted by the 'Maldon Madness, '" he wagged his finger at her reprovingly, "not the er…Walden…er…"

"Weakness," she had put in scornfully.

"I was going to say 'Wildness,'" he said, then lowered his voice and leaned closer. "If they must gossip about me, let us at least give them something meaty to get their teeth into."

She did not know whether it was his closeness or the low timbre of the words he was drawling right into her ear that had made her mouth begin to water, and her tongue snake out and lick her lips before she even knew she had meant to do it. Furious with him for having the power to evoke such a reaction, without even touching her, when she thought him quite the most obnoxious male she had ever had the misfortune to run into, she had stepped smartly back and let rip with a volley of insults that would have made any other man take to his heels in disgust.

But Viscount Maldon was not like any other man she had ever met. There had been a gleam of something like triumph in his eyes as he had bowed politely over her hand and escorted her, still spluttering, onto the dance floor.

That really would have been the end of their association, had not her aunts decided they needed to warn her that he was not an eligible party.

"You ought not to be encouraging the advances of a man like that, my dear," her Aunt Twining twittered, the next morning at the breakfast table.

Encourage him? She had done the very opposite, did they but know it. And she fully intended to give him the cut directly, the next time he tried to foist himself on her.

"There is bad blood in that family," Aunt Berry had ponderously intoned. "Everyone knows about the Maldon Madness."

She had carried on buttering her toast, on the surface taking their advice to heart. But inside she was seething. There was nothing, absolutely nothing, so irritating, as being told to do something she had already decided to do.

"To be fair, it does sometimes skip a generation," Aunt Twining had pointed out.

Hah! They had not seen him cowering behind a potted palm, nor had they been manhandled in a positively loathsome manner! The madness had clearly not skipped this particular generation.

But at that point, Aunt Berry had frowned at Aunt Twining and shaken her head so sharply her jowls had quivered. And no matter how hard Katherine pressed them, they refused to divulge what form the madness took.

Naturally, the next time Katherine ran into him, she simply had to satisfy her curiosity. She had been certain that a man who could grab her in such an ungentlemanly fashion, then be rude enough to make her feel as though it was her own fault for trying to appropriate his hiding place, would not scruple to shield her ears from indelicate topics of conversation. Nor did he.

The afternoon they spent strolling around Hyde Park had been an education.

"You wish to know all about the Maldon Madness?" he had echoed, looking wary. "Why?"

"Because my aunts," exactly as he had predicted, "have told me it makes you completely ineligible, yet they will not tell me what form, exactly, it takes!"

"Ah!" His eyes had lit with amused understanding. "Now I understand. Forbidden fruit." He had grinned in a positively wicked manner. "Nothing is more enticing, is it? But sadly—" and then his expression had sobered "—I do not suffer from it. My father was of the opinion that I am a changeling. It always shocked him when I managed to make my allowance last until the end of the quarter. Occasionally, I have even been unnatural enough to pay my tailor."

She could well believe that. His vanity would make it essential for him to keep on good terms with the man who was responsible for his appearance.

"So…the Maldon Madness is only an inability to handle money?" she asked, somewhat crestfallen.

"Alas," he said tragically, "would that it were that simple. Our estate has been brought to the verge of ruin countless times over the generations, through the excesses of the head of the family. My own father had the ailment in a mild form. He merely spent all his waking hours at the races, when he was not throwing good money after bad in card games at his club. It was my brother who had it in its truest form. He was never satisfied with the commonplace wagers that any man might make. He had to be more…creative in his profligacy. In an earlier age, I think he might well have become a pirate…" He paused then, smiling wryly. "I do not think I should sully your ears with the sordid details. Trust me when I say that the extent of his mania has left me with the unenviable task of having to marry someone wealthy, yet still so desperate for a husband she will overlook the family taint."

"It seems unfair," she said thoughtfully, "that you should have to pay the price for his excesses."

"It is not for myself I mind so much," he admitted, for once sounding perfectly sincere. "But for our sisters. They will all want to make respectable marriages in due course. But without decent dowries, who would have them? And why should they have to forfeit all this?" He waved his hand around, encompassing the fashionable people bowling along in open carriages. "Girls dream about having their season, do they not? Coming up to London, and having dozens of beaus?"

She flushed and turned away at that. "As a rule, I suppose…"

"Ah, I do not count you as a girl with romantic dreams, Miss Malahithe," he assured her. "The purchase of that hat," he said, eyeing the elaborately decorated bonnet she had allowed her Aunt Twining to persuade her into buying, "makes its own statement. Coupled with the gown you have on…" he had paused then, in the middle of the pathway, to examine her at his leisure through his quizzing glass "…A mushroom," he breathed, tucking his glass away with an expression of satisfaction. " That is what it makes you look like. A little mushroom on legs. Come," he said with a smile, offering her his arm, "and let us give it a chance to work its repelling power on as many of those with pretensions to your hand as we may meet."

She had not been able to suppress the giggle that rose up within her in a bubble of pure enjoyment. He knew she had picked the hat because it was the most unflattering item of headgear she had ever tried on. And yet, even though he cared so much about his own appearance, he was prepared to walk through the park with her looking, as he had just informed her, like a drab little mushroom with half a forest strapped to her head.

And find the disdainful looks of true aspirants to fashion highly amusing.

That night, when he had asked for a dance in proper form, she had accepted willingly. She'd had time to reflect on his behavior and see it in a new light. To begin with, he really did have sisters. The first time he had mentioned them, she had believed he was inventing them, merely to score a point off her. Now she could see that he was pursuing the women on his list, not for himself so much, but to undo the damage their older, irresponsible brother had done to them all.

The poor man wished to marry as little as she did. But unlike her, he was not free to please himself.

She still could not think of him as a suitor, obviously, but neither did she wish him ill, now that she could see that he was in as awkward a situation as she found herself.

Besides, she felt grateful to him. The trimming Aunt Twining had given her after discovering her arguing with Viscount Maldon behind the potted palm, had inspired her to adopt a new tactic.

Before coming to London, Katherine had thought that dressing dowdily would have been enough to deter prospective suitors. But by the time she ran into Viscount Maldon at Almack's, she had discovered that the men who were determined to get their greedy paws on a female's fortune cared nothing for outward appearances. She had been at her wits' end, until her aunt had warned her that a young lady should never contradict a gentleman, especially not in public.

From that moment on, she developed a great many decided opinions, which always ran counter to whichever gentleman happened to be making up to her at any particular moment. She continued with her policy of repeatedly making over her gowns and wearing her gloves until they split, and gradually, people began to murmur that her aunts had exaggerated the extent of her worth in order to make their termagant of a niece seem marriageable. She still received invitations everywhere, because her aunts had the kind of connections that meant people did not wish to offend them by excluding their niece. But the suitors who had been such a nuisance at the beginning of the season had, to her complete satisfaction, melted away like swallows flying south for the winter.

The only man, in fact, who still sought her out wherever she went was Viscount Maldon. No matter how outrageous the views she expressed, he only seemed to find her posturing amusing. It was a novel and somewhat heady experience to find a man who actually enjoyed pitting his wits against a female. She had begun to think that he looked forward to their verbal fencing matches as much as she did.

Or perhaps it was only that when the task of fawning round the ten women on his list got too much for him, squabbling with her came as something of a relief.

Ah, there he was! Lounging against a pillar on the edge of the dance floor, his arms folded across his chest in an attitude that spoke of a man holding on to his temper by the merest thread.

She wished that she was bold enough to ignore convention completely and simply walk across the crowded room and ask him what was the matter.

But then, as though she had drawn his attention merely by focussing on him, he lifted his head, looked directly at her and without a moment's hesitation, made straight to her side.

"The damnedest thing!" he blurted. "You won't believe it!"

If his language had not been enough to demonstrate he was extremely agitated, the way he stood over her—his fists clenched, his normally cool gray eyes flashing with disturbing intensity— would have done so.

"You had better tell me," she said, fiddling with her dance card, then smiling and making him a curtsy, as though their conversation was only what one would expect to take place between any lady and gentleman in a ballroom.

He bowed and held out his arm. But when she laid her hand on his sleeve, he did not take her onto the dance floor.

"Can't talk while trying to remember the sequence of steps," he muttered, steering her through a set of doors and along a short corridor. "Here," he said, flinging open twin glass doors that led into a conservatory. "I seem to remember there are some benches along here somewhere."

He led her along a flagged path, bordered by dense foliage. What little light there was came from the stars she could dimly make out through the glass panes of the roof. It struck her, as he flung himself moodily onto a bench and glared up at her, that this was exactly the kind of situation her aunts would have warned her she should never get into, not with a gazetted fortune hunter like Viscount Maldon. *Not any gentleman,* she corrected herself, sitting next to him and smoothing down her skirts primly. The place was entirely too private. Too…she craned her neck to look up at the stars, while the strains of the music floated faintly through the green misty air…*too romantic!*

"I see nothing to amuse you about all this," he snapped, seeing the smile that flitted across her face at the prospect of anything romantic occurring between her and the irascible Viscount Maldon.

"Acton has betrayed me!"

"He…what? Your man of business! How?"

"Well, not betrayed me, precisely," he grumbled, "but let me down with a display of inefficiency that only makes me wonder how much of our family misfortunes were due to my father's gambling and how much to Acton's mismanagement of our affairs!" He ran a hand through his fair hair, leaving his normally neatly combed locks rather endearingly ruffled.

"What has he done?"

"He wrote this damned list...." With a grimace, he pulled the much mangled sheet of paper out of his breast pocket and waved it at her. " Seemingly with the sole intention of preventing me getting married to anyone! All of these females are completely repulsive to me—" he suddenly ripped the page in half "—and yet I have swallowed my pride and made up to them—" he ripped the pieces in half again "—when all the time, I could have been courting a perfectly charming young woman. Actually stood a chance of marrying someone I could tolerate!" Rip, rip, rip went the paper, his fingers trembling with the violence of his feelings. And then he thrust the resultant mess into her hands, as though somehow he held her to blame for whatever it was that was making him so angry.

"Do you know how I found out about her?"

When she dumbly shook her head, he went on, "I overheard some fellows talking about her in my club. Miss Susannah Hullworthy has more money than all those females put together—" he glared down at the scraps of paper she held in her hands "—and came to London with the express purpose of catching herself a title." His voice lowered to a growl. "And Acton did not put her on my list!"

"I am sure he had a very good reason.…"

"Yes." He laughed bitterly. "And do you know what he said it was? He did not consider her suitable, because her money comes from trade! Trade!" He clutched at his already disordered locks, an expression of anguished incomprehension on his face. "What do I care where her money comes from, when she has a delectable figure, a sweet nature and a face that has artists queuing up to paint her?"

"Well," she pointed out—quite reasonably, she thought, "what is to stop you from courting her now?"

"Now? When I have made myself odious, fawning over a batch of females no self-respecting man would look twice at! Thrust my way into the mob that hang around her already, and try to convince her I am marriage-worthy when everyone in town knows I am not only tainted by the Maldon Madness, but have sunk to the level of becoming one of your insincere, oily, grubby…"

Katherine had grown accustomed to hearing

him unload some of his feelings regarding the progress of his ten concurrent courtships. But never had she seen him prey to such flat despair.

"Not grubby," she put in, hoping to re-awaken his indefatigable sense of humor. "Never grubby."

He bowed his head, his hands clasped tightly together between his knees. "It is too late in the season now to fix my interest with her. Too many others ahead of me in the game. Any minute now, she could up sticks and head for Brighton, where I simply cannot afford to follow. I have wasted all these weeks.…" He groaned.

Katherine put out a hand and patted him gently on the hunched shoulder he was presenting to her.

"It is never too late," she said gently. "From my experience of the kind of men that must be hanging about her, you will seem like a godsend. You are quite good-looking, you know, and if she really wants a title and has the least particle of common sense, she will fall head over heels for you within ten minutes of making your acquaintance."

He raised his head, frowning up at her. "Do not mock me."

She smiled. "No, really, even I can concede that you are quite handsome, when you are not scowling. I know that you can be charming, too, when you put your mind to it…."

"The answer to every maiden's prayer, in effect." He sneered.

She flinched, removing her hand from his shoulder to toy with the pieces of paper that had scattered over her skirts when she had reached out to him.

"I beg your pardon," he said. "That was uncalled for. I meant no disrespect."

"I am sure I do not know what you mean," she replied frostily.

"Oh, come now, Katherine. We have become too close for me to pretend any longer. I know you are not a virgin."

"Who told you?" She gasped.

His face softened. "You did, you sweet idiot. The very first time we met. You knew exactly what your behind had come into contact with. You understood exactly what I meant when I referred to withering foliage. And far from acting outraged, you chose to find it amusing."

"You have known from the first?" Her face grew hot. "All this time…"

"Perhaps not quite from the first," he admitted. "But when I thought about your strange behavior at Almack's that night, it was the only explanation that fit. The only reason why a girl with your wit, your vibrancy, your connections, would wish to avoid marriage."

"Fustian!" she snapped. "There may be plenty of good reasons why I do not wish to marry!"

He shook his head in reproof. "Do not think you can lie to me now, Kitty Kat. I know you too well."

"What is this? Are you trying to threaten me?"

He looked hurt. "How can you even think that? Let alone say it? After I have kept your secret all these weeks?"

"Have you?" She leaned forward and grasped his wrists. "Have you truly kept my shameful secret to yourself?"

"Is it so shameful?" he asked gently. "I find it hard to believe that you were anything but the innocent party in a seduction."

"No! No, it was not like that! We loved each other. We were going to marry, only…"

"He abandoned you." His face turned grim. "I should like to meet the bounder who seduced and betrayed you and made you feel unfit to marry anyone else. That is why you will not accept any man's suit, is it not?"

"Yes." She sat back, regarding him in wonder.

He knew, without her having to spell it out, that she could never accept a proposal from a man she liked, because it would mean having to confess her guilty secret. And knowing the pain of seeing his regard turn to disgust. And what was the point in agreeing to marry a man who did not respect her?

"But he did *not* abandon me."

"Then where is he?" he asked harshly. "Why did he not marry you?"

"He died," she said bluntly, averting her face when she heard his gasp of surprise.

"We grew up together. We were always close. He was not very well off, but he thought, once he had made his way in the world a bit, perhaps got made up to a captain, he could ask my father for my hand in marriage. I would have waited for him. Especially after we...well...did what we did the night before he went away to join his regiment...."

Viscount Maldon seized her shoulders and spun her upper body round so that she faced him. "If any man toyed with any of my sisters, as that boy did you, I would horsewhip him! What kind of man seduces a girl for his pleasure, then abandons her to bear the consequences alone? He could have got you with child!"

"It was not all his fault. The prospect of being

parted, for who knew how long, was too much for both of us. Our feelings overcame us. I could have stopped him. But…"

"Oh, yes, I know. He made you believe that if you loved him, you would not refuse."

She blinked up at him in consternation.

"That is what he did, is it not?"

She went pale. "We simply could not help ourselves," she insisted. "We loved each other so much, what happened was inevitable. It was as much my fault as his.…"

"In cases like that, it is always the man's fault. He knew what he was doing was totally, completely unacceptable, and—what the hell…?"

Two large tears were rolling down Katherine's pale cheeks. "I hate you," she breathed. "I have always, always, treasured the memory of how he made me feel that night. It was w-wonderful. B-beautiful. But now you—" she hiccupped "—with your nasty, cutting, c-cynical observations—" she drew in an enormous, ragged breath. "You have ruined it all!"

And then she buried her face in her hands and began to sob in earnest.

"Katherine, no, don't cry," he pleaded. "I take it all back. I am sure he loved you to distraction.

He was just a boy, faced with the prospect of fighting and probably scared of dying…"

"It is no use trying to take back what you said now! He did die!" she wailed. "And of course he loved me!"

"Oh, hell." He groaned, putting one arm round her shoulders, and gently running his other hand up and down her arm, while she sobbed. "Of course he loved you. What red-blooded male would not love such a passionate, giving, warm-hearted girl as you?"

"You are just saying that!"

"No," he replied, looking somewhat startled. "I really do not think I am. Katherine…Katherine…"

He tipped her face to his, by placing one finger under her chin, and stared, as though stunned, into her eyes for several heartbeats. And then, to her complete astonishment, he cupped her face in his hands and began to wipe away the tear tracks on her cheeks. And there was something in his eyes that took her breath away.

And when she gasped, his eyes fixed on her parted lips. In that instant, everything between them changed irrevocably.

When he lowered his head to kiss her, gently, almost tentatively, she felt as though she had been waiting for this moment ever since he had taken her in his arms and crushed her against his aroused body in the entrance hall of Almack's.

The mourning she had worn in her heart for David, her first love, fluttered from her like a cloak sliding from her shoulders as she reached up and put her arms about his neck.

It was all the encouragement he needed. With a low groan, he wrapped his arms about her, crushing her to his chest and kissing her with an ardor that made her blood roar through her veins. For the first time in years, she felt alive, truly alive. And so beautiful and desirable, to have roused a man as handsome and fastidious as this to such unrestrained ardor.

His hands swept the length of her back, coming to rest on her bottom. He kneaded and squeezed at her softness, making her breath hitch in her throat, her head loll back in an expression of pure sensuality. He ran his hand down the side of one leg, tugging insistently at her.

He was going to haul her onto his lap.

And she was going to let him! Because she wanted to be close to him. As close as it was possible for two people to be.

She had never felt so completely out of control.

Not even with David! He had been tentative about touching her, hesitant in expressing his desire. And she had responded partially out of an impending sense of loss. She had taken him into her body, in a vain attempt to staunch her misery. The whole thing had been a bittersweet experience.

There was nothing sweet about what Viscount Maldon was making her feel. It was hot and intense, born of passion, not the sort of tender, romantic feelings she'd had for her childhood sweetheart. His excitement stoked her own responses almost to fever pitch. She forgot that they were only a few yards away from a crowded ballroom. All she knew was the magic of his hands, the heat of his mouth on her throat, the hardness of his body.

The way he was panting for breath as his lips scorched a trail of blazing kisses down the length of her neck. The heat of his erection against her thigh that summoned an answering warmth, throbbing low in her pelvis.

She knew exactly where this was leading, and she was willing to go there with him. More than willing. Eager.

But then a wave of cold air swirled into the heated conservatory as the doors crashed open.

Katherine spun round, to see both her aunts standing in the doorway, identical expressions of horror on their faces.

"Katherine!" Aunt Twining shrieked, clutching at the doorpost for support.

"You cannot mean to fob us off with excuses about studying botany this time!" roared Aunt Berry.

Since she was sprawled half across his lap, her hands still clinging to his broad shoulders, while his own were firmly clamped to her bottom, there was no denying anything.

"Not botany, no," Viscount Maldon replied calmly.

Katherine shut her eyes, hoping that he would come up with some really, really good reason why they should be embracing each other in this darkened, secluded room.

"It was marriage we were discussing."

"Marriage?" she heard Aunt Twining say faintly.

No! She attempted in vain to wriggle out of his hold. He had to think of something better than that!

"Yes," he replied, tightening his grip on her bottom. "Miss Malahithe has just done me the very great honor of agreeing to become my wife."

"Oh, Katherine, no! Not Viscount Maldon!" protested Aunt Berry.

But before Katherine could explain that marriage had been the very last thing on either of their minds, Viscount Maldon tipped her over his arm, so that she had to cling to his shoulders or tumble to the floor.

And kissed her again.

So thoroughly that both aunts turned and fled.

Chapter 3

Katherine leapt to her feet, causing the shredded paper to flutter to the floor like a cloud of confetti.

And as her eyes were drawn to the remains of Acton's list, she saw the whole scene in an entirely different light.

She had thought Viscount Maldon had come to care for her so much he could no longer contain himself. She thought he had been as carried away by his feelings as she.

Instead, this whole evening had been a piece of cold calculation on his part.

He had admitted he had heard gossip at his club about other heiresses. He had mentioned the name of another girl whose money came from trade, but had entirely glossed over the part where he had learned of the wealth *she* had been desperately trying to downplay ever since arriving in London. Taking advantage of what she had looked upon as a friendship, he had lured her to a spot that was the perfect backdrop against which to carry on a spot of seduction, and sneakily coaxed her most intimate secret from her. She rounded on him, fists clenched at her sides. "I really do hate you."

Making sure it was her aunts that discovered them in that clinch had been a masterstroke on his part. He knew her so well! She would never risk upsetting them by trying to wriggle out of this engagement. She would never expose them to the public censure that would ensue if this snake at her side were to tell the world that her oh-so-respectable aunts had taken a fallen woman into Almack's and tried to foist her onto the ton as a decent, marriageable woman!

"To think I trusted you with my deepest secrets! And this is how you repay me!"

She could not bear to remain a moment longer in his company. Uttering an incoherent cry, she dashed towards the exit.

"Katherine, don't be like this!"

It was the note of exasperation in his voice, when she needed to hear contrition, that tipped her over the edge. Seizing the nearest plant pot, she turned round and hurled it at him. It struck one of the iron pillars that supported the roof, shattering, and showering him with finely sifted loam. She froze, stunned that it had gone anywhere near him. Her eyes had been too full of tears to have made the effort of taking aim anything but a waste of time.

"I will call on you tomorrow then," he infuriated her further by saying calmly, as he began brushing earth and clumps of roots from his waistcoat, "when you have had time to…"

His words were lost in the sound of the glass doors slamming shut behind her.

Left in the darkness, Viscount Maldon sat down, removed his shoes and tipped the soil out into the greenery behind the bench.

What a mess!

Katherine was sitting on the sofa between her aunts when he entered their drawing room the next morning. She looked wan. As though all the life had drained out of her during a night spent pacing her bedroom floor.

"I have come to take Miss Malahithe out for a drive," he announced. "It is such a beautiful day, and some fresh air is bound to put the roses back into her cheeks."

He received two baleful glares from the aunts, but a thoughtful expression appeared on Katherine's face. And in next to no time, she was sitting beside him in the curricle he had borrowed, rigid backed and with her ugliest hat rammed firmly on her head.

It was only when busy streets began to give way to green fields that she seemed to take note of anything but the bleakness of her thoughts.

"Are you intent," she asked icily, after a few more minutes, "upon adding abduction to your list of crimes?"

"Not a bit of it. I intend only to ensure we have some privacy, so that we can properly finish the discussion we began last night."

"I do not recall any discussion taking place. I only recall your disgraceful behavior in luring me into that romantic spot, filling my ears with nonsense and then kissing me senseless."

"Is that what you recall?" he replied, skillfully tooling the curricle into an inn yard. "How interesting."

The groom, who had been riding up behind, jumped down to take the horses' heads while Viscount Maldon handed Katherine down from the bench seat.

"Would you like to take some refreshment before we set out?"

"Set out where?"

Viscount Maldon indicated a cobbled lane leading from the inn yard, which soon petered out into a track that meandered onto some woodland. "I thought we could take a walk. While we talk. But if you would prefer our discussion to take place in the coffee room...?" He tipped his head towards a low door, leading into the dim interior of the bustling posting house.

She did not want to risk anyone overhearing what she had decided she was going to say to him! She had spent all night alternately pacing her bedroom, shredding his character and falling onto her bed to indulge in bouts of weeping. There was not an insult in the dictionary she was not now ready to apply to his person. In fact, she could not wait to get somewhere that she could give him a no-holds-barred account of exactly what she thought of his amoral, beastly, conniving, duplicitous...

Snapping her parasol open with a decided click, Katherine began to march briskly down the lane to the woods.

"You are still upset," she heard him observe from several paces behind. "But you have no need to be. I understand your reasons for not wishing to marry, and I assure you, I do not mind a bit."

No, she was sure he did not! What did it matter that she was not a virgin, when his knowledge of that very fact served to place her very firmly in his power! She had no choice but to agree to this shameful engagement. But, oh, if she had her way…

He caught up with her just as she plunged into a copse of beech trees, and steered her down the left-hand fork of the track. Katherine shook her arm free. His very insouciance was making her angrier by the second. And as he passed her, she pressed her lips into a thin line. She had long since established that the scoundrel was impervious to insults, so she might as well save her breath! He led her into a clearing, sauntered across to a fallen log, withdrew a handkerchief from his pocket with a flourish and spread it over the mossy bark. He had so obviously chosen this spot with cool, calm deliberation, that Katherine's anger heated by a few more degrees.

"Do sit down," he said, blithely ignoring her fulminating glare.

She sat, consoling herself by remembering the look on his face when her random throw had showered his previously pristine waistcoat with damp soil.

"It is not as if I am without taint, either," he said, linking his hands behind his back, in the manner of a man about to make his excuses before a meeting of his creditors. "People will always whisper about the Maldon Madness whenever we walk by. Even if we live lives of unimpeachable virtue, they will only be waiting for the taint to appear in our children or grandchildren. So I understand, Katherine, why you have done all you could to avoid falling under a similar cloud."

She decided she would just wait for him to finish his cleverly rehearsed little speech, designed, no doubt, to lull her into a state of meek compliance, and then she would calmly inform him that all her money was tied up so that he could never touch a penny of it! Not that it was true, but oh, how he would sweat until he could get to see her lawyers! It would be worth telling just one lie to get some measure of revenge for the way he had betrayed her trust in him!

He began to pace up and down the clearing in front of her log now, his hands linked behind his back, his head bowed – the very picture of sincerity! But she could see through him now. She was not going to believe one word that slithered from those lying lips....

"I have been up all night working out this plan," he was saying. "So please, do not interrupt until you have heard the whole."

He did look somewhat drawn. She had noticed, the very moment he had come into the drawing room, that his usually immaculate appearance was marred by bruise-like shadows under his eyes and grim lines bracketing his mouth. She had ruthlessly dismissed a fleeting notion that he looked just like a man whose conscience had given him a sleepless night. She knew him better than that. It was more likely carousing that had given his skin that unhealthy pallor. He had probably been up all night, celebrating the end to all his financial problems with his cronies in some dark drinking den…wherever it was that fortune hunters slithered off to when they were not insinuating themselves into the hearts…she had terminated such thoughts at once. He had no place in her heart. None at all!

"I love you, you know, and I am sure you do not dislike me as much as you say you do.…"

Katherine almost fell backwards off her log. *Love her!* How could he compound all his villainy by telling her such a monstrous lie? A tangled mass of emotions rose up from her breast and clogged in her throat, preventing her from doing more than uttering a sort of choking snarl.

"So I am sure we can make a success of our marriage. Once we have settled my family's debts."

That was more like it! The debts. The sole reason he had come to London. To hunt for a susceptible heiress. And she had been the gullible fool to fall for his charm. Oh, how hard she had fallen! Even now, angry as she was, she knew it would not all hurt so much if she had been deceived by anyone but Viscount Maldon.

"So I am going to tell Acton to sell the estate."

What? Her head snapped round to follow his progress across the clearing. His back was to her at the moment. Could she possibly have misheard him? He could not really have just said he was going to sell the estate!

He turned round and began to pace back towards her. "It is just the sort of place that would appeal to one of these newly wealthy men from the north, I suspect. Someone who wants to make an impressive show. For the priory is impressive, you know," he said wistfully. "It came to my family at the dissolution of the monasteries. Stuffed with family portraits and collections from various campaigns…We even have a ghost. One of the priors still guards the wine cellars…" His face brightened. "He might even drive the price of the place up a bit, if we can find the right type of buyer."

Katherine shook her head, feeling completely bemused.

Why was he talking about selling the estate? He was marrying her to save it, surely? That had been the whole purpose of all his plotting and planning.

"Now that will fetch enough to wipe out the debts and leave a tidy sum over, which I am hoping will be sufficient to put all five of my sisters through school. And by the time it comes to the first of their presentations—" he dropped to his knees before her, and clasped her hands in his. "Now, this is where I am going to have to ask you to be very brave, my love. It is going to have to be India for us."

"India?" Katherine was completely bemused.

"Lots of fellows go out there and make immense fortunes, you know. Why should not I? I am as sharp as a tack. And you are so full of pluck, I am sure you could cope…no, more than cope. You are stifled here in London, bound by its rigid conventions. You are made for a life of adventure."

She looked at him, her eyes filling with tears as

it suddenly dawned on her what he had been saying.

"You would sell the estate?"

He nodded.

"Put the girls in school. And go off to India?"

"Without a backward glance." He grinned. "So long as you come with me."

"But…but then why did you go on and on about how vital it was for you to marry an heiress?"

"Oh, that was old Acton's solution to the situation," he said, with a dismissive gesture of his hand. "But there is no need for me to sacrifice myself on the altar of propriety now. No, now that we've compromised each other, we can put everyone else's expectations to one side, skip the country and live any way we dashed well please!"

Katherine shook her head. "You are trying to make it sound as though marrying me, and going out to India and working for a living is exactly what you have always wanted. But surely, you do not wish to figure in your family's history as the man who lost your estate?"

He reached up, and stroked her cheek. "Is that what has been bothering you? Is that why you think you do not want to marry me? You are afraid that I might one day regret finding you too luscious to resist and hold you to blame for losing the estate? Ah no, my sweet Kitty Kat, I do not regret a thing. I did my best to salvage something from the wreckage my father and brother left behind them, but last night, when I realized it was all gone, I felt nothing but relief."

Her heart began to hammer in her breast. *What did he mean, it had all gone?* It sounded as though he really believed he *had* to sell his estate to settle his inherited debts.

"Do you know how miserable I would have been if I had married one of those rich girls, for whom I felt nothing but…well…a kind of pity, I suppose?"

One of those rich girls? Did he truly have no suspicion that she was one of them?

"Yes, I would have kept the estate going, and yes, I would have provided for the girls. But I would have slowly died inside. Well, you saw how sick it made me feel, to have to walk into Almack's and let the world watch me demean myself in that way."

"What kind of fortune hunter are you?"

"A fatally flawed one." He grinned again. "I found it well nigh impossible to make up to women I don't like. It made me hate myself. But now—" his eyes lit up with fervor as he grasped her hands more tightly "—I am the happiest man alive. I knew you were something exceptional the very first moment I clapped eyes on you, sidling out of a respectable ballroom to hide behind that potted plant with me. Don't you think we were made for each other? Kitty Kat? Don't you think you could be happy as my wife?"

"Viscount Maldon," she replied, easing her hands from between his so that she could cup his face. "Do you really mean to tell me that you don't care if we never have a penny to our name?"

"Tarquin," he corrected, his eyes fixed on her softly parted lips. "If you mean to kiss me like you did last night—and I very much hope you do—then we should be on first-name terms, don't you think?"

"But the money," she persisted.

"Hang the money," he breathed, hauling her into his arms and taking the initiative by kissing her passionately. "I do not want any money I have not earned through my own endeavors." He did not notice her wince. He was too busy untying the strings of her bonnet. "I was never any good at being a fortune hunter," he declared, tossing the bonnet towards a clump of bracken, into which it vanished without trace. "Fortune hunters need far thicker skins than I seem to possess."

A determined look came to her face. Very calmly, she tugged off her gloves, then slid her hand into the gap that had ridden up under his waistcoat.

"Your skin feels exactly right to me." She purred.

"Kitty Kat." He groaned, when she tugged his shirt from his breeches so that she could more easily slide her hands up the satin-sleek muscles of his back, "Please, do not do that...."

"Do you not like it?" she enquired pertly, knowing from the expression on his face that he was enjoying her exploration immensely.

"You know I do," he breathed. "But if you carry on like this much longer, I will forget all my scruples—" He gasped as she leaned forward to nibble at the small patch of skin behind his ear. He gave a soft groan and angled his head to grant her better access.

"I do not think those kind of scruples stand much chance against what has sprung up between us," she breathed into his ear as she reached down to stroke the evidence of his passion for her.

"It is love, kitten," he protested with the last remaining scrap of his sanity.

"I know," she replied, undoing the flap of his breeches.

"Grass stains…" he moaned as her fingers reached inside, and almost sent him straight to heaven. " A dead giveaway."

He seized her wrist, hauled her to her feet and swung her into his arms. "I may be about to behave in a completely reprehensible fashion, but I have not so far lost my wits that I would shame you by letting anyone else know about it."

She fell in love with him a little bit more. He would never have used his knowledge about her experience to bend her to his will. Oh, how she had wronged him!

He dropped her to her feet, at the base of a tree. Her legs trembled so much when he reached down and began bunching up her skirts, she had to lean back against it for support.

He paused. "Are you completely sure about this?"

By way of an answer, she flung her arms round his neck and kissed him as ardently as she knew how. And then, as soon as her legs were freed from the restricting swathes of her walking dress, she wrapped them round his waist.

"God, I love your bottom." He groaned as he grasped it tightly. "It was the first part of you I fell in love with."

"There is no part of you I do not love." Katherine sighed, as he slid deep inside her.

And then there was no more talking.

And it seemed to Katherine that there was no more fitting place to consummate their love than here, under the leafy green canopy with the wind soughing through the branches, natures counterpoint to their own sighs and moans.

Tarquin was not gentle with her. But it thrilled her to feel his passion raging so very far beyond his control. She reveled in every forceful thrust, the way he grasped her soft flesh with a grip like iron, even the way he sank his teeth into her neck with a predatory growl. It sent her spiralling up, up, until she felt like a bird spreading its wings and soaring into the sun.

Total rapture burst through her, shattering her into a million pieces, then drawing her back together, reforming her as a woman who was more whole than she had ever dreamed it was possible to feel.

With Tarquin in her arms.

He was only a heartbeat behind. She cradled him as he shuddered to his own moment of rapture, a serene smile on her lips.

"I cannot believe—" he growled, withdrawing

and straightening their clothing hastily "—that we just did that."

Katherine just sighed dreamily, her eyes half shut as she gazed up into the lacy greenery shimmering overhead.

"You will have to marry me now," she murmured drowsily as he swept her into his arms and carried her back to the fallen log, "in case you have got me with child."

He settled her onto his lap, his arms round her waist, and she rested her head on his shoulder.

"And soon," she sighed.

"It will have to be banns, love." He frowned, kissing her absently on the crown of her head. "A special license would cost too much."

"Oh, not necessarily," she said, risking a peek up at him through lowered lashes. "And we do not *need* to go to India, either."

"Well, no," he agreed, giving her a hug. "I dare say we could live in a modest fashion in this country, if you really do not want to go abroad. It is just that I should like to set you up in style, if only I could. And since I have some very useful connections with the East India Company, I thought that would be the obvious way to go about it."

"I can think of a much more obvious way for us to live in style."

"Can you?" he asked, kissing the crown of her head. "My clever little Kitty Kat, tell me what it is."

"You could simply…use my money. Because," she said, sitting up straight, so she could look him directly in the eye as she broke the news. "Susannah Hullworthy's name was not the only one Acton should have put on your list. I am worth almost as much as her."

He flinched, turning pale. "The devil you say!"

"Please do not be angry. My money comes from…coal."

"I did not know," he grated. "You have to believe me.…" He seized her hands, a look of anguish contorting his features. She reached up, and soothed his frown with her fingertips. "I know. That is why I had to…compromise you." She blushed, her eyes darting furtively towards the tree. "I was suddenly scared that you might try to wriggle out of our engagement, if you thought there might be any suspicion you had deliberately targeted me for my money—"

He leapt to his feet. "You seduced me!" For a moment, he looked aghast. And then, to Katherine's relief, his lips twitched, a gleam came to his eye, and then he began to laugh.

"My God," he said, when he could eventually form words, "the fortune hunter hunted! Tell me, what was it about me—" he sat down beside her and hauled her into his arms "—that drove you to such lengths? My looks?" He kissed her hard on the mouth. "My rapier-like wit?"

She pretended to look pensive. "Your sense of honor," she said with a grin, which sent him off into peals of laughter all over again.

"Now, seriously, Tarquin," she said, "there is no need for you to sell your estate and put the girls into school. They can have a governess—"

"Oh, no they can't!" he objected. "If I cannot spirit you away to India and become a nabob— which was the height of my ambition, you know," he said in mock disappointment, "then at least I can have you all to myself. I am not having those hoydens underfoot. Nor would I wish to subject some poor female to their terror tactics. It would not be fair."

"Very well, we shall send them to school," she said meekly.

"Oh, I do like the sound of that."

He kissed her again.

"I had no idea you disliked your sisters so much!" She frowned.

"Oh, no, you mistake me. It was you saying *we* shall send them to school. Hearing you making plans for the both of us was what I liked the sound of so much. For it struck me, that from now on, it will always be *we* and *us.*"

"Then I have only one more thing to say about our future, Tarquin,"

"What is it, my love?"

"*We* are going to live happily ever after."

"I think you may be right," he said. Then, after spending several minutes kissing her, amended that to, "Yes, most definitely right."

* * * * *

REGENCY
Silk & Scandal

A season of secrets, scandal and seduction in high society!

Volume 1 – 4th June 2010
The Lord and the Wayward Lady
by Louise Allen

Volume 2 – 2nd July 2010
Paying the Virgin's Price
by Christine Merrill

Volume 3 – 6th August 2010
The Smuggler and the Society Bride
by Julia Justiss

Volume 4 – 3rd September 2010
Claiming the Forbidden Bride
by Gayle Wilson

8 VOLUMES IN ALL TO COLLECT!

www.millsandboon.co.uk   M&B

REGENCY
Silk & Scandal

*A season of secrets, scandal and
seduction in high society!*

Volume 5 – 1st October 2010
The Viscount and the Virgin
by Annie Burrows

Volume 6 – 5th November 2010
Unlacing the Innocent Miss
by Margaret McPhee

Volume 7 – 3rd December 2010
The Officer and the Proper Lady
by Louise Allen

Volume 8 – 7th January 2011
Taken by the Wicked Rake
by Christine Merrill

8 VOLUMES IN ALL TO COLLECT!

www.millsandboon.co.uk

M&B

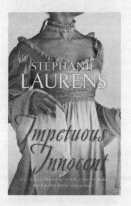

millsandboon.co.uk Community

Join Us!

The Community is the perfect place to meet and chat to kindred spirits who love books and reading as much as you do, but it's also the place to:

- Get the inside scoop from authors about their latest books
- Learn how to write a romance book with advice from our editors
- Help us to continue publishing the best in women's fiction
- Share your thoughts on the books we publish
- Befriend other users

Forums: Interact with each other as well as authors, editors and a whole host of other users worldwide.

Blogs: Every registered community member has their own blog to tell the world what they're up to and what's on their mind.

Book Challenge: We're aiming to read 5,000 books and have joined forces with The Reading Agency in our inaugural Book Challenge.

Profile Page: Showcase yourself and keep a record of your recent community activity.

Social Networking: We've added buttons at the end of every post to share via digg, Facebook, Google, Yahoo, technorati and de.licio.us.

www.millsandboon.co.uk